FROM DREAM TO DISCOVERY

Other Books by Hans Selye

STRESS, 1950

THE STORY OF THE ADAPTATION SYNDROME
(told in the form of informal illustrated lectures), 1952

TEXTBOOK OF ENDOCRINOLOGY, 2d edition, 1949

"The Steroids," 4 vols., in
ENCYCLOPEDIA OF ENDOCRINOLOGY, 1943

"Ovarian Tumors," 2 vols., in
ENCYCLOPEDIA OF ENDOCRINOLOGY, 1946

"On the Experimental Morphology of the Adrenal
Cortex," in AMERICAN LECTURES IN ENDOCRINOLOGY
(in collaboration with H. Stone), 1950

THE STRESS OF LIFE, 1956

ANNUAL REPORTS ON STRESS
(in collaboration with G. Heuser and A. Horava),
Vols. I–V, 1951–1956

THE CHEMICAL PREVENTION OF CARDIAC NECROSES, 1958

THE PLURICAUSAL CARDIOPATHIES, 1961

CALCIPHYLAXIS, 1962

SYMBOLIC SHORTHAND SYSTEM FOR PHYSIOLOGY AND MEDICINE
(in collaboration with G. Ember), 4th edition, 1964

FROM DREAM
TO DISCOVERY

On Being a Scientist

by Hans Selye

McGRAW-HILL BOOK COMPANY
New York   Toronto   London

FROM DREAM TO DISCOVERY

Library of Congress Catalog Card Number: 63-23306

FIRST EDITION

56207

Dedicated to GABRIELLE SELYE
who so patiently shared with the author
the stress of compiling these Notes.

*"I am born to this position; I must take it, and
neither you nor I can help or hinder me. Surely, then,
I need not fret myself to guard my own dignity."*

—RALPH WALDO EMERSON

ACKNOWLEDGMENTS

Among the members of our Institute, I am first of all indebted to Miss E. A. Middleton and Mr. A. Jones for editing and proofreading this book. Valuable assistance has also been received from Mrs. E. Staub and her staff, who typed most of the manuscript and helped in the collection and verification of the quotations. Mr. G. Ember prepared the Index, Miss M. Barath, the drawings and photographs.

Very useful advice has been received from the McGraw-Hill Book Company, as well as from my literary agents, Messrs. Paul R. Reynolds and Oliver G. Swan.

I am sincerely grateful to the many friends and colleagues, who took the trouble of reading a rough first copy of the manuscript, particularly to doctors Albert Delaunay, Sydney M. Friedman, Giulio Gabbiani, Octavia and Charles Hall, Hugh Hood, Charles Huggins, Dwight J. Ingle, Pierre Jean, Franklin C. McLean, Irvine H. Page, Plinio Prioreschi, Ignacio de Salcedo, Karl Stern, and Beatriz Tuchweber. Although many of their suggestions have improved the text, it must not be assumed that all these colleagues necessarily approve the views expressed here.

Last but not least, my gratitude is due to all the authors cited in my bibliography, whose views on science and scientists have greatly stimulated my thinking. From their writings I have also gathered many a pithy epigram on the philosophy of science, and numerous instructive anecdotes about the way discoveries are made. I have borrowed so freely from their works that a large portion of my book is hardly original. In this respect, I can only console myself by one thought: if you annex a single sentence from another man's work, that is plagiarism, but if you select the best from everyone who ever wrote about the subject, that is creative synthesis. All that can be said about science has already been said; the only way I could achieve some small measure of originality was by the choice of what to accept and what to reject. "For I have neither wit, nor words, nor worth, action, nor utterance, nor power of speech, to stir men's blood; I only speak right on; I tell you that which you yourselves do know."

[William Shakespeare]

CONTENTS

viii *Contents*

PREFACE

The object of this book is to present certain problems of science through the portrait of one scientist—the only one I know really well. It is not an attempt to picture the ideal scientist which the beginner should try to emulate, nor is it an *apologia pro vita sua*. This is merely a human document, a case report of what one laboratory man has done, why and how he has done it. It could never be more, since no two scientists are, or should be, the same.

I have tried to do a ruthless autopsy of my mind, describing and analyzing all of its characteristics as objectively as I can, whether I approve or disapprove of them. Consequently, not all of this book will make pleasant reading. You will see certain aspects of my personality as serious character flaws. You may even be shocked and perhaps rightly so. But you might as well learn from the start that in real life scientists are full of imperfections that are tactfully eliminated from their obituaries and sometimes even from their biographies.

By speaking freely about all my views, I shall also reveal a great naïveness and ignorance on topics about which I should either know more or remain silent. These sections could easily have been suppressed to save my dignity. But there are many decorously retouched biographies and memoirs of much greater scientists; if you are to learn anything from my remarks, I feel they should be uncensored. You will be irritated to see me worry about trivialities, and I am afraid you will consider some of my critical remarks and attitudes tactless. But the point is not to describe what I should have been, but what I am. If the story is to be honest, then the ugly must not be withheld.

Besides, how do we know that success in some spheres does not depend upon certain defects and even deformities. Quasimodo, in Victor Hugo's *Hunchback of Notre Dame,* was one of literature's ugliest monsters. And yet, his twisted grotesque frame hid a soul capable of infinite pity and love. It would be difficult to imagine a Quasimodo, normally built, with the regular features of a healthy French peasant, having the capacity of yearning so much for tenderness and the chance to show it by serving.

DEAR JOHN,

Since you say you would like to continue my kind of research, I am sending you this bunch of loose Notes that I have jotted down in the course of the past thirty-five years about my impressions of science and scientists. They are rather intimate, personal reflections, "glimpses behind the scenes," none of which can be gathered from my technical papers and books. Yet I feel that what they reveal has played the decisive role in directing, not only my work, but my whole way of life. Of course, I do not want to force my views on you; you have to live your own life. All I ask is that you leaf through these Notes in moments of leisure, to see whether you might not profit a little from my experience, accepting the good, rejecting the bad. In a sense, this would splice our lives together, and you could start with what took me so long to acquire.

If I had known at the start what I know now, I would certainly have done things better; it takes time to polish the rough spots. The style of that first paper on "A syndrome produced by various nocuous agents" (written at the age of twenty-eight) was nothing to be proud of. Indeed, if I had known then what I know now, I'm sure I could have formulated the stress syndrome with half the lab work and on a tenth of the paper. I think I could also have avoided much of the antagonism aroused by incidental speculations that did not mean much to me anyway. I certainly would have known better than to be bothered so much by whatever criticism is unavoidably leveled at any new concept.

If I had known how to handle my chiefs when I was an assistant and my assistants when I became a chief! If I had known then how to get money and staff for research; how to organize sooner this big library of ours so one might really find what one is looking for; how to construct a set of labs to make them functional . . . by Jove, John, if I had known then what I know now, I might even have found you a couple of decades earlier—perhaps several of you—and think of what we could have done together!

I can already hear you say (or at least respectfully suggest in your inimitable way) that I have no statistical evidence of having made any progress since the beginning. But you must admit that I did not have nearly as much trouble with my later projects, such as the cardiac necroses or calciphylaxis. And the atmosphere in the lab is undoubtedly more congenial now than it was at the outset.

Perhaps the most important thing I have learned is self-confidence; nowadays I no longer waste so much time in justifying my ways to others and to myself. It is difficult for an objective young man to have self-confidence when he still lacks the evidence to prove that he is on the right track.

Take, for example, my great preference for the simplest possible methods. I like to hold a rat in the palm of my hand and just watch it. I like to look at its organs with a loupe or on histologic sections stained with the simplest methods. Despite my Ph.D. in chemistry, I have never used complex chemical procedures. I have never employed isotope techniques, the electron microscope, X-ray diffraction or any of the more sophisticated new tools—not because I fail to appreciate their worth, but merely because I am more interested in the general picture than in details. Somehow I feel much closer to Mother Nature when I can observe her directly with the sense organs she herself gave me than when there are instruments between us that so often distort her picture. Easily recognized, manifest changes in shape or behavior, are not only less subject to "instrument-error," but, because of their simplicity, they lend themselves better to the large-scale experimentation needed for the broad integration and correlation of many vital reactions.

For a while I was afraid that I was becoming obsolete in my passion for simplicity and the panoramic approach. The tendency in science today is all in the opposite direction. They are building ever more complex tools to dig ever deeper at one selected point. Of course, this must also be done, but not by all of us, John. Not by all of us! The specialist loses perspective, and by now I am sure that there will always be a need for integrators, for naturalists who keep trying to survey the broad fields. I am no longer worried about missing some of the details. There must remain a few of us who train men and perfect tools to scan the horizons rather than to look ever closer at the infinitely small. We must train men who can lead large teams to survey an extensive area, even though only with simple methods. We must construct huge documentation systems to keep us well informed on many things. Some of these problems are not yet yours at this stage, but I hope with a little time you will look into them. In any event, I could use your support to help me with what I am trying to do along these lines.

But I had another, much more personal and selfish reason for taking the time to edit these Notes for you. Up to now, there was really no one with whom I could share the world in which I live, the things that really interest me, the ideals that I consider worth living for. Most people consider me quite self-sufficient, but I do need the intimacy of sharing as much as anybody else does; probably more, because where my mind likes to be, there are no genial crowds. In fact, as far as I can see, there is no one really close by with whom I could talk things over properly, to whom I could feel bound by the kind of natural kinship that makes all defense and pretense unnecessary, and thereby offers a chance for mutually checking our bearings in the journey through life.

As regards the usual everyday problems, such intimate, warm relationships usually develop between members of the same family or clan, but the motives that most decisively direct my course are not the usual ones. I like the warmth of family life; I need the feeling of security that comes from doing something for others. But the satisfactions and contributions that are most characteristically mine, stem from a kind of resonance with the general laws of Nature. These are too grandiose to stimulate any feeling but admiration unless their appreciation can be fully shared with others. This sharing is no easy matter for us. The farther you advance into the unknown, the fewer fellow travelers remain with you. In the forefront of your advance, if it is really beyond the point that anyone else has reached, you are finally alone. To me, you John, are the symbol of the one who stays the course. That is why I have been looking for you all my life.

When I was very young, I imagined you as a father or teacher, later as a brother or wife, and now as a son or pupil; I have been lucky in finding warm kinships of all these kinds, but the gifts they brought me were of another nature. I value my relationships with them all, but now I am well past fifty and still searching for your kind.

Perhaps there are many of you. Perhaps even you are only a figment of my need. Perhaps my mind has no real, close kin. But time is running out and, while I do not know whether you really exist, I do know that I need you. That is why I had to invent you. In research, we soon learn that abstractions are often just as, or even more, effective than tangible, individual facts. So I have created you, John, as my spiritual younger brother and successor, with whom I can talk things over.

For, who is my brother? The man of my blood, even if we have nothing else in common—or the man of my mind, to whom I am bound only by the warmth of mutual understanding and common ideals? I keep on hoping that somewhere, sometime, you will materialize. Perhaps, by publishing these Notes, I may actually bring you into existence, thereby assuring my succession in the way of life with Nature that has given me so much pleasure.

Hans Selye

Université de Montréal
February, 1964

FROM DREAM TO DISCOVERY

INTRODUCTION

It was in medical school that I first became fascinated by the possibilities of experimental research. It was then that I had to make the most important decision of my career, namely, whether to select this speciality from among so many others open to an M.D. Yet, at that time I knew virtually nothing about what I was going in for. The idea of science that one gets from textbooks—the picture of a scientist, as reflected by his lectures or biography—is a far cry from reality. I suspected this then as much as I know it now.

I can still vividly remember how eager I was for a man-to-man talk with one or other of my professors who were engaged in medical research—men who wrote textbooks or, even better, created the material that goes into textbooks. I felt vaguely that there was a great deal to be learned from these men if I could only get them to open up and let their hair down; not merely to teach me facts from the lecture platform, or through their books, but to tell me what made them tick. Most likely, I could not even have formulated my questions precisely, then. But what I really wanted to know was the nature of the satisfactions they derived from their successes, the basic causes of their frustrations and failures, the kind of talents required to lead their way of life. I wanted to learn so many things that only they could tell me! Now, after all these years, I am still not sure I know just what to ask, and much less do I know how to answer. There are no precedents for the way these subjects should be treated; it will not be easy to write about them. But then, if the task is important enough, lack of precedent makes the challenge only more alluring.

Presumably, no one will ever be able to write the kind of exhaustive treatise about all the problems of experimental medicine that Claude Bernard had in mind; but then, perhaps that is not what is most urgently needed. As I shall try to show later, concise, simple formulation of facts is one of the principal aims of science in general, and concise simplicity—perhaps a little tempered with human warmth—will have to be the keynote of these pages. We are at the dawn of what will undoubtedly go down in history as the Age of Basic Research. Surely it is worthwhile to pause briefly and try to formulate the basic problems of experimental medicine that confront us now.

It is difficult to say who should attempt to write Notes of this kind. I am painfully aware that my almost complete lack of formal training in philosophy, logic and many of the physical sciences constitutes a serious handicap. Worst of all, my experience in the art of writing is limited to technical texts. But at least I have one qualification for this job that none of my colleagues seems to possess—I am willing to try.

The questions that I used to ask as a beginner and that so many others have asked me since, are nearly always the same. With my compulsive need for categorization I have classified them into the following six groups:

1. *Why?* Why do you select a scientific career? What is your motivation? What satisfactions do you derive from it?

2. *Who?* Who should go in for research? What are the most useful aptitudes for it?

3. *What?* What is a good subject? How can you assess the importance and feasability of a project when you embark upon it and cannot yet know the outcome?

4. *When?* When is it best to do one thing or another? What is the "order of priority" in research?

5. *Where?* Where should you work? What constitutes a good climate for research?

6. *How?* How should you conduct your research once you have decided upon the topic?

Of course, the last mentioned is the most all-embracing category of problems. It includes the techniques of laboratory work, the general rules about the design of experiments and theories, the use of logic, statistics and intuition in the critical evaluation of results. It includes even your personal conduct in the lab and outside it, your attitude toward criticism, the perennial struggle between the need for independence and the advantages of teamwork. It includes the manifold problems of laboratory organization, fund raising, selection of assistants. It includes a great many things.

As you read the following pages, be sure to remember that I am not trying to press any views on you. What is good for me may not be good for you; in this career, there is no general code of conduct, no single best way. Scientists are probably the most individualistic bunch of people in the world. All of us are and should be essentially different; there would be no purpose in trying to fit us into a common mold. All I can say is that, if I had known at the onset of my career what I have learned by trial and error (mostly by error, I am afraid), I am sure it would have helped me immensely. I hope it will help you too.

1. Why Should You Do Research?

It is not easy to explain why people want to do research, and not everybody has the same motivation. "Researchers" will work for money, power, social position, but there are more efficacious ways of getting all these rewards. True scientists are rarely motivated by them.

Nowadays, scientific accomplishments give you a great deal of recognition, and scientists need an occasional approving pat on the back just as much as anyone else—although, for some reason they are very reluctant to admit it.

Of course, it is not the decibels of applause that count, but what you are applauded for and by whom. Few scientists seek anonymity and many put up bitter fights to defend their priorities; but they want to be recognized by competent colleagues—and for a very special kind of accomplishment. They want the kind of acknowledgment that confirms them in their belief that they have really understood some hidden laws of Nature. They want to be able to say with the divine in Shakespeare's *Antony and Cleopatra:* "In Nature's infinite Book of Secrecy a little I can read." And many of them, especially the physicians, derive their greatest satisfaction from having relieved human suffering through this understanding. Of course, a lawyer may avert suffering by a clever defense of his client; a politician can do this on an even larger scale by helping to enact a law, and a general can save thousands of lives by a strategic move. But all these people protect man against man, often at the expense of other men. The gain is always temporary and limited to certain people. A secret of Nature, once revealed, permanently enriches humanity as a whole.

Yet, neither the glory science can bring nor its potential usefulness are its only charms—certainly not its usefulness as most people understand it. The principal "use" of basic research, like that of

5

a rose, a song, or a beautiful landscape is that it gives us pleasure. Every scientific discovery reveals new harmonies in the lawfulness of Nature for our passive enjoyment. But research is not a mere "spectator sport," the scientist actively participates in the unveiling of the enjoyable, and this type of activity is as close as the human mind can come to the process of creation.

Of course, if you have not yet known this feeling, my description of it will not be very meaningful; if you have, it will not be very necessary. It has been said about the pleasure of a kiss that those who have never experienced it will not gain much by a verbal description, while those who have will hardly need it. But the instinctive anticipation of pleasure is there before the kiss, before the discovery, and all those who eventually became scientists must have felt it vaguely before, or else they would not have thought of making research their career.

If you are a young physician interested in science, the best my remarks can do is to help you analyze your own feelings. I thought that such an analysis might in itself be useful now, when you have to make that most important decision of your career: the choice between basic research and the practice of medicine. You may be a physician by temperament, and, if you decide for practice, your choice is not necessarily guided merely by material considerations; all true physicians enjoy direct contact with the patient. If you decide for basic research, you will never see the grateful eyes of a mother whose child you have saved; you will never be able to say that, unless you had been there, this man would have died. But if you are successful in the impersonal solitude of your laboratory, you will have the satisfaction of knowing that, had you not unveiled it, no practitioner could have applied the law of Nature that you found for the benefit of his patient.

To a young beginner, my remarks cannot have the same meaning as they have for me, but this is the way I can best explain why I am doing research. And if you were born to be an investigator, you will understand.

Yet scientists have very diverse incentives for doing research. We must now consider these in detail, for no advice I could give in these Notes is more important than to examine your motivation very frankly and determine whether this is really what you want to do. Misfits in science are pathetic creatures, and many are the maladjusted who drifted into research careers by mere accident.

Some of the incentives for scientific work are accepted by society as praiseworthy; others are frowned upon as disgusting. Let me not

judge them on this basis, but merely say that, as far as I can see
—whether they seem beautiful or ugly to you—the following have
the necessary force to make an otherwise qualified man succeed
and be happy in a career of basic research:

> *Detached love of Nature and truth.*
> *Admiration for the beauty of lawfulness.*
> *Simple curiosity.*
> *The desire to be useful.*
> *The need for approval.*
> *The glory of success.*
> And, last but not least: *The fear of boredom.*

Detached Love of Nature and Truth

"Avoid, as you would the plague, a man of God who is also a man of
business." [St. Jerome]

"It is preoccupation with possession, more than anything else, that
prevents men from living freely and nobly." [Bertrand Russell]

"And then, despite their faults and vices, scientists have more or less the
same kind of soul. They all profess the cult of truth in itself. For them
science is a religion." [Charles Richet [59]]

"Probably, what characterizes all scientists, whatever they may be,
archivists, mathematicians, chemists, astronomists, physicists, is that
they do not seek to reach a practical conclusion by their work."
[Charles Richet [59]]

It may seem odd that people should work so hard to unravel the
truths of Nature without any practical aim in sight. But what is
practical? As Benjamin Franklin said: "What is the use of a newborn baby?" Not everything important to us is practical in the accepted sense of the word. The recognized values of success—money,
power, ever shorter working hours—are but the means to buy
happiness, and often they bring only a very shabby form of it at
that. The baby is not a potential token or currency with which to
buy something else that makes us happy; the baby, itself, makes us
happy. The generally accepted tokens of practical value are all only
means to happiness. Why not skip the intermediates and reach out
directly for the end? Pure art—a great painting, a piece of music
—is useful since it lifts us beyond the preoccupations of everyday
life; it brings us peace, serenity and happiness. Basic research, the
study of natural laws, is often undertaken for the same reasons.

Certain things are good for something; others are good in themselves; still others are both good for something and good in them-

selves. Money is useful only because we can buy something with it; it has no value as such. The pleasure of listening to a great symphony or of enjoying an excellent cigar is good in itself, but we can buy nothing in exchange for it. On the other hand, most things that are good in themselves are also good for something: it is enjoyable to eat a good meal; in addition, we derive useful calories from it. Nature has cunningly spiced most things that are useful to its purpose with subjective feelings that in themselves are agreeable. This is true not only of nutrition and reproduction, but also of understanding. Discovery through basic research is enjoyable, irrespective of its possible practical applications. But sooner or later the knowledge thus acquired does become useful in that it increases our power over Nature.

It is remarkable that good things so often also act as tokens with which we can buy other good things that the distinction between means and aims may become difficult. The miser likes to fondle his gold—and, curiously, some (few) scientists actually enjoy writing their papers—because the mere handling of the means for credit evokes the pleasant feeling of its aim. These are not pretty thoughts, I am afraid, but to the scientist, even the ugliest truth is more beautiful than the loveliest pretense.

The Beauty of Lawfulness

"The fairest thing we can experience is the mysterious. It is the fundamental emotion which stands at the cradle of true art and true science. He who knows it not and can no longer wonder, no longer feel amazement, is as good as dead, a snuffed-out candle."   [Albert Einstein [32]]

"I do not know what I may appear to the world; but to myself I seem to have been only like a boy playing on the seashore, and diverting myself in now and then finding a smoother pebble or a prettier shell than ordinary, whilst the great ocean of truth lay all undiscovered before me."

[Sir Isaac Newton]

It is difficult to explain the beauty of the transition from mystery to lawfulness. The collector of stamps, matchboxes or butterflies, the solver of crossword puzzles, enjoys the feeling of having completed an orderly series, of having found the key according to which a large number of apparently dissimilar items can be arranged in a logical fashion. The more diverse, the more peculiar and puzzling the items are, the more satisfactory it is to detect the laws that permit us to put them into a manageable, harmonious arrangement that brings their manifold features closer to understanding.

As children we all have what it takes to enjoy wonderful and mysterious things. When a child points out something unusual which he has never seen before—a colorful butterfly, an elephant, or a sea shell—just watch his eyes as he cries out with enthusiasm, "Look, Daddy!" and you will know what I mean.

No sensitive person can look at the sky on a cloudless night without asking himself where the stars come from, where they go, and what keeps the universe in order. We ask the same kind of questions when we look at the self-perpetuating, eternal universe within the human body, or even just at that pair of sensitive and searching human eyes which constantly strives to bridge the gap between these two universes.

The capacity to contemplate the harmonious elegance of Nature, at least with some degree of understanding, is one of the most satisfactory experiences of which man is capable. This is a noble and gratifying aim in itself, quite apart from any material advantages it may offer. But actually it does help us in our everyday life, very much in the same way as a deep religious faith or a well-balanced philosophic outlook helps us. Looking at something infinitely greater than our conscious selves makes all our daily troubles appear to shrink by comparison. There is an equanimity and a peace of mind which can be achieved only through contact with the sublime.

But as time goes by, most of us—not all—lose this gift of pure enjoyment. When we have seen most of the things that are encountered in everyday life, custom begins to stale variety. The petty routine of daily problems also tends to blunt our sensitivity to the detached enjoyment of greatness and wonder. It is a pity that nowadays most people are so bent on being practical, on getting ahead in life, that they no longer find time to make sure where they really want to go. After a while, the prosperous businessman, the efficient administrator, begins to get that lost feeling of aimlessly drifting from day to day—toward retirement and death.

So many people work hard and intelligently for some immediate objective which promises leisure to enjoy life tomorrow; but tomorrow never becomes today. There is always another objective which promises even more leisure in exchange for just a little more work. That is why so few people in the usual walks of life retain that wonderful gift which they all possessed as children: the ability to really enjoy themselves. But it hurts to be conscious of this defect, so adults dope themselves with more work (or alcohol) to divert attention from their loss. The inspired painter, poet, composer, astronomer, or biologist never grows up in this respect; he does not lose the abstract treasures of his naïve innocence, no matter how poor or how old he may be. He retains the childlike ability to enjoy the impractical. And pleasures are always impractical; they can lead us to no reward. They are the reward.

The really acquisitive person is so busy reinvesting that he never learns how to cash in. "Realistic people" who pursue "practical aims" are rarely as realistic and practical, in the long run of life, as the dreamers who pursue only their dreams. True scientists—even when they become very old—retain a certain romanticism, a dreamy, imaginative habit of mind; they continue to dwell on the adventurous, the picturesque, the unusual; they never cease to be thrilled by the heroic grandeur and infallible consistency of the laws that govern the harmony of Nature in and around man.

Curiosity

"Every man ought to be inquisitive through every hour of his great adventure down to the day when he shall no longer cast a shadow in the sun. For if he dies without a question in his heart, what excuse is there for his continuance?"   [Frank Moore Colby]

There is a certain opprobrium attached to inquisitiveness but only because people tend to confuse curiosity and nosiness. The curious wants to know that which is of concern to him; the nosy inquires into the personal concerns of others. The true scientist thrives on curiosity; he could not live without it. Whenever an investigator loses this driving force—because his efforts have been too often frustrated, or because he has become complacently satisfied by "practical achievements"—he retires from science and takes refuge in self-commiseration or the smug enjoyment of his prosperity. But we need not say much about scientific curiosity in particular, for it is superimposed upon all the other motives.

The Desire to be Useful

"They know that perhaps because of them, some light will appear on the crests of the dark ocean in which humanity struggles frantically. And all scientists, all without exception, have this magnificent hope to sustain them in their hard labors, that they will be useful to their human brothers."   [Charles Richet [59]]

"Young man, I say, If you want to discover a new truth, do not worry about its practical applications. Don't ask yourself how medicine, commerce or industry will profit by it; for, if you do, you will find nothing. You want to solve the problem that you consider important: embark on its solution without worrying about the consequences. Approach the question from its simplest side. Do not let the injunctions of journalists, hygienists, engineers, pharmacists, or physicians stop you. Let them talk. Go straight at your problem by the shortest route. Leave to the practitioners the cumbersome task of conclusions and industrial complications. *Veritas lucet ipsa per se.* Truth is self-sufficient".... "Where would we be if Galvani, instead of touching the legs of his frogs with iron and copper, had wanted to construct a telephone? Soubeiran, in discovering trichlorinated methane, which he called chloroform, did not at all try to find an anesthetic, no more than Röntgen had looked for ways to facilitate surgical operations." [Charles Richet [59]]

"The first step, the fashioning of a world picture from life, is a task of pure science. The second step, the utilization of the scientific world picture for practical purposes, is the task of technology. The first task is just as important as the other and, since each of them claims the whole man, the individual investigator, if he really wants to promote his work, must concentrate all his strength on a single point and leave aside meanwhile the thought about other implications and interests. Therefore, let us not scold the scientist too much because of his unworldliness and his lack of participation in the important problems of public life. Without such a one-sided attitude, Heinrich Hertz would not have discovered the wireless waves, nor Robert Koch the tubercle bacillus." [Max Planck [55]]

A former United States Secretary of Defense, Charles E. Wilson, said that basic research is "what you do when you don't know what you are doing." I cannot quite agree with this definition.

More commonly, basic research is thought of as the opposite of "practical" research, the kind that can be immediately applied. This suggests a disassociation from man's everyday problems. The development of weapons, television sets, or vaccines, is obviously practical. Studies of the inner temperature of distant stars, of the habits of infinitely small living beings, of the laws governing the inheritable coloration of pea blossoms, all seemed eminently impractical—at least when first undertaken. They were viewed as sophisticated pastimes, pursued by intelligent, but somewhat eccentric, maladjusted people whose otherwise excellent minds had been sidetracked by a queer interest in the farfetched and useless.

Of course, basic research is rarely undertaken with its practical applications in mind; indeed, these are never predictable. I still remember my own reaction in school when I was taught how astrophysicists estimate the inner temperature of distant stars. Cunning, I thought, but why should anybody want to know? When Louis Pasteur reported that germs might transmit diseases, he was ridiculed. Fancy a grown man worrying about being attacked by bugs so small no one could see them! When the Austrian monk, Gregor Johann

Mendel, amused himself by observing the results of crossbreeding red- with white-flowering peas in the monastery garden, even his most farsighted contemporaries failed to imagine the momentous implications of his findings.

Yet, without basic knowledge of the behavior of distant stars, we would not be placing satellites in orbit today. Without knowledge about bacteria, there would be no vaccines, serums and antibiotics. And without those observations on the inheritance of color in peas, modern genetics—with all its importance to agriculture, animal breeding and medicine—could never have developed.

The more manifestly sensible and practical a research project, the closer it is to the commonplace we already know. Thus, paradoxically, knowledge about the seemingly most farfetched, impractical phenomena may prove the likeliest to yield novel basic information and to lead us to new heights of discovery. But usually this takes time, often much time. Basic research neither becomes nor ceases to be useful as soon as the applied kind.

Some insist that basic research must proceed in the same spirit as "art for art's sake," and should not be appraised by its practical applicability. Yet, in defending this view they usually argue that even the most abstruse research may eventually yield practical results. It is odd that the study of the impractical should have to be justified by its potential usefulness.

Whatever our motives for undertaking it, basic research certainly can become practically useful. But to the scientist, how important is the motive of being useful to others? Man is essentially an egocentric and egotistic creature. It is not within my province to question why he was thus created nor to explore whether it is strength or weakness that seems to make some people disinterested in themselves. In any event, such totally altruistic individuals are exceedingly rare in the general population and—as far as I have been able to establish—they do not occur among scientists. The basic research man sets his sights high; he believes in the inherent value of his interests and is prepared to make, and press others to make, great sacrifices for them. If this is egotism, he must admit to being an egotist. It would be incompatible with his sense of honesty and objectivity to bluff himself into believing that he has no thought for his own interests.

Egotism is the most characteristic, the most ancient, and the most essential property of life. All living beings, from the simplest amoeba to man, are of necessity closest to themselves and the most natural protectors of their own interests. I see no reason why we should expect someone else to look after us more conscientiously than after himself. Selfishness is natural, yet it is ugly; we are so much repulsed by it that we try to deny its existence in ourselves. It is also dangerous to society. We are afraid of it, because it harbors the seeds of fight and revenge. Yet, despite their egotism, many scientists, especially among physicians, are strongly motivated by humanitarian impulses.

I do not believe that these two apparently contradictory drives reflect a schizoid trait, a kind of double personality, in which the instinct for self-preservation constantly fights the wish to help others. To me, even altruism is a modified form of egotism, a kind of collective selfishness that helps the community. Unconsciously, we sense that altruism engenders gratitude. By awakening in another person the wish that we should prosper because of what we have done for him, we elicit gratitude which is perhaps the most characteristically human way of assuring our security (homeostasis). It takes away the motive for a clash between selfish and selfless tendencies. By inspiring the feeling of gratitude, we induce others to share with us our natural wish for our own well-being. The less a person is conversant with the ecology of living beings, the more is he repulsed by this kind of reasoning. But the biologist is not called upon to question the wisdom of creation; he merely analyzes its structure.

Whatever their conscious motives, many scientists have a sincere wish to be useful to society. That is why, even among those who do basic research without any expectation of practical applicability, few are completely indifferent to the hope that their discoveries may help to relieve suffering and to promote happiness. One of the most important reasons for this desire is the need for approval.

The Need for Approval—The Thirst for Credit—Vanity

"Xenophon says that there is no sound more pleasing than one's own praises." [Plutarch]

"A friend once said to Cato the Elder, 'It's a scandal that no statue has been erected to you in Rome! I am going to form a committee.'
" 'No,' " said Cato, " 'I would rather have people ask "Why isn't there a statue to Cato?" than "Why is there one?" ' " [Thomas L. Masson]

"All this shows how ambitious I was; but I think I can say with truth that in after years, though I cared in the highest degree for the approbation of such men as Lyell and Hooker, who were my friends, I did not care much about the general public. I do not mean to say that a favourable review or a large sale of my books did not please me greatly, but the pleasure was a fleeting one, and I am sure that I have never turned one inch out of my course to gain fame . . .

"My books have sold largely in England, have been translated into many languages, and passed through several editions in foreign countries. I have heard it said that the success of a work abroad is the best test of its enduring value. I doubt whether this is at all trustworthy; but judged by this standard my name ought to last for a few years . . .

"But I was also ambitious to take a fair place among scientific men, —whether more ambitious or less so than most of my fellow-workers, I can form no opinion."   [Charles Darwin [26]]

"Since the real world in the absolute sense is independent of individual personalities, indeed independent of all human intelligence, every discovery made by an individual acquires a very general significance. This gives the scientist, who struggles with his problem in quiet isolation, the certainty that every result which he finds, will be appreciated by all specialists throughout the world, and this feeling of the significance of his work is his joy, it gives him full compensation for many a sacrifice in his daily life."   [Max Planck [55]]

I have met few scientists, if any, who are uninterested in the approval of their colleagues and do not care whether or not they get credit for their discoveries. Few of them pick up a book or a reprint on their own subject without immediately consulting the author index to see whether they are quoted. Why are most of them so desperately ashamed of this?

We have established a visiting professorship at our Institute which has brought us into contact with some of the most eminent medical scientists of our time. It has become our tradition to invite these distinguished guests for an informal dinner followed by a leisurely chat. This gives us a chance to learn more about the intimate characteristics, drives and satisfactions of these men. One question which is always asked, concerns the motives for research. The most common answer is, "Curiosity." When pressed for additional motives, a scientist may also mention his wish to be useful, or even admit that he got into his career by sheer accident because there was an opening in a research laboratory and he needed the money. But a desire for credit is always violently denied. Why?

I shall never forget the time when my youngest graduate student innocently asked our distinguished guest on such an occasion: "Well, sir, in that case, would you mind if I published the experiment you showed us this afternoon? I have been assisting you with it and I did quite similar work—though, I admit, not very successfully—

before. It would be a useful addition to my thesis, sir . . . That is if you don't mind, sir." It did not prove to be a practical request, but it was a good question.

Scientific curiosity can be satisfied much more easily by reading the publications of others than by working in the lab. It may take years to prove by experimentation what we can learn in the few minutes needed to read the published end result. So let us not fool ourselves; the driving force is hardly sheer curiosity. Could it merely be the wish to do good? Few scientists would get much pleasure from doing good by political or charitable activities, or by providing livelihoods through business.

The fact is that we are vain, very vain. We adore the feeling of having found some important law of Nature through our own ingenuity. Why should we be so ashamed of it? "Vanity as an impulse has without doubt been of far more benefit to civilization than modesty has ever been" [William E. Woodward].

Vanity becomes objectionable only when the legitimate pride in a recognized accomplishment turns into an indiscriminate craving after fame for its own sake. No scientist worthy of the name measures his success by the number of people who acclaim him. No scientist wants credit for a discovery erroneously attributed to him, nor would he trade places with the most famous politicians, millionaires or generals. No scientist that I ever knew could possibly have felt envy for the enormous fame of a ventriloquist admired on the television screens by millions throughout the nation. Scientists are vain, they like recognition, they are not immune to the pleasures of fame; but they are very choosy about whom they want to be recognized by and what they want to be famous for.

Actually, scientists are extremely discriminating in this respect. The greater they are, the smaller the number of people whose recognition means something to them. But it is a heart-warming experience for one who has assiduously labored in the solitude of his laboratory on a highly intricate mechanism of Nature to know that, somewhere in the world, there are some people—even though perhaps only half a dozen—who truly understand the importance of his work and appreciate the difficulties he had to surmount. These colleagues he accepts as his peers and he is deeply gratified that, through his work, he has acquired their spiritual kinship. He has earned a place in their select, intellectual aristocracy. He can communicate with them across the enormous geographic distances, the language and social barriers, and all the petty hatreds and competitions that separate other men.

In this age of cold and shooting wars, of bitter racial, political, and religious intolerance, or of simply trite platitude of purpose, I do not think that the basic scientist need be ashamed of his vanity.

The Glory of Success; Hero-worship and a Desire to Imitate Our Heroes

"Men of genius do not excel in any profession because they labour in it, but they labour in it, because they excel."   [William Hazlitt]

"Which one of us has not gained fortitude and faith from the incarnation of ideas in men, from the wisdom of Socrates, from the wondrous creativity of Shakespeare, from the strength of Washington, from the compassion of Lincoln, and above all, perhaps, from the life and death of Jesus?"   [Arthur Schlesinger, Jr. [63]]

I am a passionate hero-worshipper myself; my great ideals are Claude Bernard, Louis Pasteur, Robert Koch, Paul Ehrlich and Walter Cannon. But I profited mainly from Dr. Cannon, whom I knew personally as a pure man and a pure scientist. He had the greatest influence on me, and throughout my life I always felt very close to him. My work on stress has been largely inspired by his discovery of the sympathetic "emergency reactions" and even these Notes bear the imprint of his spirit. I seem to be tied to Dr. Cannon by bonds I cannot sever. I hope that he would not mind if he were still alive. After all, he himself said:

"I am a son of Bowditch, who led me into physiological investigation. Dr. Bowditch in turn was the son of Karl Ludwig, to whose laboratory in Leipzig in the last century he resorted together with other young men from many lands. Through my grandfather Ludwig, I am related to others of his descendants, among them the Italian physiologist Mosso, the English pharmacologist Brinton, and the Russian physiologist Pavlov. In my own place in this sequence of familial relationship I have scattered sons—and some grandsons."   [Walter Cannon [16]]

I have embraced so many of Cannon's ideas! I can only be grateful, but I cannot help it. For sons cannot help resembling their fathers; it would be irreverent if the offspring tried to be different just to avoid being accused of imitation. Besides, transmitted characteristics manifest themselves differently in successive generations. No scientist arises spontaneously without predecessors, but, unlike the son by blood, the son by mind can at least choose his parent.

The development of real excellence and genius has been greatly impeded by a misunderstanding of what Lincoln meant when, on the battlefield of Gettysburg, he dedicated his nation to "the proposition that all men are created equal." Taken literally, this proposition is obviously untrue: Some men are small, others big; some are fat, others thin; some are intelligent, others stupid. What Lincoln meant was that all men should have the same birthright to develop whatever qualifications they possess.

In practice, even this is impossible, so we are told to do the next best thing and treat everybody in the manner that suits most people. We cannot adjust our teaching to every pupil in the class—so the "democratic" thing is to adjust it to the mean. This turns Lincoln's proposition into a motto of mediocrity, especially if even in daily life, every measure—from taxes to prejudice—is leveled against those who rise above the mean. There must always be an aristocracy of some kind (in royalist, democratic, and communist societies alike), or else the gifted receive neither the chance nor the inducement to develop their excellence and the nation must remain middle-class. It is most unfortunate that:

"Our contemporary American society...has little use for the individualist. Individualism implies dissent from the group; dissent implies conflict; and conflict suddenly seems divisive, un-American and generally unbearable. Our greatest new industry is evidently the production of techniques to eliminate conflict, from positive thoughts through public relations to psychoanalysis, applied everywhere from the couch to the pulpit. Our national aspiration has become peace of mind, peace of soul. The symptomatic drug of our age is the tranquilizer. 'Togetherness' is the banner under which we march into the brave new world."

[Arthur Schlesinger, Jr. [63]]

Under present circumstances, it may not be practical to decide general community problems otherwise than by a majority vote but in scientific, artistic and other cultural matters it is certainly true that: "Any man more right than his neighbors, constitutes a majority of one" [Henry David Thoreau].

The Fear of Boredom

Much has been written about all these motives that unceasingly push the creative mind on to the path of glory; but I have heard little about boredom—one of the mightiest motives of all which acts by ruthlessly blocking all other avenues of escape.

All living things have to do or die. The mouse can restlessly dart hither and thither, but it cannot keep still for long; the bird must fly, the fish must swim, even the plant must grow.

The minimum requirement for activity varies from species to species, from individual to individual, from time to time. It drops quite low when life is slow during sleep or hibernation, during senility or severe disease; it rises high when body and mind are blooming and bursting with the vigor of youth.

The need for physical exercise tends to decrease more rapidly with age than the craving for mental activity. Usually, the body ages sooner than the mind. But if we find no outlet for our energies, they viciously begin to bore inward, destroying themselves and their casing by morbid self-dissection. Enforced inactivity—be it due to laziness or compulsory retirement—breeds insecurity, depression, and hypochondriac preoccupation with body and mind. Busy people have no time to worry even about major setbacks; the inactive fret themselves to while the time away.

Creative people have a tremendous appetite for spiritual outlets; since they have acquired a taste for the great adventures of the mind, nothing else seems to them worthwhile by comparison. Few scientists are amused by anything but science, and I believe that their terrifying fear of boredom drives them away from more wordly occupations just as strongly as their enthusiasm for science attracts them toward research.

2. Who Should Do Research?

"My success as a man of science, whatever this may have amounted to, has been determined, as far as I can judge, by complex and diversified mental qualities and conditions. Of these, the most important have been —the love of science—unbounded patience in long reflecting over any subject—industry in observing and collecting facts—and a fair share of invention as well as of common sense....

"I attempted mathematics, and even went during the summer of 1828 with a private tutor to Barmouth, but I got on very slowly. The work was repugnant to me....

"On the favourable side of the balance, I think that I am superior to the common run of men in noticing things which easily escape attention, and in observing them carefully. My industry has been nearly as great as it could have been in the observation and collection of facts. What is far more important, my love of natural science has been steady and ardent....

"This pure love has, however, been much aided by the ambition to be esteemed by my fellow naturalists."   [Charles Darwin [26]]

"In listing the traits which have seemed to me important for a career of investigation—curiosity, imaginative insight, critical judgement, thorough honesty, a retentive memory, patience, good health, generosity, and the rest—I have not attempted to weigh their relative values. Anyhow, that would be difficult."   [Walter Cannon [16]]

"To summarize their ways concisely, I would say that they put as much audacity into hypothesis as meticulousness into experimentation."
            [Charles Richet [59]]

Of all the questions dealt with in these Notes, the one that I hear most frequently is: "Do you think I have the qualifications needed for research?" But what are these qualifications? The question is of cardinal importance. It is in the belief that he possesses these talents that a person decides to go in for science and is selected for

19

research positions. Even the established investigator must ask himself which of his features he should try to develop or suppress. I have discussed this matter with many people (scientists, educators, psychologists, and officers of granting agencies), but opinions differ enormously. Intelligence, imagination, curiosity, perseverance, the power of observation or of abstract thinking, initiative, technical skill and many other qualifications are singled out as being especially important. Can one generalize? The morphologist will need the power of visual observation much more than the biostatistician; the experimental surgeon or the developer of new instruments will depend more on technical skill than the medical historian.

I am not competent to discuss the qualifications needed for all types of research; let us, therefore, take first the kind I like. I strongly feel that we need more correlators to integrate the enormous mass of data published in the medical journals nowadays; but the more that is published, the fewer the people willing to attempt its integration. Still, remember that the essence of science is the orderly correlation and classification of knowledge, not the mere registration of facts. The unceasing search for new details, and the perfection of methods will and should go on, but this type of work requires a specialized kind of craftsmanship more than true scientific talent.

In any case, as far as possible, I want to speak about things I know from personal experience and not from armchair speculation. To do so, I shall have to use as examples discoveries made by our own group—even if much more important ones can be found in the literature. I know from our seminars how difficult it always is to retrace a trend of thought that has guided us to some new finding; hindsight always tends to idealize, and the retouching may reach monstrous proportions when we try to reconstruct the way others have made their discoveries. Medical literature records the extraordinary foresight, or the complete lack of it, attributed to us by different critics who analyzed the same discovery. The chance of such misunderstandings is ever so much greater in dealing with our predecessors of past centuries, whose personalities, coworkers and working conditions are virtually unknown to us.

In my now nonexistent native land, the Austro-Hungarian Empire, they used to say, *"Wo nichts ist, hat selbst der Kaiser sein Recht verloren"* (Where there is nothing, even the Emperor has lost his rights). Those who just haven't got it won't profit from an analysis of scientific talent. Genius need not be taught. Yet, in that wide range between the most mediocre researcher and the genius, everyone can gain something from an objective survey of his aptitudes.

How should we go about this analysis? In studying disease, it is customary first to consider entire complex syndromes and then to dissect their constituent parts. For example, we must first learn to distinguish between such maladies as tuberculosis, typhoid, and cancer, before we can determine what individual manifestations in various organs are the elements of these diseases. Why not do the same in our analysis of the scientific mentality? Let us first sketch a few of the characteristic, whole personality-types that we meet in labs and then examine their individual basic aptitudes—and inaptitudes.

PERSONALITY TYPES

Sketches of personality types tend to become caricatures or idealized portraits if you have strong feelings about your subject. I cannot help being prejudiced toward certain types of scientists, I might as well admit it. Some types I love and admire, others I hate and despise, so let me start by bringing out through exaggeration the features that I dislike most in them. Then, I shall draw idealized portraits of the perfect chief and perfect disciple. None of these characters exist in a pure state, but it would take a Tolstoi or a Dostoevski to picture scientific personalities as they really are. These sketches of the repulsive and the divine in the scientists I knew, are the best I can offer to remind us of what to avoid and what to emulate. (Just between us, in myself I can discern at least traces of all these types.)

THE DOERS

1. The fact collector. He is interested only in the discovery of new facts. As long as they have not been previously published, all findings are equally interesting (and equally meaningless) to him, because he does not try to evaluate them; any attempt at evaluation strikes him as objectionable blabber.

This type is usually a good observer and very conscientious about his work, but he completely lacks imagination. He keeps regular hours, but rarely has any inducement to work overtime. His teachers or colleagues feel compelled to suggest that he should try a dynamic analysis of his findings, but their remarks invariably fall upon deaf ears. For example, he may spend years on a meticulous examination of the microscopic structure of the tiny pineal gland in all animal species to which he can gain access, without ever attempting to perform a pinealectomy or to prepare a pineal extract in order to find out what this organ is good for. He may conscientiously determine the effect of every newly synthesized steroid hormone upon the preputial gland without ever examining any other effects of these compounds or showing any interest in the function of this gland.

Fact Collectors may find things that are subsequently useful to others—still, I am glad that this type rarely occurs in pure form.

2. The gadgeteer. This kind is closely related to the preceding one. He constantly tries to improve apparatus or techniques and becomes so interested in their perfection that he never gets to use them. Like the Fact Collector, he considers material for discovery as an end in itself. However, the Gadgeteer is much more original, imaginative and emotionally involved in his work; he rarely limits his activity to regular hours.

THE THINKERS

1. The bookworm. This is the purest form of theoretician. He reads voraciously and may accumulate encyclopedic knowledge. The Bookworm is usually very intelligent and shows a great disposition for philosophy, mathematics or statistics; he is well informed about the most complex theoretic aspects of biochemistry and biophysics. Owing to the hours spent in the library, the Bookworm is awkward with his hands in the lab, so he rarely uses them, which makes them still more awkward. He must know everything about his field before starting an experiment and then he decides not to do it after all, because it has been done before or would not reveal anything.

"He who can does. He who cannot, teaches" [George Bernard Shaw [77]]. The Bookworm likes to teach and teaches well. His lessons are highly informative but impersonal. Like the superannuated ballet dancer, he can teach his art to others without being able to perform it any more—the difference being that the Bookworm never was able to perform. He is implacable at examinations, which he uses largely to show off his own knowledge. His superb memory and experience in the construction of indexes and files, often combined with a talent for the clear expression of his views, may become a formidable tool in committee work. The Bookworm agrees to sit on many committees and to do much teaching as welcome excuses for his failure in the laboratory.

2. The classifier. As a child, he used to collect stamps, matchbox covers, butterflies or plants, which he arranged in albums. As a

scientist, he may still collect butterflies or plants for Linnaean systematization, or he may classify scientific literature, steroid hormones, pharmacologic actions, anything that lends itself to the dis-
pelling of confusion by bringing like items together. The Classifier
is closely related to the Fact Collector, but likes only closely related
facts that fit into a series. To a certain extent he is a theorist, since
he assumes something inherently common in the groups he creates;
but he rarely goes on to analyze the nature of this commonness.
Instead, he labels his groups, which satisfies his need in this respect.
Among the medical specialities, dermatology has been most intensely
subjected to the work of Classifiers. Following the example of zoo-
logic, botanical, and microbiologic terminologies, innumerable minor
variants of skin diseases have received scholarly Greco-Latin designations (often embodying the names of the baptizers).

Classifiers have had a great share in the creation of modern
science. As we shall see, the identification of natural units and their
classification into a system is the first step in theory formation. The
Classifier has a true scientific soul; he derives pleasure from the
contemplation of lawfulness in nature, although he rarely explores
further after he has succeeded in putting similar things together. His
greatest dangers are the arrangement of items according to irrelevant
characteristics, and a plethora of neologisms, sometimes aggravated
by egocentric eponymism.

3. The analyst. As a boy, he took his wrist watch apart (although he could not put it together again) because he just had to
know what made it tick. Later, as a scientist, he continued to display the same type of curiosity. One of the purest variants of this
personality is the analytical chemist, who spends all his time in the
search for components, without giving much thought to the manufacture of new compounds by synthesis. In medicine, the Analyst
likes anatomy, histology and analytical biochemistry. (As these
Notes show, he may even become curious about what makes himself
and his friends tick, and feel the urge to analyze the scientific
mentality.)

Some analytical work is an indispensable prerequisite for all classification and synthesis; hence, no investigation can have a broad
scope without it. The danger lies in forgetting that the only purpose
in taking things apart is to find out how they are put together—
preferably with improvements.

4. The synthetist. As a child, he liked to build card houses, or
bridges and towers out of putty and matches. In science, his synthetic
talent depends largely upon certain manual and intellectual skills.

The gift for synthesis shows up well in the most varied fields: synthetic chemistry, instrumentation, theory construction, or plastic surgery. The Synthetist is the highest type of scientist, because analysis and classification are only preambles for synthesis. His greatest danger is that he may forget to ask himself whether the thing he tries to put together is really worth having. Synthesis, like all other skills, may become an aim in itself and never get past the card house stage.

THE EMOTIONALISTS

1. The big boss.   As a child, he was the captain of the team— the winning team. Later he went into science because it has "class." He knew he could win at this game too, and he was right, for he is the born "Fuehrer." His main aim is success, success in anything, success for its own sake. His distorted mind is directed by a monumental inferiority complex, which he despises, and he must hide behind a self-certain, iron façade. His deep wounds were acquired early in childhood. They may have been caused by abject poverty, the ugliness of his features, or social ostracism of his family because of race, religion, alcohol or crime. In any case he was determined to get out from down under; he would show them that, in this big tavern of a world, he can lick anyone at his own game. He might have made almost the same career in business, politics, or the army —but circumstances got him into the "science racket" and, being an opportunist, he wasn't going to miss his chance.

During his early days, as a research assistant, he published some quite creditable work in association with others, but it never became very clear how much of it was done by himself.

He had many love affairs which he always terminated quite brutally, and finally he "married well," thereby improving his social and financial position. Being an excellent politician, committee man, and organizer, it did not take him long to become chief of a research department.

Even now, his greatest asset is string-pulling and making others do his work. His shifty eyes never look straight at you, except to give an order which he knows will be obeyed. Despite his egocentric cruelty, he is hearty, in a condescendingly back-slapping way. He is easily on first-name terms, even with his subordinates, and loves to use jargon. His expressions are hypererudite or vulgar, depending upon the occasion; he uses them with equal ease to play the role of the remote Olympian or the democratic "good guy," as required by the circumstances. He has a prima-donna complex and is essentially a narcissist, very proud of his "vision for what is important in science," although his extroverted, self-centered, cast-iron mind refuses to understand the real values beneath the surface. By skillful participation on the advisory boards of granting agencies and at the dinner tables of millionaires, he succeeds in attracting a great deal of money to his university. Thereby, he manages to enlarge his department and staff to a point where he can keep informed about their work just sufficiently to report on it (though not always correctly) at meetings with "important people." He no longer has time for the lab, but after all, he did just as well as the best among the eggheads, the ivory-tower dreamers, when it came to the tangible status symbols of research. He is satisfied. But, during the rare moments of introspection—when he is tired or slightly drunk—he wonders . . . he wishes he had . . . but no, all he needs is a rest.

As you may gather, I don't like this type very much, but don't underrate him; one or the other variant of him will have power over you throughout your life.

2. The eager beaver. He is so anxious to get there fast that he has no time to think about where he really wants to go. Being an opportunist and a compulsive worker, he explores questions, not because they interest him particularly, but because he happens to have everything needed for a quick solution. When he is young, he hurries to get on the next rung of the career ladder, because there is still such a long stretch to the top—and when he is on top, he hurries because there is so little time left. Actually, he likes speed for its own sake, as the sportsman does.

These young men in a hurry do not love Nature, but merely rape her. They may possess her body as much as we do—but not her spirit.

3. The cold fish. He is the ostentatiously unemotional skeptic. With his blank face he murmurs the mottoes of his breed: "Take it easy"; "This is not likely to work"; "You didn't prove your point and there is really no way to prove it"; "You aren't the first to find this." His social life is guided by the code: "Ask no favors, do no favors." And at the end of his course we find the epitaph: "No hits, no runs, no errors."

4. The desiccated-laboratory-female. She is the bitter, hostile, bossy and unimaginative female counterpart of the Cold Fish. Usually a technician, she rarely gets past the B.Sc., or at most, the M.Sc. degree, but she may be a Ph.D., less commonly an M.D. In any event, she assumes a dominant position in her own group, has very little understanding of human frailties among her subordinates and almost invariably falls in love with her immediate boss. She may be very useful in performing exacting, dull jobs herself and in enforcing discipline upon others, but tends to create more tension and dissatisfaction than the results warrant. Some women make excellent scientists, but this type never does.

5. The narcissist. The embodiment of pure egocentricity, he stands in constant awe of his own talents and is ready for any sacrifice to promote their fulfillment. Each time he performs an operation he relates, to everyone within reach, the incredible complications that have arisen and how they were all successfully overcome. Each time he makes a new (or not so new), significant (or not so significant) observation, he ennumerates all the far-reaching consequences this discovery may have upon the progress of science. Sometimes he takes pains to emphasize the great intricacy and originality of his train of thought and the almost insuperable technical difficulties that had to be mastered to make his observation possible. But, curiously, at other times he derives just as much pleasure from having done it all with the greatest of ease, or even by sheer accident. To the Narcissist, the conquest of obstacles and the stroke of luck are equally eloquent witnesses of his greatness. Since he is not unintelligent, he sometimes senses the danger of inviting derision, if not hostility, by what others may consider obnoxiously ostentatious vanity, but this does not faze him. He merely suggests, with a contented smile, that his apparent immodesty is only make-believe, or a charming exaggeration for fun—but of course, facts are facts, and we are allowed to read between the lines of his modest remarks.

The self-assured Narcissist goes no further, but there are two insecure variants of this type who constantly scan the horizon for possible threats to their prestige and honor:

(a) The *mimosa type* responds to most stimuli by freezing in his tracks and assuming the pouting countenance of complete indifference. He often feels boycotted or left out of things and complains, "Nobody ever tells ME anything."

(b) The cantankerous *toreador type* creates emergencies on purpose so that he may exhibit the manly courage with which he can meet them. "No one is going to tell ME what to do," he says, kicking up a terrible row whenever he thinks someone might question his authority.

6. The aggressive-arguer. In school he was the smart aleck who knew it all, and in the research laboratory he remains insufferably cocksure. In scientific arguments, he is interested mainly in being right and defends his point by special pleading, using misleading argument or even straight bluff. This is a dangerous variant of the Narcissist; he can singlehandedly create tensions which destroy the harmony of even the most congenial group.

7. The credit-shark. His main preoccupation is with getting his name on as many papers as possible. In the lab, he constantly irritates his colleagues by suggesting that whatever they are doing was actually stimulated by his own earlier remarks. He may be brutally blunt about this if he thinks he is right, or he will take great care to camouflage his assertions in an air of self-evidence, if he knows he is bluffing. For example, he may exclaim with enthusiasm: "As I was saying just the other day, this is exactly the kind of work you should be doing," or "This is a beautiful confirmation of my thesis that...." At the autopsy table, he hurries to a colleague's animals, so that he may be first to point out anatomic changes that anyone would have observed in due course. In papers, he writes long legalistic introductions to prove that, although what he is about to describe has been seen by many others, he is the first to describe and interpret it quite the right way, and his contribution is what really counts.

8. The saint. Truly chaste in thought, word and deed, he is the Knight of the Holy Grail. As a boy scout, he vowed to do not one, but ten good deeds a day. Later, he went into medicine only because of its humanitarian goals. At first, the Saint studied tropical medicine, because he planned to practice in a leprosarium; but upon reading Sinclair Lewis' "Arrowsmith," he came to the conclusion that in the laboratory he could do even more for his fellow man. He does not play the role of the Saint, he really is one. And although his self-effacing altruism represents a terrible handicap to his efficiency in the lab, I lack the courage to draw the caricature of such a truly likeable and respectable person. The qualifications of the Saint would have suited him better for the leprosarium than for the laboratory. He should not have chosen the life of an investigator, but the desecration of icons is in bad taste, even if they do not render special services. In any event, he is only one in a million, so let us keep his image untarnished as a symbol of purity, beyond the reach of our worldly critique.

9. The saintly one. He imitates the real Saint. With an ostentatiously modest, sanctimonious bearing, he strikes the attitude of the "knight in shining armor" when he speaks about his aims in medicine. His smile is benign and self-righteous; it suggests tolerance

and compassion for his colleagues who just do not have a properly
developed sense of right and wrong. This type is almost as rarely
found in laboratories as the true Saint.

10. *The goody-goody.* In grade school he was the teacher's pet;
in medical school, he asked the professor, "What are we responsible
for at examinations?" After he got married, he became a conscientious breadwinner, but his work as a scientist suffers severely from
his sincere desire to give his wife the attention she deserves. He lives
mainly for her and for his children and is willing to do (or renounce)
anything for their happiness. Despite the superficial resemblance,
he is quite unlike the Saint who, on the contrary, sacrifices the family to his moral ideals. The Goody-Goody may be quite intelligent,
but his insipid innocence, his complete lack of imagination and
initiative disqualify him for meaningful scientific research, and he
tends to use his self-imposed restrictions as an excuse for inefficiency.
He is willing to sacrifice his career for that of his children, who
must receive all the privileges that he never had; the Goody-Goody
does not feel that in the succession of generations he is the one whose
work should bear fruit. His desires are honorable, but he forgets that
he could have fulfilled them better had he chosen another walk of
life.

The basic defects of the preceding ten personality types are excessive self-effacement or egocentricity and exhibitionism which over-
shadow all other forms of scientific motivation. These personality
traits, whether morally good or bad, are sterilizing because they
focus attention upon the investigator rather than the investigation.
Both the Saint and the Narcissist, to take extreme opposites, are
more preoccupied with the value of their own conduct than with
the progress of knowledge. We may admire or despise them, but their
place is not in the laboratory.

THE IDEALS

1. *Faust: the ideal teacher and chief.* The pure philosopher-
scientist has a religious reverence for Nature, but is humbly aware
of man's limited power to explore its secrets. He has a profound
and compassionate understanding for human frailties, but his kindness does not mislead him into unwarranted tolerance for lack of
discipline, superficiality of work, or any other form of behavior incompatible with his calling. His somewhat romantic attitude toward research exhibits sentiment, but no sentimentality. His main
assets are: an enthusiasm for the possibilities of research rather

than for his own possibilities; respect for the interests of others; a great capacity for singling out important facts; a keen power of observation; lack of blinding prejudice toward man and scientific data; an iron-cast self-discipline, as well as great originality and imagination, combined with scrupulous attention to detail both in laboratory technique and in the logical evaluation of results.

He is neither broken by failure, nor corrupted by victory. Having decided early in life what he considers to be worth living for, he follows a steady course uninhibited by remorse, temptation, fear or even success. Despite the infinite complications of his work, he remains a simple and real person; no amount of adulation can turn him into a "distinguished personage."

2. *Famulus: the ideal pupil and assistant.* I left him to the last for, like his master, he is the perfect blend of all other types, but in addition he represents the Future. Famulus combines some of the Saint's austere idealism with just enough of each kind of sinful lust to give him the worldliness and healthy appetite needed for an eager and efficient exploration of the world in and around us. The ideal junior basic scientist differs from his teacher and chief only in that we meet him at an earlier point in his course—when he is still less mellowed by experience. His mind is not as mature as that of his spiritual father, still not necessarily richer in youthful vigor. Daring and perseverance in strenuous tasks are qualities we associate with the vigor and strength of youth. Yet, young Famulus may be more cautious and preoccupied with his own security than old Faust, and his less trained mind may not be as resistant to the stress of prolonged abstract thinking. But his body stands up much better to the exigencies of the lab; his eyesight is keener, his movements more certain; he can stand at the work bench for hours without fatigue, and, most important of all, he has so much more time ahead to make his dreams come true. That is why Famulus is really the most important of our personages. But I need not explain him to you, young man. You know him well already. For you want to be he as much as I want to be Faust, though neither of us can ever succeed. Ideals are not created to be attained, but to point the way. It is good to see clearly in whose image we should try, as best we can, to create ourselves.

Epilogue

None of these prototypes exist in pure form; their characteristics overlap and many other personality traits may be so dominant in certain individuals as to justify the listing of innumerable additional types. Here, I have tried to sketch only the type of people whom I have met most often, or who left the most profound impressions upon me—good or bad.

If we now look back upon our list, we see that some scientists are predominantly doers, others thinkers, and yet others, the emotionalists, so intensely preoccupied with themselves that their interest in Nature takes second place.

The ideal scientist is not, and perhaps even should not be free of characteristics distasteful to the average citizen. Society sanctions the motives that are best for the majority, and scientists are a very small minority. Men are not created equal and should not try to be alike. The splendid musculature of the athlete is admired but not coveted by his wife; the scientist's passion for objectivity would be no asset to the nonobjective painter.

In my long career, I have met no outstanding scientist who was entirely free of egotism or vanity, and in the single-minded pursuit of their aims, few of them spent as much time with their families or gave as much attention to political problems as the average good citizen should. To my mind, the highest qualities of mankind are a warmhearted attitude toward our kin, and particularly compassion for all who suffer from disease, poverty or oppression. Yet, each of us needs different, additional motivations and skills to contribute his best in the service of his fellow man. My purpose here is not to sit in judgment over good and bad, but merely to identify the basic qualifications that characterize the scientists I know. Such an analysis can help each of us select and reject what does or does not fit his personality. All I can do is to dissect and characterize the parts that I have learned to see, but the reader of these Notes will have to do the selecting and rejecting himself, in consonance with his own needs and abilities.

Now that we have introduced the "dramatis personae" as general types, we can proceed to analyze the basic aptitudes and drives which make them what they are.

BASIC QUALIFICATIONS

The same word—especially if attached to abstract concepts—has different meanings for different people. The terms "originality," "independence of thought," "imagination" and "intuition" are often used interchangeably, yet, for our purposes, we shall have to differentiate between such shadings in meaning. Formal definitions will not be enough, because again their interpretation depends upon the meaning we attach to words; besides, dictionaries give so many alternative definitions of abstract ideas that it is difficult to know which to accept in a given case. In the following pages we shall have to use a great many abstract terms, and by way of introduction it may help to list them with a few explanatory remarks. Later, in the course of our more detailed discussion, the precise meaning attached to each term will become more evident.

To my mind, the innumerable mental and physical qualifications that make a scientist, can be roughly classified into six principal categories:

1. *Enthusiasm and Perseverance.*
2. *Originality.* Independence of thought, imagination, intuition, genius.
3. *Intelligence.* Logic, memory, experience, concentration, abstraction.
4. *Ethics.* Honesty with self.
5. *Contact with Nature.* Observation, technical skill.
6. *Contact with People.* Understanding of self and others, compatibility, organization of teams, convincing others and listening to argument.

The perennial question "Which gift is most important?" can hardly be answered. In the context of the scientist's environment and special subject, success may be more or less dependent upon technical skill, the gift of observation, or the ability to get along with associates. But the other qualifications are indispensable whatever his field of interest, whatever the social setting in which he works. Any attempt to list these basic qualifications according to their importance would be arbitrary; but there is no doubt in my mind that the rarest gift is originality. I mentioned enthusiasm first in the preceding list, because, without motivation to do research, none of the other qualifications do any good. In practice, however, lack of enthusiasm is rarely a problem; laziness is very uncommon among scientists. The reverse is true of originality. Independence of thought, initiative, imagination, intuitiveness and genius —the principal manifestations of originality in research—are undoubtedly the most exceptional gifts that characterize only the elite among scientists and it is astonishing to what extent this one gift can compensate for deficiencies in all other respects.

ENTHUSIASM AND PERSEVERANCE

Enthusiasm means interest, zeal, fervor, or passion; a strong feeling of excitement on behalf of a cause. It provides intense motivation to achieve certain aims, and a power of perseverance in the face of obstacles. The principal ingredients of the scientific mentality are enthusiasm for progress and a habitual dissatisfaction with things as they are. No placid, contented type has ever achieved scientific eminence. But the motivation for enthusiasm has already been discussed (p. 5); here we shall speak only of perseverance.

Perseverance is the power for the continued, steadfast pursuit of an undertaking. It depends on single-mindedness of purpose without obstinacy; it requires resistance to failure, to dullness, and even to success; it derives strength from healthy optimism, courage, and faith.

Single-Mindedness of Purpose

"The lame in the path outstrip the swift who wander from it."
[Francis Bacon]

"Art is a jealous mistress, and, if a man have a genius for painting, poetry, music, architecture, or philosophy, he makes a bad husband, and an ill-provider."   [Ralph Waldo Emerson]

"What is the use of redoubling our efforts, if we have forgotten our goal?"   [G. K. Chesterton]

"However, science demands much greater sacrifices. It does not permit any sharing. It demands that certain men devote to it their whole existence, their whole intelligence, their whole labour."   [Charles Richet [59]]

"To know when to persevere and when to stop, that is the gift of talent and almost of genius."   [Charles Richet [59]]

As I have said, simple laziness is very exceptional among scientists, although many of them work in spurts interrupted by periods when they are just not in the mood. It takes considerable will power to overcome the feeling of letdown after a difficult task is completed— or the sense of frustration that comes from long continued failure. But, perhaps worst of all are the paralyzing guilt feelings about things we should, but do not want, to do.

The scientist who is indefatigable in amassing references may be too lazy to repeat a somewhat ambiguous experiment or vice versa. The investigator who works assiduously for months in the lab may then find the most childish excuses for postponing the task of collating and describing his data. As a class, scientists are extremely disinclined to do anything they do not particularly like to do. They are willing to work hard even on a painstaking, repetitive, and boring routine, but only if and when they are fully convinced that this kind of work is indispensable for the solution of an important problem. Often, they are consciously or subconsciously uncertain about whether more laboratory work should be done, or whether the time has come to write up their findings. In the resulting indecision, they may be able to do neither. This kind of laziness is common among scientists; a great deal of introspection and self-discipline is necessary to overcome it. Yet it is not sufficient to make a discovery or even to describe it briefly. Despite all difficulties, it has to be worked out to a point where others will accept the idea and carry on the work. Steinhaeuser discovered in 1840 that cod-liver oil cures rickets, but this enormously important fact remained no more than an opinion and, hence, unexploited for the next eighty years [Wilfred Trotter [84]].

There are many other threats to perseverance. The work of the scientist may also be too frequently interrupted by overconscientious attendance to demands on his time made by his wife, family, and friends; he is much less inclined to have scruples about refusing participation in committee work, undergraduate teaching, academic, and formal social functions. Researchers in industry, engineers, physicians, lawyers, businessmen or teachers may be very competent in their professions without the need for such single-mindedness of purpose, but most career scientists have few "outside" or parascientific interests (p. 145).

Even after a certain balance has been reached between scientific and other activities, the great problem remains: how long should we persist with work on a research project which just refuses to yield results? It is not easy to draw the line between patience and obstinacy.

Few really great investigators succumb to the temptation of working on many totally unrelated problems. Usually, the first really significant discovery gives direction to the whole subsequent life of its discoverer. In the course of this tenacious effort to follow one big problem, wherever it may lead, the scientist is highly adaptable; he will learn or actually invent new techniques or develop completely unexpected applications of his discovery, rather than change his field.

Pasteur, who started out by studying bacterial fermentation, stuck to this problem throughout his life and, although he was not a physician, he eventually revolutionized medicine by demonstrating the widespread participation of microorganisms in biology. He began by studying the effect of fermentation upon grapes and found that what he called the "diseases of wines" are due to the enzymatic actions of microorganisms. Then he went on to look for germs as the possible cause of diseases among silkworms and eventually founded clinical bacteriology.

Similarly, Claude Bernard, one of the greatest physiologists of all times, started out in 1843 as a very young man by determining sugar in blood and urine, and his last article, published after his death in 1878, was still related to glucose determinations. This single-mindedness of purpose is not due to lack of ideas. On the contrary, it represents the victory of a highly imaginative mind which, despite all obstacles and temptations, is kept on a single, fruitful path by an iron will. This kind of perseverance is characteristic of genius. In a few apparently unimportant observations the highly gifted mind can discern the seeds for an immense field which needs undivided attention to become sufficiently obvious for subsequent exploitation by the masses. "The genius of a good leader is to leave behind him a situation which common sense, without the grace of genius, can deal with successfully" [Walter Lippmann].

Resistance to Failure and Dullness

"It is a rough road that leads to the heights of greatness."   [Seneca]

"...And yet it was in this miserable old shed that the best and happiest years of our life were spent, entirely consecrated to work. Often I have prepared our meals on the spot, so that we should not have to interrupt some particularly important operation. I sometimes passed the whole day stirring a mass in ebullition, with an iron rod nearly as big as myself. In the evening I was broken with fatigue."   [Eve Curie [24]]

In general, original thinkers are especially sensitive to dullness. The imaginative mind is eager to fly from discovery to discovery and resents being constantly grounded by the need to check its bearings through meticulous measurement. In fact, it has often been said that one of the most characteristic features of the exceptional genius is the rare combination of bold imagination with meticulous attention to detail in the objective verification of ideas.

For young people especially, it is difficult to resist the temptation to get bored with time-consuming, complex problems and to follow up every promising new lead, whenever they stumble upon readily accessible but unimportant things. Here, a great deal of faith and courage is needed for perseverance, because the farther we reach out from the commonplace into the unknown the more inaccessible our aim—and the less understanding and support can we expect from others.

In my own limited field, I have had to learn this by bitter experience. After my first observations on the production of a stereotyped syndrome by various agents had led me to the formulation of the stress concept,* I met with little encouragement to persevere along these lines. I remember the reaction of one senior investigator whom I admired very much, and whose opinion meant a great deal to me. He was a real friend who seriously wanted to help me with my research efforts. One day I was asked into his office for a good heart-to-heart talk. He reminded me that for months now he had attempted to convince me that I must abandon this futile line of research on whatever I called "stress." He assured me that, in his opinion, I possessed all the essential qualifications of an investigator and that I could undoubtedly contribute something even to the generally recognized and accepted field of endocrinology in which I had been active before. So why bother with this wild-goose chase? With the youthful enthusiasm of my twenty-eight years I met these remarks only by an outburst of uncontrolled confidence in the new point of view. I outlined again, as I had done so often before, the immense possibilities inherent in a study of the stress which must accompany all diseases and all but the mildest medications and exertions.

When he he saw me thus launched on yet another enraptured description of what I had observed in animals stressed with this or that impure, toxic material, he looked at me with desperately sad eyes and said in obvious despair, "But, Selye, try to realize what you are doing before it is too late! You have now decided to spend your entire life studying *the phrarmacology of dirt!*"

Of course, he was right. Nobody could have expressed it more poignantly. That is why it hurt so much that I still remember the phrase today, twenty-seven years later. Pharmacology is the science which explores the actions of specific drugs or poisons, and I was going to study nothing but their undesired, incidental, that is, non-specific side effects that they share with any kind of dirt. But to me, "the pharmacology of dirt" seemed the most promising subject in medicine.

Now, after all these years I look at my favorite topic, perhaps with a little more objective detachment, but I do not regret having stuck to it. Even my current subject of calciphylaxis † is but another outgrowth of the original idea that nonspecific, connective-tissue

---

* The sum of all nonspecific changes caused by function or damage; also defined as the rate of wear and tear in the body. (For detailed description see p. 239.)

† A biologic mechanism through which the organism can send large amounts of calcium and phosphate selectively to certain regions. (For detailed description see p. 241.)

reactions to injury are largely conditioned by humoral factors which can be analyzed, identified, and, within limits, influenced at will.

Of course, it is probable that the same facts to which I was led through the stress concept would have been found by someone else guided by an entirely different theory. In the great network of Nature, all parts are interrelated and the same point may be reached by different pathways. If you look at a person through red glasses, you can see and recognize him, although you think he is all red; someone else who looks at him through green glasses sees him just as well, though in a different color. But what is the point of changing glasses all the time? We get much further if we adapt our eyes to those we have on. It usually takes a whole lifetime to learn how to look through the wide-angle lenses of a broad, theoretic concept. That is why neither temporary failures nor the monotony of meticulous verification should break our perseverance if the final aim seems worthwhile.

At this point it may be rewarding to say a few words about the very important problem of overcoming inhibitions and feelings of inferiority in the early stages of a scientific career. It is estimated (John Keats, *Life* magazine, June 21, 1963) that six of every ten students who enter college leave before graduation, most of them at the end of the sophomore year. Quitting school, even by those who can afford advanced learning, has become a major national problem. E. R. Iffert of the United States Department of Health, Education and Welfare, one of the government's leading authorities on college drop-outs says, "College students almost unanimously complain that most college teaching is bad. The withdrawal from college is not associated so much with dissatisfactions, as with the inability or unwillingness to endure dissatisfaction." Some students just refuse to put up with anything they depise. College drop-outs are often very talented and original thinkers, but they are unable to adjust themselves to the established routine of the school. Even at the best colleges an intelligent student cannot help noticing that some courses are bad, that some obligatory lab work is useless because he knows it already, that some exam questions are silly.

At my alma mater the students used to say with some malice that, in general, profs can be grouped into three categories according to the exam questions they ask: 1) the narcissists, who ask questions to show how bright they are; 2) the vicious ones, to show how stupid the students are; 3) the kindly ones, to show how bright the students are. Only the exceptionally few remaining profs examine merely to find out what the student knows. That may be a slight exaggeration, but in any event, the strong personality adapts himself to his teachers as far as necessary and does not waste time grumbling about the unavoidable.

Another difficulty of the college drop-out is that he dreads the necessity of having to perform when told, right here and now. More particularly, he refuses to face the possibility of humiliation in competitive effort where his performance is continually compared with that of his colleagues. He may not even want to participate in competitive sports, although he may like noncompetitive physical exercises and be very efficient at them. This attitude is often wrongly ascribed to laziness. The typical college quitter is not lazy, only inflexible and unwilling to be integrated into a group or to shoulder full responsibility for a complex task.

In research, the same kind of person will do well just puttering about in the lab; he can never fully exploit the field by planned systematic work, especially if this requires taking charge of a group or, at least, becoming part of it. He can also write excellent little papers but never an extensive review or monograph. In the literary sphere he may become a first-rate critic, but the original novel or even short story that he is always planning to write never materializes. He may even talk himself into believing that there is no point in a college education because he can learn as much by studying on his own. The truth is, he just does not have enough self-discipline to overcome the terrible inhibitions that almost every writer faces when he has to stop vaguely talking and dreaming about his work; when the time comes to sit down and write definite text whose shortcomings stare bleakly back at their creator, making all but the strongest-willed blench and crawl back to the comfort of leisurely mediocrity.

There are even students who prefer to think that they quit because they are not good enough for college. My experience is virtually limited to Ph.D. candidates, but among these, alas, those who lacked talent could never be made to see this—while I lost many a truly gifted student because of his insurmountable feelings of inferiority.

Resistance to Success

"Among all the great scientists that I have known, Mrs. Curie was the only one who remained totally unspoiled by success."   [Albert Einstein]

Many more people can face failure than success. Adversity may even ennoble a man by bringing out the best in him, while fame degrades all but the greatest to the state of conceited authority

symbols or, at best, reduces them to benign patrons of the fame-
less.

Just as the work of talent leads to fame, so does fame lead talent
away from work. It does so in many ways. First, there is that feeling
of letdown whenever an arduous task is finally achieved. "The mel-
ancholia of everything completed!" [Friedrich Wilhelm Nietzsche]
During a concerted effort, the investigator's mind, his assistants, his
instruments, are all adjusted to a certain type of work which, no
matter how original, becomes standardized in its detail. When the
aim is reached, the habit of the daily routine is suddenly broken.
During the ensuing sinister lull there is no enticing goal to work for.
The scientist is faced only with the depressing task of dismantling
the whole, highly perfected machinery of specialized thoughts and
facilities, of clearing mind and lab alike for some new use. But for
what? The investigator has been so much absorbed in the preceding
task that his mind is now ill prepared for anything else. If his work
has led to an outstanding accomplishment, nothing seems worthwhile
by comparison.

Many—no, I should say most—scientists, are eventually bogged
down by the by-products of their own successes. They are given large
institutes which must be administered; they have a voluminous correspondence; invitations come for lectures, monographs, reviews,
dedication of new labs or hospitals; more and more visitors must be
received; innumerable former students ask for letters of recommendation every time they change their jobs, etc., etc. None of these interruptions in the scientist's work can be avoided easily. He may even
welcome some of them—but eventually there is nothing left but interruptions.

Success also stultifies by the adulation it creates. Through fame
the person becomes a personage. Like it or not, he has to submit
gracefully to a certain amount of celebration—press, radio, television,
academic convocations—or else his reticence will offend. Then the
personage becomes an oracle. Even if his training is limited to biochemistry, his opinion will be sought on all kinds of political,
philosophic or even religious questions; and if he considers himself
incompetent to answer, he will only be accused of conceited indifference. Finally, the Great Man must "lend his name" to every
worthy cause, and that includes writing articles, speech-making, or
at least sitting silently for hours on platforms and at speakers' tables
with no other task at hand but that of putting on an impressive
countenance.

Thus, inexorably, fame kills the real person by petrifying the man into a monument of his own past accomplishments. This is not the kind of recognition the scientist needs, but it may take as much energy to fight the consequences of fame as it took to do the work that made him famous.

Courage

"The mariner of old said thus to Neptune in a great tempest, 'O, God! thou mayest save me if thou wilt, and if thou wilt, thou mayest destroy me; but whether or no, I will steer my rudder true.' "

[Michel de Montaigne]

We must educate our youth to understand that in this Age of Basic Research man's great wars will not be fought with the strength of youthful muscles; his battles will not be won by the glorious, intoxicating, momentary courage to face a bayonet and to die for a cause if need be. Our children must learn that from now on man's great fights in peace, as in war, will be won by heroes of a different stamp, men with the strength of intellect and that more exceptional, persistent kind of courage—the sober determination to dedicate their whole life to what they think is a worthwhile aim for existence. Youth will have to learn that it is much more difficult to live for a cause than to die for it.

Few people would think of courage as a particularly important qualification for a scientific career. In the usual sense of the word it is not. It is true that occasionally a bacteriologist accidentally infects himself with a deadly germ; some early X-ray workers (including Walter Cannon) suffered permanent damage when appropriate protective measures were not yet known; a toxicologist may fall victim to one of his fatal poisons. Because of their human appeal, such accidents are often overdramatized, but they are not more common among scientists than in other walks of life. Despite these hazards, it certainly takes no great bravery to become an investigator.

Sometimes a physician performs some experiments on himself but they are rarely dangerous. This voluntary exposure to risk makes an even greater impression upon the public than do accidents. Yet, I think it is rather silly for a scientist to make his contribution by acting as a guinea pig, except in very rare instances when no other form of experimentation could bring us the solution of a truly important problem. Each person should give according to his finest talents; let us leave the glory of sheer physical valor to the armed forces.

The scientist needs a less spectacular but more lasting kind of courage to enter a career which he knows will be so exacting as largely to deprive him of family life, wealth, and leisure. As a young physician he must be willing to accept a poorly paid laboratory position when he could easily make two or three times as much in practice. As he becomes more proficient he will have to be very brave to resist the inevitable offers of highly paid and influential administrative posts. Even greater courage will be needed to go on with unorthodox scientific projects that receive neither moral nor financial support.

A young man who wants to enter the career of research must be able to reassess his values and renounce many of the accepted symbols of success, particularly the trite cult of the "high living standard." This takes considerable courage and faith, above all faith in his own, still untested capacities.

Faith

We have become accustomed to thinking that while religions are built on faith, and poetry on dreams, the prime prerequisite for research is pure intellect. Yet, the basic researcher must also be able to dream and have faith in his own dreams. To make a great dream come true, the first requirement is a great capacity to dream; the second is persistence—continued faith in the dream. Pure intellect is largely a quality of the middle-class mind. The lowliest hooligan and the greatest creator in any field of human endeavor are driven by imponderable instincts and emotions, especially by an unreasoned desire for, and faith in, success. Scientific research—the most purely intellectual creative effort of which man is capable—represents no exception in this respect. The initial impulse and the strength to persevere both feed on emotion; intellect is merely a powerful weapon that faith uses to attain its goal.

The following poem, or prayer—I don't know which, perhaps both, perhaps neither—was written at a time when its author reached an important crossroad between the safe but by now commonplace and the hazardous but still excitingly new. He had to choose between either continuing work on the then accepted lines of classic stress research—for which his Institute was equipped and financed—or shifting over to the new, wholly untested field of calciphylaxis. The decision was difficult; it implied the complete reorientation of a large institute (118 people and several hundred thousand dollars were involved), and the choice had to be made on the basis of a few chance observations whose only fascination was that they did not seem to fit anywhere into what was then known.

Almighty Drive who, through the ages,
Have kept men trying to master Nature by understanding,
Give me faith—for that is what I need most now.

This is a rare and solemn moment in my life:
I stumbled across what seems to be
A new path into the unknown.
A road that promises to lead me closer to You:
The law behind the unknown.

I think I have the instinctive feeling,
And patiently, through the years, I have acquired the kind of knowledge
Needed to explore Your laws.
But my faith was weakened by this apprenticeship.
No longer can it steer me steadily towards my goal.
For I have come to distrust faith and overvalue proof.
So, let reverence for the unfailing power of all Your known laws
Be the source of my faith in the worth of discovering the next commandment.

Sometimes I feel lonesome, uncertain on my new trail,
For where I go no one has been before
And there is no one with whom to share the things I see—or think I see.
Still, to succeed, I must convince others to follow me and help;
For I also need their faith in me to reinforce my own
Which has so little evidence to lean on now,
For now is the beginning.

A long and hazardous course lies between me and my goal,
How could I travel alone?
How could I force this fog of half-understanding,
That confuses my sense of direction?

The other shore is not in sight—alas, there may be none:
Yet I—like all those who, before me,
Have succumbed to the lure of the vast unknown—
Must take this risk in exchange
For each chance to experience the thrill of discovery.

And that thrill I need, or my mind will perish,
For—thanks to You—it was not built to stand
The stale security of well-charted shore waters.

I cannot know whether You listen,
But I do know that I must pray:

Almighty Drive who, through the ages,
Have kept men trying to master Nature by understanding.
Give me faith now—for that is what I need most.

Health and Vigor

"It is easy to see that vigorous health is a great advantage in research as in other activities."   [Walter Cannon [16]]

"I have known no man of genius who had not to pay, in some affliction or defect either physical or spiritual, for what the gods had given him."
[Max Beerbohm]

It may seem superfluous to mention health and vigor as useful assets in the pursuit of scientific research. They are more or less essential for any career and perhaps less so for the sedentary life of a scientist than for most other occupations. The basic researcher certainly does not need a powerful musculature; but a weak, disease-ridden body or one softened by excessive pampering does not stand up well to the hard exigencies of peak accomplishment in any field. The scientist who has to spend long hours on his feet in the lab, or to muster up all his mental forces for long periods of abstract thinking, should have a disciplined, wiry—I would almost say Spartan —personality. He has to find ways to keep fit despite the artificial living habits imposed by lab work.

It is true that sometimes a physical or spiritual defect may be the driving force that induces a man to sublimate his talents into creative, intellectual activity, but if so, he will be even more dependent than the average person upon a disciplined attention to fitness.

ORIGINALITY

The power of original, creative thought reflects an independent freshness of aspect. By independence of thought I mean particularly initiative and resourcefulness in taking the introductory step. This, in turn, depends upon imagination, the power to form a conscious idea of something not previously perceived in reality. It requires vision, the discernment and foresight of what is important at a time when importance is not yet obvious.

Independence of Thought

"He is great who is what he is from Nature, and who never reminds us of others."   [Ralph Waldo Emerson]

"Genius, in truth, means little more than the faculty of perceiving in an unhabitual way."   [William James]

The hopeless inadequacy of words as vehicles of information is most painfully obvious when we want to explain the nature of originality. Words are symbols for things we know from previous experience; it is the very essence of the original to be unlike anything previously experienced. If I had to make some generalization about originality, I would say that the most usual aspect of all its manifestations is their unusualness. But, of course, this is not all. The madman's mind is unusual, but he pushes independence of thought to a point where contact with reality is lost. He is unlike anyone else. He perceives things in an unhabitual way, but, having gone too far into the land of imagination, he cannot come back to us with the fruits reaped by his novel way of looking at the world.

Genius can have almost equally fantastic dreams and yet wake up to check, by meticulous, objective tests, what aspects of a dream reflect reality. It is this capacity during dreams to remain sufficiently in touch with the world, to discern values meaningful to mankind, that is most characteristic of the originality and independence of creative thought. Genius is not only capable of going out far into the unknown; it can also come back to earth.

The would-be painter in the *Quartier Latin* of Paris who wears a funny beret with a bright red scarf and grows a vandyke beard is unusual—but not necessarily a Van Dyke. He confuses superficial peculiarities in the external appearance of old masters with the profound originality that made them great. He is like the Famulus in Goethe's Faust who tried to emulate his great master by clearing his throat and spitting the way his chief did.

Scientific resourcefulness, independence from established custom in taking the introductory step, is a form of opportunism, but a very special kind. The common opportunist does not think of farfetched things in an original way; on the contrary, he takes advantage of opportunities as they arise, to the disregard of higher aims that are perhaps more, though not immediately, beneficial.

Resourcefulness is a valuable attribute, even at the lower levels of research activity, but far-reaching independence of thought is also the basis of imagination and intuition, the most important attributes of scientific genius.

Control of Prejudice

"The dispassionate intellect, the open mind, the unprejudiced observer, exist in an exact sense only in a sort of intellectualist folk-lore; states even approaching them cannot be reached without a moral and emotional effort most of us cannot or will not make."   [Wilfred Trotter [84]]

"Prejudice, preconceived ideas and systems of ideas, enthusiasm for his own point of view—these are the working attributes of a productive scientist. Yet he must unerringly, in the crisis of a contradiction, by the data, of all he has cherished in theory or prediction, renounce Love for Duty (like the hero of a Victorian novel)."   [Alan C. Burton [15]]

On the one hand, we are told with great justification that the true scientist must be able to rid himself of prejudice, to shake himself out of the accustomed channels of thought, for only thus can he have an open mind and observe something that he was not looking for ("Peripheral Vision" p. 78) or formulate an entirely novel thought. On the other hand, the really unprejudiced thinker knows that he cannot and should not rid himself of prejudice. If he did, he would lose all the advantages of experience that his mind has acquired not only during his own life but in the course of evolution throughout the ages. The totally unprejudiced individual who gives equal consideration to every possibility, would be unfit not only for science but even for survival. The fact is that creative scientists are full of preconceived ideas and passions. They consider certain results likely, others unlikely; they want to prove their pet theories and are very disappointed if they can't. And why shouldn't they be prejudiced? Their prejudices are the most valuable fruits of their experience. Without them they could never choose among the countless possible paths that can be taken.

What we really mean by the "unprejudiced mind" of the scientist is a mentality that has control over its numerous prejudices, and is always willing to reconsider them in the face of contrary evidence. Though his mind is most strongly prejudiced in favor of logic, the scientist must accept a fact, even if it is contrary to logic. That is why creative research cannot be guided by formal logic. Indeed, since the scientist will always accept the primacy of the fact whether it seems rational or not, the highest type of scientific work is paradoxically antilogical or at least nonlogical.

Imagination

"Man consists of body, mind, and imagination. His body is faulty, his mind untrustworthy, but his imagination has made him remarkable. In some centuries, his imagination has made life on this planet an intense practice of all the lovelier energies."   [John Masefield]

Imagination depends so much upon independence of thought that there is little need to add much here. It is through independent original thought that the mind forms conscious ideas of something, that it imagines something not previously perceived in reality.

In order to be useful in science, imagination must be combined with a keen sense for what is important. This assessment must, of necessity, be made instinctively on insufficient evidence at a time when importance is not yet demonstrable. Here, perhaps more than in any other respect, the scientist must depend on innate gifts. It is virtually impossible to teach imagination. Only our vision for the importance of things can be sharpened through experience, by trial and error. This dependence of critical judgment upon experience explains why, in the course of life, it takes so much longer to develop a sense of values than to exhibit the largely innate power of imagination. The flair for the potential practical or theoretic importance of the things that we imagine is not itself imagination; it is merely a prerequisite for the selection, among innumerable imaginary pictures, of those having significant applications in reality.

The combined activity of first imagining and then fixing the important aspects of the imagined picture on to conscious reality is the basis of creative thought—the most elevating and satisfying activity of which the human mind is capable. The act of scientific and artistic creation, much like that of procreation, gives the enjoyment of release from the tensions of a need—a hunger—which, when appeased, leaves our whole being delightfully flagged by the sense of fulfillment.

Most of the discoveries which are usually attributed to chance are actually made by virtue of a prodigious power of imagination which immediately visualizes manifold general applications of the chance observation. The following are a few classic and often cited examples of discoveries attributed to chance.

Two German physiologists, von Mering and Minkowski, were studying the function of the pancreas in digestion. For this purpose, they performed pancreatectomies (surgical removal of the pancreas) to see how the digestion of food would proceed in the absence of this gland. One day, their animal caretaker wanted to quit; he complained that he could not keep the lab clean, because the urine of the pancreatectomized dogs attracted swarms of flies. Thereupon, Minkowski analyzed the urine and found sugar in it. This finding was the first clue to some relationship between diabetes and the pancreas; it formed the very basis of the subsequent discovery of insulin [Walter Cannon [16]].

The great French physiologist, Charles Richet, cruising on the pleasure yacht of the Prince of Monaco, was injecting dogs with an extract made from the tentacles of a sea anemone, to determine the toxic dose. Once, when he reinjected a dog with this same extract, he noted that a very small dose is promptly fatal. This result was so unexpected that he refused to believe it and at first did not ascribe it to anything he had done. But repetition of the experiment showed that pretreatment with this extract induces a sensitization to it. This is how Richet discovered the phenomenon of anaphylaxis which, according to his own statement, he never would have thought to be possible [Walter Cannon [16]].

Sidney Ringer developed the solution which now bears his name because of his perspicacity in evaluating a "technical error" in experimentation. He worked with frogs' hearts which he perfused with a sodium chloride solution in distilled water, as was the custom at the time, and the hearts kept beating for perhaps half an hour. Once, however, these hearts continued to beat for many hours and at first he ascribed this to a seasonal effect; indeed he even suggested this possibility in print. Later, however, it turned out that his technician had used tap water instead of distilled water to make up the saline solution. This called Ringer's attention to the fact that salts other than sodium chloride may also play a part [Henry Dale [25]].

Gowland Hopkins, the founder of biochemistry, gave his class a well-known test for proteins as an exercise. To his surprise, none of the students obtained a positive reaction. Examination showed that the test is positive only when the acetic acid solution employed contains glyoxylic acid as an accidental impurity. This finding started Hopkins on an extensive study which eventually led him to the isolation of tryptophane, the part of the protein which reacts with glyoxylic acid [M. Stephenson [82]].

When the Italian physiologist Luigi Galvani looked at frog-legs which were hanging (ready to fry) from an iron wire in his home at Bologna, he noticed that sometimes their muscles contracted. Upon closer examination, he realized that the twitching occurred when one part of the leg was in contact with the iron wire and another with a piece of copper wire accidentally attached at one end to the iron. It was this observation that led him to construct the so-called metallic arc which eventually led to the understanding of current electricity and the subsequent invention of the voltaic cell by Volta [James B. Conant [23]].

The German physicist, Röntgen, was experimenting with electrical discharges in a high vacuum by using barium platinocyanide as a means of making the otherwise invisible rays detectable. He had no idea that these rays would penetrate opaque materials, but accidentally he observed that the barium platinocyanide left near the vacuum tube would become fluorescent even if separated by black paper from the tube. Later, he modestly pointed out that: "I found by accident that the rays penetrated the 'black paper'" [J. R. Baker [5]]. Actually, it took a great capacity for imagination not only to see this fact but to perceive its enormous implications.

Intuition

"There is no logical way to the discovery of these elemental laws. There is only the way of intuition, which is helped by a feeling for the order lying behind the appearance." [Albert Einstein [33]]

DEFINITION. Intuition is the unconscious intelligence that leads to knowledge without reasoning or inferring. It is an immediate apprehension or cognition without rational thought. Intuition is the spark for all forms of originality, inventiveness and ingenuity. It is the flash needed to connect conscious thought with imagination. The intuitive "hunch" has been defined as "a unifying or clarifying idea which springs into consciousness as a solution to a problem in which we are intensely interested" [Platt & Baker [56]]. It is perhaps significant that, in the language of the ancient Peruvian Indians, there was only one word (*hamavec*) for both poet and inventor [Charles J. H. Nicolle [50]].

In discussing intuitive flashes with others, I find that most scientists have experienced them quite unexpectedly while falling asleep, awakening, or doing something quite unrelated to the problem at hand. After hard, conscious work on a solution, a hunch may come, for example, while taking a walk, listening to an opera, or reading the newspaper. On the other hand, physical fatigue, annoyance of any kind, interruptions, and pressure to meet a deadline definitely block intuition.

We must first gather facts through observation, then store them away in our memory. Following this, we can arrange them logically in the order dictated by rational thought. Sometimes this process in itself is sufficient to reach a satisfactory solution. But if, after conscious reasoning and inferring, the facts do not make a harmonious picture, consciousness, with its ingrained habit of imposing conventional order, must look away to allow fantasy free play. Then, innumerable more or less random associations are made under the guidance of uninhibited imagination. These are like dreams—and conventional intellect disregards them as silly. But sometimes one of the many random fact-mosaics, constructed by the kaleidoscope of fantasy, comes so close to reality as to evoke an intuitive flash whose explosive force shoots the idea into consciousness. In other words, imagination is the unconscious power to mix facts in novel ways; while intuition is the gift of bringing usable dream-pictures into consciousness.

Creation itself is always unconscious; only the verification and exploitation of its products lend themselves to conscious analysis. Instinct creates thoughts, without knowing how to think; intellect knows how to use thoughts, but cannot create them.

EXAMPLES. *How our nerves function.* Otto Loewi, one of the greatest medical scientists of our time, told me that the idea for his most important experiment came to him one night when he awoke suddenly from sleep. He immediately realized the transcendent importance of the dream and jotted down his thoughts on a piece of paper. But next morning, though aware of having had an inspiration, he could not read his scribble. Try as he would, he was unable to remember what the hunch was until the following night when he again awoke with the same flash of insight as before. This time he tried to arouse himself sufficiently to take legible notes, and next day he performed his famous experiment on the chemical transmission of nerve impulses. He showed that if two frog hearts are perfused with the same solution, stimulation of the nerve of one heart causes a change in cardiac rhythm which is transmitted to the other heart by the perfusing fluid.

This extremely simple and elegant experimental arrangement, conceived so easily by the unconscious mind, opened up an entire new field of research. The possibility of such chemical mediation of nervous activity had been suspected before by many scientists, including Loewi himself, but no one could think of a good way to prove it.

The discovery of insulin. Another interesting example of how the unconscious mind works is furnished by the discovery of the antidiabetic hormone. Since I had the opportunity of personally discussing with Sir Frederick Banting the psychologic motives involved in his discovery, I should like to relate them here in detail.

After the First World War, Banting—returning from military service—took up medical practice in the then quite small town of London, in the Canadian Province of Ontario. One evening he read an article on the degenerative changes that take place in the pancreas after blockage of its duct by concrements. He went to bed but could not sleep, because of the intriguing though vague impression that such degenerative changes might help the elucidation of the then mysterious part played by the pancreas in diabetes. It was not until about two o'clock in the morning that an idea suddenly crystallized in his mind. He immediately wrote it down in these words: "Ligate pancreatic ducts of dogs. Wait six to eight weeks for degeneration. Remove the residue and extract."

Many investigators find it difficult to formulate an idea clearly in the presence of the countless psychologic inhibitions which arise when one is fully awake; on the other hand, in the half-conscious state, while about to fall asleep or to awaken, instinctively felt conceptions tend to present themselves clearly, without any effort.

Banting could not carry out his plan in London, Ontario, hence, he visited Professor J. J. R. Macleod, at the University of Toronto, from whom he received the advice and the facilities necessary to perform his experiments. Work began on the sixteenth of May, 1921, with a highly talented young student, C. H. Best, who was already familiar with the tricky and then still little-known technique of accurately determining the sugar content of small blood samples. Best, now Professor of Physiology in Toronto, continued to help Banting during the rest of the work and contributed many fertile thoughts to make this enterprise successful.

After several failures, on July 27, 1921, Banting and Best finally had a duct-tied dog with a degenerated pancreatic residue and a severely diabetic, completely depancreatized dog. The degenerated pancreatic remnant of the first animal was removed, cut up in small pieces and extracted in the cold, with about 100 cc. of saline. Five cc. of this extract was given intravenously to the depancreatized dog and 2 hours later, its blood sugar had fallen from 200 to 110 mg. per 100 cc. By January, 1922, the first diabetic patients were treated with cattle pancreas extracts at a hospital in Toronto.

First inkling of the germ theory. In 1847, when Semmelweis was greatly worried about the high mortality from childbed fever in Vienna, his colleague Kolletschka died from a minor wound in his finger, sustained during an autopsy. Semmelweis wrote:

"In the excited condition in which I then was, it rushed into my mind with irresistible clearness that the disease from which Kolletschka had died was identical with that from which I had seen so many hundreds of lying-in women die.... Day and night the vision of Kolletschka's malady haunted me, and with ever increasing conviction I realised the identity of the disease."   [W. J. Sinclair [78]]

Phagocytosis. This is Metchnikoff's account of the origin of the idea of phagocytosis, the ingestion of foreign materials by cells, for the defense of the body:

"One day when the whole family had gone to the circus to see some extraordinary performing apes, I remained alone with my microscope, observing life in the mobile cells of a transparent starfish larva, when a new thought suddenly flashed across my brain. It struck me that similar cells might serve in the defence of the organism against intruders. Feeling that there was in this something of surpassing interest, I felt so excited that I began striding up and down the room and even went to the seashore to collect my thoughts."

[Elie Metchnikoff, quoted by B. M. Fried [48]]

Evolution. It was during an illness that A. R. Wallace read Malthus' *Principles of Population* in which the conclusion was reached that the various checks to the increase in the human population eliminate the least fit. From this, Wallace drew the conclusion that the same may be true in the animal world.

"Vaguely thinking over the enormous and constant destruction this implied, it occurred to me to ask the question, 'Why do some die and some live?' and the answer was clearly that on the whole the best fitted live.... Then it suddenly flashed upon me that this self-acting process would improve the race... the fittest would survive. Then at once I seemed to see the whole effect of this."   [Alfred R. Wallace [86]]

The ring structure of benzene.   The German chemist Kekulé was trying to put order into his thoughts about the structure of benzene, ideas which eventually revolutionized organic chemistry:

"But it did not go well; my spirit was with other things. I turned the chair to the fireplace and sank into a half sleep. The atoms flitted before my eyes. Long rows, variously, more closely united; all in movement wriggling and turning like snakes. And see, what was that? One of the snakes seized its own tail and the image whirled scornfully before my eyes. As though from a flash of lightning I awoke; I occupied the rest of the night in working out the consequences of the hypothesis.... Let us learn to dream, gentlemen."

[Friedrich A. Kekulé, quoted by G. Schutz [45]]

The discovery of a mathematical law.   The eminent French mathematician, Henri Poincaré, relates the story of how he made the greatest of his discoveries on the so-called Fuchsian functions, after weeks of unsuccessful efforts.

"One evening, against my custom, I drank a cup of black coffee and could not sleep. Innumerable ideas came to my mind and I felt them knocking against each other until two of them stuck together, so to speak, and formed a stable combination. By morning, I had established the existence of a class of Fuchsian functions, which are derivatives of the hypergeometric series. All I had to do was to write down the results, which took me only a few hours."   [Henri Poincaré [57]]

It is no mere coincidence that so many examples of intuitive flashes occurred in a semisomnolent condition and we shall have occasion to show that this is by no means exceptional.

The discovery of the stress syndrome. It may perhaps be permissible to add a few words here about the discovery whose elements I know best, even if its value is in no way comparable to that of the previously cited examples. As I explained elsewhere (Selye [70]), I first hit upon the concept of stress and the general adaptation syndrome (G.A.S.) in 1925 when I studied medicine at the University of Prague. I had just completed my courses in anatomy, physiology, biochemistry, and the other preclinical subjects which were required as a preparation before we saw a patient. I had stuffed myself full of theoretical knowledge to the limit of my abilities and was burning with enthusiasm for the art of healing, but I had only vague ideas about clinical medicine. Then came the great day, which I shall never forget, when we were to hear our first lecture in internal medicine and see how one examines a patient.

It so happened that, on that day, by way of an introduction, we were shown several instances of the earliest stages of various infectious diseases. As each patient was brought into the lecture room, the professor carefully questioned and examined him. It turned out that each of these patients felt and looked ill, had a coated tongue, complained of more or less diffuse aches and pains in the joints, and of intestinal disturbances with loss of appetite. Most of them also had fever (sometimes with mental confusion), an enlarged spleen or liver, inflamed tonsils, and so forth. All this was quite evident, but the professor attached very little significance to any of it.

Then, he enumerated a few "characteristic" signs which might help in the diagnosis of the disease. These I could not see. They were absent or, at least, so inconspicuous that my untrained eye could not distinguish them; yet these, we were told, were the important changes to which we would have to give all our attention. At present, our teacher said, most of the characteristic signs were still absent, and, until they appeared, not much could be done. Without them it was impossible to know precisely what the patient suffered from, and hence it was obviously not feasible to recommend any efficient treatment. It was clear that the many features of disease which were already manifest did not interest our teacher very much because they were "nonspecific" (not characteristic of any one disease), and, hence, of no use to the physician.

Since these were my first patients, I was still capable of looking at them without being biased by current medical thought. Had I known more, I would never have asked questions, because everything was handled "just the way it should be," that is, "just the way every good physician does it." Had I known more, I would certainly have been stopped by the biggest of all blocks to improvement: the certainty of being right. But I did not know what was right.

I could understand that our professor had to find specific disease manifestations in order to identify the particular cause of disease in each of these patients. This, I clearly realized, was necessary so that suitable drugs might be prescribed, medicines having the specific effect of killing the germs or neutralizing the poisons that made these people sick.

I could see this all right; but what impressed me, the novice, much more was that apparently only a few signs are actually characteristic of any one disease; most of them are apparently common to many, or perhaps even to all diseases.

Why is it, I asked myself, that such widely different disease-producing agents as those which cause measles, scarlet fever, or influenza, share with a number of drugs, allergens, etc., the property of evoking the nonspecific manifestations which have just been mentioned? Yet evidently they do share them; indeed, they share them to such an extent that, at an early stage, it might be quite impossible —even for our eminent professor—to distinguish between various diseases, because they all look alike.

I could not understand why, ever since the dawn of medical history, physicians should have attempted to concentrate all their efforts upon the recognition of *individual* diseases and the discovery of *specific* remedies for them, without giving any attention to the much more obvious "syndrome of just being sick." I knew that a syndrome is "a group of signs and symptoms that occur together and characterize a disease." Well, the patients we had just seen had a syndrome, but this seemed to be the syndrome that characterized disease as such, not any one disease. Would it be possible to analyze the mechanism of this "general syndrome of sickness" and perhaps even to find drugs which act against the nonspecific factor in disease? It was not until a decade later, however, that I managed to put all this into the precise language of experimentally established scientific description.

At that time I was working in the Biochemistry Department of McGill University trying to find a new ovarian hormone in extracts of cattle ovaries. All the extracts, no matter how prepared, produced the same syndrome characterized by enlargement of the adrenal cortex*, gastrointestinal ulcers, and involution of the thymus and lymph nodes. Although at first I ascribed all these changes to some new ovarian hormone in my extract it soon turned out that extracts of other organs—in fact, even toxic substances of all kinds—produced the same changes. It was only then that I suddenly remembered my classroom impression of the "syndrome of just being sick." In a flash I realized that what I had produced with my impure extracts and toxic drugs was an experimental replica of this condition. This model was then employed in the analysis of the stress syndrome using the adrenal enlargement, gastrointestinal ulcers and thymicolymphatic involution as objective indices of stress. This simple hunch of a connection between the almost forgotten, purely speculative, clinical concept of student days and the reproducible and objectively measurable changes in the animal experiments at hand was the basis for the development of the entire stress concept.

It could be shown that stress is the rate of wear and tear in the human machinery that accompanies any vital activity and, in a sense, parallels the intensity of life. It is increased during nervous tension, physical injury, infections, muscular work or any other strenuous activity, and it is connected with a nonspecific defense mechanism which increases resistance to stressful or "stressor" agents. An important part of this defense mechanism is the increased secretion by the hypophysis (a small gland at the base of the brain) of the so-called adrenocorticotrophic hormone (ACTH) which in turn stimulates the adrenal cortex to produce corticoids. Most important among the latter are the glucocorticoids such as cortisone (which influence glucose and, in general, organic metabolism) as well as the mineralocorticoids such as aldosterone or desoxycorticosterone (which regulate mineral metabolism). Various derangements in the secretion of these hormones can lead to maladies which I called "diseases of adaptation" because they are not directly due to any particular pathogen (disease producer) but to a faulty adaptive response to the stress induced by some pathogen.

The whole stress syndrome, or general adaptation syndrome (G.A.S.), evolves in three stages: 1. the "alarm reaction" during which defensive forces are mobilized; 2. the "stage of resistance" which reflects full adaptation to the stressor; 3. the "stage of ex-

---

* The adrenal is a hormone-producing or endocrine gland, situated just above the kidney on each side. It consists of an outer shell or cortex (which produces corticoid hormones) and an inner core or medulla (which secretes adrenaline and related hormones).

haustion" which inexorably follows as long as the stressor is severe enough and applied for a sufficient length of time since the "adaptation energy" or adaptability of a living being is always finite.

MECHANISM.   Innumerable vital processes go on continually in the various parts of the body at the same time: some are conscious (e.g., voluntary muscular movements); others unconscious (e.g., glandular secretions, intestinal movements); while yet others are normally unconscious, but can be pulled into consciousness at will (e.g., breathing). The great advantage of conscious activities is that they are subject to intentional regulation by will and intellect. But the chief weakness of the conscious mind is that it can handle only one problem at a time.

It is difficult to perform even two simple but different manual movements simultaneously, unless we succeed in pushing at least one out of the way into the unconscious. Only with the greatest difficulty can I draw circles with my left hand and squares with my right by mechanizing one of the two activities, after having launched it under conscious control. For example, if I pick up two pencils and first concentrate on making circle over circle with the left hand, I can push this repetitive activity into the unconscious by merely giving the order, "Carry on," to my left; then, while my circling motion continues, I can concentrate on drawing a square with the right hand.

We can consciously establish an abnormally deep and slow breathing pattern and then order this type of respiration to continue while we concentrate on something else, but during the initiation of this form of breathing our conscious mind is fully occupied by it. We can learn a language by consciously memorizing its rules and words, but we could not even speak our native tongue by consciously planning the grammar and syntax of each sentence as we talk. While our mind is occupied with the conscious analysis of a problem, we can breathe, digest, pump our blood, and walk along the street, without being aware of any of these activities. However, if we want to change our course and cross the street, we must, at least for an instant, abandon the subject that has occupied our conscious mind and direct attention to the problem of walking.

The same is true if an unexpected event calls for "repair" in an unconscious mechanism. If a pebble gets into my shoe, I have to stop the mechanical walking and direct my conscious effort to the removal of the source of pain; then I can walk on automatically again and redirect my conscious mind to the problem which was occupying it before the disturbance. Pain is the most common warning sign that calls attention to the need for conscious intervention. Even otherwise unconscious physiologic processes can call for this kind of help through the pain signal. Many a patient would die if the normally unconscious activities of his internal organs did not call for help in disease by becoming painfully conscious.

The harmonious interaction between the conscious and the unconscious mind plays a particularly important part in the mechanism of intuitive thinking. If man has much more power over Nature than understanding of her ways, it is because his conscious intellect can study only one idea at a time, while his actions are aided by all his unconsciously stored experiences and ideas. From the dark stores of our innate and acquired unconscious information, we can pull out only one problem at a time for logical analysis in the light of consciousness; at that time, the rest of our knowledge is not subject to such planned examination. All the data that have ever been thrown into the great mixer of our unconscious memory constantly hit against each other, until cognate elements combine to form useful associations. Such newly formed idea-sets can involuntarily direct purposeful actions, even without becoming conscious, just as instincts do; they become subject to rational analysis and intentional use only if they flash into consciousness through an intuitive hunch. Unconscious thinking goes on all the time, especially during sleep when undisturbed by logic, while fully conscious thinking needs the clear light of complete wakefulness. It is in the twilight, at the rim of consciousness, that dreams can best flash into reality through the spark of intuition.

A simple mechanical analogy may help to visualize how the disorderly unconscious manipulation of thoughts might prepare them for conscious, will-directed manipulation as a single unit, merely by bringing related ideas together through countless haphazard combinations which are normally suppressed. A multitude of balls, differing in weight and color can, at will, be arranged under the control of intellect so that like objects come to lie together; but this is time-consuming, for each of the many balls must be identified as to its characteristics and then placed into proper position without disarranging those already in order. It is much easier to pour them all randomly into a bowl and shake until order is automatically achieved. Eventually, the gray steel balls will be at the bottom, the brown wooden ones in the middle and the white celluloid ones on top. Here, we have exerted no intellect-directed control over the movements of individual balls. Yet they fell into an order in which like objects are conveniently approximated for conscious comparison, or for handling as a single layer which forms a unit. In this analogy, the color of the balls plays no part in the establishment of order, it merely helps to identify them. In the more complex problems of science, such inactive incidentals are often confused with causative properties. We shall have more to say about this important cause of error in discussing the "silent marker" fallacy (p. 316).

Since intuitive mental activity can proceed only behind a screen that protects it from conscious control, a true scientific analysis of intuition is impossible. Conscious intellect cannot reason about things beyond the reach of its perception, any more than a blind man can interpret color patterns. Fortunately, we are not totally blind to the unconscious. We can grasp at little bits that come up for moments here and there on the fringe of consciousness, if we are quick enough to catch hold of the elusive fragments before they dive back again into the dark ocean of the unconscious. Intuition also depends upon conscious preparation by fact-gathering and by the evaluation of ideas. If observant, we can learn a good deal about the pathways of a thought even if, by necessity, our analysis must be limited to those portions of the track that traverse consciousness.

Most students of the mechanism of scientific thought recognize that intuition takes place during a period of unconscious incubation. The material that has been, at least in part, consciously gathered before incubation must be consciously verified again after it has been molded into an idea [Platt & Baker [56], Graham Wallas [87], Hermann von Helmholtz [40]].

It may be sheer coincidence and, again, it may be a deep-rooted natural law that accounts for the extraordinary similarity in the mechanism of scientific creation and of procreation. But as far as I can see, both processes go through seven stages which we shall designate by terms customarily employed in the physiology of reproduction, although we intend to apply them to scientific creativity. This analysis of the mechanism of creative thought will also give us an opportunity to reconsider the prerequisites for discovery.

1. Love or, at least, desire. The first prerequisite for scientific discovery is an avid enthusiasm, an unrelenting thirst for knowledge, that must be satisfied. This enthusiasm may be nourished by love of Nature, longing for truth, vanity and the need for recognition, simple curiosity, a desire to be useful, or by any other motive, but it must be sufficiently passionate to overcome all obstacles in its way.

2. Fertilization. No matter how great its potential creative power, the mind remains sterile unless it has been previously fertilized by facts gathered through observation and learning. There are individual variations in the amount of erudition that best serves an intuitive mind. Some scientists, especially the great correlators, must acquire an encyclopedic knowledge to construct their broad, unifying concepts. Others, the specialists, who probe deeper but in a more limited field, need less information; they may even be handicapped by too much knowledge irrelevant to their purpose. But, in the history of every scientific discovery, we find this indispensable preparatory period of gathering and conscious exploration of facts and ideas that may act as seeds for an essentially new contribution.

3. Gestation. During this stage, the scientist is pregnant with an idea. At the beginning, he may not even realize it, but all those who have attempted to analyze the mechanism of intuition agree that, when conscious analysis of a problem leads us no further, it should be put aside to mature by being unconsciously compared with an enormous number of other experiences. Then, related facts hit upon each other and form fruitful combinations.

As I have said before, this unconscious part of the thinking process is not amenable to conscious intellectual analysis, but my intuitive feeling about it is that incubation helps in two ways:

a. As the study of physiologic phenomena has shown, unconscious (e.g., biochemical) activities can proceed on a very large scale and concurrently in essentially different directions. Perhaps this is true of unconscious thinking also. Perhaps our unconscious mind can think simultaneously of the most varied subjects and, hence, compare the seed of a new idea with many more potentially relevant facts than conscious intellect could.

b. Unjustified prejudices, the habitual approach to a problem from an unapproachable side, and other mistakes about the way we consciously handle a subject are forgotten while the conscious mind is otherwise occupied or asleep. Consequently, when our idea comes up from incubation to the fringe of consciousness again, it is not only more mature but we are more likely to catch it. When unexpectedly faced with a glimpse of its outlines we are then more likely to grasp the idea through a new approach by a sudden, unpremeditated mental reflex. In other words, during incubation, established fruitless associations lapse from memory and thereby give new, potentially fruitful associations a chance.

Probably everyone has had the experience of trying to retrieve a name from the unconscious, by the handle of that part of it which we think we remember. Such trains of thought often go something like this one, which confused me only a few weeks ago: "Just what was the name of Biedl's book?" I asked myself. *"The Hormones?* No ... *Textbook on Hormones?* That isn't it either ... *Principles of Hormone Research?* No, that still doesn't sound right. But I am sure it was something about hormones..." Once I began thinking along these lines, all efforts to recall the title were built around this one fixed point: it was about hormones. That I remembered distinctly, but the name still did not present itself. However, days later, while thinking about something quite unrelated, it suddenly occurred to me that the name of the book was *The Internal Secretions.* The reason I could not retrieve this title from my memory was that I tried to grasp for it, starting with the premise that it contained the word "hormones." Actually, it did refer to hormones but by a synonymous designation, "internal secretions," which I could not recollect until I forgot what I believed to be my one certain memory about it.

Only yesterday, I made a similar observation on my little son, André. I asked him: "How much is six times seven?" He said, "Thirty." I repeated the question several times, and allowed him to think about it as much as he wanted to, but the answer was always "Thirty." Then I changed the subject and, after we spoke about other things for a few minutes, I repeated the original question. He answered without hesitation, "Forty-two," because he forgot the wrong answer. But, actually, with our present methods we cannot even find out just what goes on in our mind, when we give the right answer to such a simple question as "6 × 7," or when we remember the correct title of a book. It is possible that, at some future date, improvement in neurophysiologic techniques, particularly in electroencephalography, may permit us to follow the fate of an idea after it plunges into the unconscious mind. At present this is impossible. But we can learn a lot about the evolution of a thought even if we follow it only during its trajectory through the conscious mind to the border of the unconscious. We must merely keep in mind that thereafter important but inscrutable work continues to go on in the unconscious.

4. Birth pangs. Whenever I feel pregnant with an idea, I suffer. It is difficult to describe the nature of this suffering in precise terms, but it is quite bad. Not being a woman, I cannot compare it, from actual experience, with the feeling of birth pangs but I imagine it has much in common with them. It bears a definite element of frustration, a feeling that there is something in you that must come out, though you don't know how to push. This is probably what Poincaré had in mind when he said that he felt his ideas "knocking against each other."

For those who have not experienced the feeling, it is difficult to describe it other than by analogies from everyday life, and these necessarily sound ridiculous when used to characterize the birth of an idea. But when I discussed this sensation with other scientists, they immediately knew what I meant when I compared it to what we feel when we want to sneeze and cannot, or when a word is on the tip of our tongue and we are unable to utter it. If I were not afraid that these Notes might fall into the gentle hands of a lady, I would compare this suffering to that of monumental gas pains—a very appropriate analogy, since the majority of all mental gestations gives birth to nothing but gas. Unfortunately, before birth, the nature of the gestation product cannot be determined; as far as I can tell, the birth pangs that precede the delivery of valuable and worthless ideas are the same.

Undoubtedly, some kind of aura often presages the arrival of a solution. Wallas [87], in his remarkable book *The Art of Thought*, speaks of this sensation as an "intimation just preceding the actual illumination." It is of practical importance to be aware of this aura because it puts us on our guard against losing the idea when it flashes into consciousness just for a moment. As we have seen, the birth of a thought, like that of a baby, frequently occurs at night in bed; but because the emergence of an idea is unaccompanied by pain, it often does not arouse us sufficiently to get a firm grasp of the new thought and deliver it into consciousness before it slips back into the unconscious. Since I have become aware of the aura, I try to wake myself up to full alertness as soon as I experience this feeling, and, if a constructive idea presents itself, I immediately make a note of it for future reference.

5. Birth. Here, my analogy falls down because, unlike the delivery of even the finest baby, the birth of a really good idea is an extremely pleasant sensation. At least in my own experience, new ideas have never reached the surface of my consciousness amid birth pangs, but quite unexpectedly and much later, usually when I was just about to fall asleep or awaken. Sometimes the solution to a problem comes when, in a perfectly relaxed mood, I am comparing experimental protocols, or making new observations at the microscope or autopsy table. However, just as frequently, the badly needed idea is born outside the lab quite unexpectedly, while I am watching a play, reading a novel, or listening to music. It is perhaps significant that, in earlier years, I used to have good ideas while walking between my home and the garage; but since I fell out of a maple tree and developed a painful traumatic arthritis, I have never again had a useful idea while in the upright position. I mention this circumstance because, as we shall see later, all students of creative activity agree that pain of any kind interferes with unconscious thinking.

Intuitive flashes are usually followed by feelings of great happiness, exhilaration, and relief. All the accumulated fatigue and frustration of the preceding periods of fact-gathering and incubation disappears at once. It is replaced by the sensation of extreme well-being and energy which gives us, at least temporarily, the impression of being up to any task that may present itself in the future. At the same time—at least in my case—there comes the "eureka impulse," the desire to sally forth and tell everybody. It makes me very unhappy if there is no one around who would understand the meaning of my finding when I hit upon something that I think is really important. I am proud to say I have never given in to this impulse quite as much as did Archimedes who hurried out of his bathtub and into the streets unclad. But then, never having discovered anything as important as the law of specific gravity, I am not at all sure that I could have resisted the degree of temptation to which he was exposed. It is pleasant and relaxing to give in to the "eureka impulse," but we must also learn to keep it under reasonable control; even if the temptation is not strong enough to make us rush out with insufficient clothing in search of a public, it may make us rush into print with insufficient evidence.

After the need to share our newly found treasure wears off, there may be a swing of mood in the opposite direction. As the initial exhilaration gradually diminishes and blends imperceptibly into the resumption of our normal routine, there comes a feeling of letdown. This may even grow into severe depression, because everything we do seems trifling by comparison with the importance of the preceding success. I have known several scientists who went through manic-depressive cycles of this kind all the time.

It is interesting that many scientists remember for the rest of their lives even the most inconsequential detail associated with their discovery (such as the place where they stood, or the people present), although their mind was presumably fully occupied with their problem at the time. Charles Darwin [26], in commenting about the moment when the idea occurred to him that natural selection is the directing influence in evolution, wrote: "I can remember the very spot in the road whilst, in my carriage, to my joy the solution occurred to me." Few of us have a comparably dramatic discovery to remember, but I can recall exactly where, and under what circumstances, even my much less consequential ideas about stress, calciphylaxis and the chemical preventability of cardiac necroses crystallized in my mind, because, for better or for worse, these were the highlights in my scientific life.

6. Examination. When the baby is born, we immediately examine it to see whether it is viable and free of malformations. This is true also of our mental babies. As soon as the newly born idea emerges from the unconscious, it must be examined and checked by conscious reasoning and logically planned experimentation. It is impossible to verify, teach or regulate unconscious intuitive logic, because the unconscious cannot be approached by consciousness and has no apparent logic. But our intuitive thinking must be checked and its errors repaired above the surface of consciousness.

7. Life. After the new idea has been properly tested and found viable, it is ready for life—that is, for application. All discoveries worthy of the name have theoretic applications in that they promote understanding, but some thought should always be given to possible practical application as well.

TEACHABILITY. What is the best way to assist intuitive thinking? Can it be taught? These are undoubtedly questions of the utmost practical importance, but it is difficult to see how unconscious intuitive mental work could be helped by any conscious regulation of its mechanism. Yet I am firmly convinced that here, as in so many other aspects of research, much can be learned from experience. The mere empirical application of observations concerning the stimuli that we found to promote or impede creative thought can help, even if we do not understand how these factors work. Even a process that must go on automatically in the unconscious can be set in motion by a conscious, calculated effort.

While the laws of intuitive thought cannot be consciously analyzed, used, or taught, the products of intuitive thinking must be checked, and their faults corrected above the surface of consciousness. The situation here is like that of a submarine, which works under water, out of reach, but must be brought to the surface from time to time for check-ups and repairs. It is the same with many other activities. Oratory, tennis, painting, or music can be taught— at least to the gifted—and their correct practice can be consciously verified, although the thought and action patterns in all these fields must become subconscious and automatic to be effective. As Wallas [87] says: "The process of learning an art should, even in the case of those who have the finest natural endowment for it, be more conscious than its practice."

The exploration of the unconscious mind, be it even only with the most primitive, indirect techniques now available, is certainly rewarding; there is as much mental power stored away in the core of the mind as there is physical power in the nucleus of the atom. Fortunately, a few scientists have taken the trouble to explore the factors that promote or inhibit their intuitive thinking [Graham Wallas [87], Platt & Baker [56], Henri Poincaré [57], Albert Einstein [32], Eve Curie [24], Charles Richet [59]] and we can learn much from their experience, combined with self-analysis—the object of these notes.

FAVORABLE FACTORS. *Formulate your questions clearly*. First, the problem must be precisely defined. "A question clearly stated is half answered," but in basic research it is often difficult, if not impossible, to formulate a problem in precise terms when it first presents itself. For example, in the course of work on calciphylaxis (p. 241) it soon became evident that several agents must act in order to obtain selective calcification in an organ, but I could not formulate my questions more precisely than: "What kind of agents must act?" or: "Why do certain combinations of agents produce calcification?" These are not practical questions. They are not sufficiently precise to be useful. Only after empirically testing many agents, alone and in combination (more or less at random, though presumably guided by unconscious motives), did it become possible to ask more precise questions concerning the possible group classification of the evocative factors. We asked: "Do some agents merely sensitize the body for other agents?" "Do certain agents precipitate calcification only after sensitization with other agents?" "Is the exact timing in the application of different groups of agents important?" These formulations were more practical; they proved to lend themselves to experimental verification and led to the following three fundamental conclusions:

a. Certain agents are "sensitizers." They merely produce a susceptibility for local tissue calcification by their action upon calcium metabolism in general. Among these are vitamin-D derivatives and parathyroid hormone.

b. Other agents are "challengers." After sensitization they provoke calcification wherever they are directly applied, or wherever they are deposited when injected into the circulating blood. Many, but not all of these challengers are metallic salts.

c. A "critical period" must elapse between the application of a sensitizer and a challenger.

The literature on intuitive thinking justly places great emphasis upon the precise formulation of questions as the first step, but, as the preceding example shows, the problem may not lend itself to precise formulation before many data are accumulated. The gathering of facts, through original experimentation and perusal of related literature, must precede the clear definition of the problem. The hunt is usually motivated by an intriguing idea or observation which, when it first becomes conscious, can merely excite our curiosity: but hereby it stimulates us to probe around more or less empirically, guided only by subconscious instinct, until enough facts become available to formulate a definite problem in clear terms.

Use guides for your thoughts. Once we know more or less precisely just what we are looking for, we can again do much by conscious effort. We can accumulate more material by experimentation and by reading in cognate fields; we can think about the problem without permitting our attention to be deviated. Such concentrated meditation can be greatly aided by various activities that serve as a skeleton or scaffolding for relevant thought. It is very difficult to sit down and concentrate on the same subject for a long time if there is nothing on which to focus our attention. Observing the progress of an experiment, or studying protocols, histologic slides and other material related to the problem at hand not only fixes our attention on it, but brings forth additional findings which may catalyze the incubation of ideas. Similarly, reading a paper or book concerned with some aspect of our problem, and then looking up the references quoted in these writings, not only guide our thoughts, but illuminate them by the experiences of many others who worked on related topics in different countries and at different times.

Discuss your ideas with others. Perhaps the most fruitful external stimulus to creative thought is direct contact with other scientific minds. This should take the form of informal discussions, preferably limited to a very small group of two to four competent people who like each other and are interested in each other's problem. Large groups tend to become too formal and offer little opportunity for the participation of each member. Besides, a single person, who does not understand the problem and just wants to attract attention, can spoil everything with irrelevant or aggressive remarks. It is especially disturbing if a discussant is too anxious to defend his priority or to display his flippant wit on such occasions. The most productive discussions are not the regular, planned seminars but the unpremeditated exchange of ideas by people who happen to get into conversation about something that occupies their mind.

In our Institute, we also try to stimulate thought by bringing up our unsolved problems at the daily autopsy conference ("brainstorming"). I have noticed that interruptions by irrelevant or self-centered comments are least common if these discussions come up at week ends when only a small, really interested, group is present.

Another good way to produce a guide for our own thoughts is to explain the problem to people who know very little about it. Here, we cannot expect much external stimulation but, since we have to reduce the subject to its simplest and, hence, usually most important aspects, we are forced to reconsider our fundamental tenets.

Stimulate thought associations. It sometimes helps to stimulate associative ideas if we think of related subjects. It is well known that association is stimulated by continuity (calcium in the blood reminds you of the bones and food from which it comes), similarity (calcium reminds you of magnesium, another alkaline earth), and contrast (hypocalcemia reminds you of hypercalcemia). We believe so strongly in the thought-stimulating effect of such associations, that our whole library classification (p. 228) is based upon a system that brings similar and contrasting material together in the files containing the subject cards.

Jot it down. At the risk of repeating myself, let me re-emphasize the great importance of always carrying a notebook and jotting down (legibly!) any promising new ideas that reach our consciousness as a consequence of all these thought-stimulating devices. I make profuse notes of this type in the lab, at home, on trips, or wherever I may be. Then, as soon as I get a chance, I dictate brief résumés from these telegraphic notes and insert them in one of the many loose-leaf binders on my desk. I keep notebooks on the most varied subjects; scientific observations, lecture plans, administrative problems, material for future papers and books.

Put it aside. If all these efforts, planned specifically to stimulate associative thoughts, fail, there is no point in trying to force a solution by sheer stubbornness; in this event it is best to let the problem slip from the sphere of conscious intellectual analysis and incubate in the unconscious. At this stage, we should get away from it all into a setting generally favorable to imaginative thinking: a walk through the woods or on the ocean shore, fishing, golfing, music, solitude, or simply sleep. As I have said repeatedly, intuitive ideas commonly present themselves on the fringe of consciousness, while falling asleep or awakening. Therefore, I like to go over my problem just before retiring—or even in the middle of the night if I happen to wake up—always keeping pencil and paper within reach even at night because nocturnal ideas tend to vanish, leaving no trace by the morning.

Profit even by adversity. Another factor which repeatedly stimulated my intuitive thinking—although I would not recommend its intentional use—is fever, presumably because a high temperature also creates a condition of half consciousness. I have repeatedly experienced the sensation of a particularly clear, general view of a broad scientific problem, while lying in bed with a fever. I immediately reached for the note pad on the night table and sometimes found the ideas thus conceived to be useful. I must admit, however, that just as often what I thought in my feverish dreams to be a wonderful solution turned out to be perfectly useless when reexamined after recovery.

Still, many discoveries of historic importance were made during illness. "A. R. Wallace, for instance, hit upon the theory of evolution by natural selection, in his berth during an attack of malarial fever at sea; and Darwin was compelled by ill-health to spend the greater part of his waking hours in physical and mental relaxation" [Graham Wallas [87]].

When Einstein announced his profound generalization concerning space and time, he stated that the idea occurred to him while sick in bed [Platt & Baker [56]].

It seems that, after we have saturated ourselves with all the material necessary for the appraisal of a new correlation, we invariably are too close to this or that aspect of it to see things in their true perspective. Besides, in the lab or office, the visible aspects of our subject (chemicals, microscope, experimental animals, papers, books) focus attention too one-sidedly on details which interfere with the big intuitive leap necessary for making a great new correlation. That is perhaps why so many scientists have occasion to exclaim "Eureka!" in the bathtub, in bed, or on any other occasion when the mind is freewheeling.

UNFAVORABLE FACTORS. An unexpected solution to a difficult problem is most unlikely to present itself at times of fatigue and tension, or while we are making a desperate conscious effort to find it. Administrative and private worries, as well as the frequent interruption of our train of thought are particularly unfavorable. A scientist must learn to design his whole way of life in such a manner as to protect himself against these sterilizing influences, or he will not be able to succeed, no matter how great his special talents may be. Creative thinking is blocked by such factors as: mental and physical exhaustion, petty irritations, noise, worry over domestic or financial matters, depression, anger, or working under pressure.

Few of the most successful scientists depend much upon hobbies or other nonscientific activities for relaxation. A moderate amount of play, family life, and cultural interests are certainly stimulating, but too intense and time-consuming nonscientific interests (particularly politics and business) are incompatible with complete devotion to science.

If I had to pick out the three greatest impediments to creative thought in North America, the factors that cause most of the frustration and failure among talented scientists, I would mention: 1. Administrative duties, with all the petty personality problems, red tape and committee work that characterize them; 2. Routine teaching of elementary courses; 3. Interruptions by visitors, assistants, etc., as a result of poor planning of the daily agenda, or the more common and equally tantalizing fear that one may be interrupted at any time.

These disturbing factors partly overlap, but the scientist who succeeds in creating for himself a climate free of these deadly enemies of originality can call himself very fortunate indeed. Personally, I cannot write about this subject without a feeling of deep gratitude toward the administrators of the Université de Montréal, who have provided me with a virtually perfect climate in all of these respects.

GENIUS

"Genius is only a great aptitude for patience."
[Attr. to Georges-Louis Leclerc de Buffon by Hérault de Séchelles]

"Genius . . . has been defined as a supreme capacity for taking trouble . . . It might be more fitly described as a supreme capacity for getting its possessors into trouble of all kinds and keeping them therein so long as the genius remains."   [Samuel Butler]

"Genius and madness have a borderline where they may even overlap."
[Arthur Schopenhauer]

"There is no great genius without some touch of madness."   [Seneca]

"Great wits are sure to madness near allied, and thin partitions do their bounds divide."   [John Dryden]

Which is it now—sober, patient attention to detail or wild, uncontrolled madness?

The term "genius" has been used in a great variety of senses, but
in science I believe its most outstanding characteristic is originality.
Therein it differs from talent, whose creations may sometimes appear
more accomplished, because of greater perfection in their execution.
In practice, however, it is very difficult to distinguish sharply between genius, superior intelligence, talent, and that degree of originality that borders on madness. The reason for this is that some
measure of all of these qualities must combine to create a work of
genius.

To conceive a highly original idea, the mind must first rid itself
of the inhibitions normally imposed upon it by the blind acceptance
of conventional logic and conduct. This emancipation is aided by
the "touch of madness" characteristic of the great nonconformists
and dreamers. That is perhaps why so many scientists tell of having
their best ideas on the fringe of consciousness, while half-asleep, or
suffering from fever.

On the other hand, even the most original idea is worthless if
we cannot grasp and fix its meaning in terms of conscious intellect.
Even the most original idea conceived in the madman's imagination
or the sane person's dream is of no use, because it cannot be thus
translated. Genius must not only be able to dream, but also to
articulate those dreams. In science, this process of articulation, this
work of translation into logically and experimentally verifiable
terms, requires talent, skill, and infinite attention to detail.

These qualifications for effective creative work may also explain
the peculiar personality traits of the genius. The extraordinary
development of some of his mental powers often results in a one-
sided, single-minded personality, which may be regarded as distorted,
intolerant of weakness, lacking in culture, and even amoral. Yet,
scientific genius is highly cultured and strictly moral, though not
necessarily in the conventional sense. His great originality and independence of judgment, turn him into a nonconformist who recoils
from the acceptance of standards imposed by people less competent
than he is in making value judgments. His rigid moral code imposes
upon him a very strong sense of duty. In view of his novel approach
this may be the duty of civil disobedience, but who would feel
competent to correct him?

Genius deals with the supralogical. It is characterized by an immense, though unconscious, capacity to calculate the statistical

probability of chance on the basis of instinct and past experience. It is manifested by the constancy with which it can correctly predict things of unexpected generalizability on insufficient evidence. Its primary function is to capture things too complex to grasp by pure intellect alone. Genius translates the unknown into terms simple enough to become accessible by the step-by-step analysis of logic that even mere intellect can employ.

It would be presumptuous for intellect to belittle the creative genius of instinct. The Indians who created the Mayan language and culture could not have analyzed them as well as a modern anthropologist. It is not an understanding of embryology, but far less intellectual talents that enable a woman to create a baby. Casanova was no specialist in sex hormones.

Instinct and logic are constantly at odds within us; for what we want is often not logical and what is logical, we often do not want.

Instinct and intellect forever despise each other, for one only does, the other only knows why. Genius builds bridges between instinct and intellect, between feeling and logic.

INTELLIGENCE

Intelligence is usually defined as the power of understanding. It is the ability to use conscious knowledge in meeting new situations and to foresee problems by thinking abstractly of relationships in symbols. It depends upon a general mental acuteness or sagacity for the meticulous, objective, conscious evaluation of observations.

Like imagination and intuition, intelligence works by combining the facts stored away in memory, but it does so not by fanciful play in the darkness of the unconscious, but by logical analysis in the full light of consciousness. Its main tools are: logic, memory, and the power of concentration upon a single topic with its corollary, the gift of abstraction, the disregard of the irrelevant.

Logic

"Some of my critics have said, 'Oh, he is a good observer, but he has no power of reasoning!' I do not think that this can be true, for the *Origin of Species* is one long argument from the beginning to the end and it has convinced not a few able men. No one could have written it without having some power of reasoning. I have a fair share of invention, and of common sense or judgment, such as every fairly successful lawyer or doctor must have, but not, I believe, in any higher degree."

[Charles Darwin [26]]

The dictionaries define logic as the science that deals with the criteria of validity in thought and demonstration. It comprises the principles of definition, classification, correct use of terms, correct predication, demonstration, and reasoning in general. In essence, it is a system of the formal principles used in subjecting a problem to consciously planned intellectual analysis.

As we shall see later (p. 263), it is rarely possible to give sufficiently stringent definitions of biologic concepts, to classify or interpret them by rigid application of the laws of logic. In addition, even the simplest manifestations of life are so complex that an exhaustive logical analysis of all their ingredients is impractical. Therefore, biologic research must depend largely upon purely instinctive or intuitive evaluation. In acquiring this instinct for biology, we are aided much more by experience than by the consciously guided application of logic. Unfortunately, instinct is too uncertain and logic too slow for the analysis of natural phenomena. Hence, instead of formal logic, we must use a kind of "semi-intuitive" logic (p. 266) in which entire patterns of thought are used as such, after their efficacy has been proven by experience. We need not dissect these typical thought-patterns nor check the validity of their individual components each time we use them. We come to trust them and learn to handle them intact, as guides to reasoning by analogy.

It is not only unnecessary and quite impractical to apply the canons of formal logic to all the problems we meet in the biologic laboratory, but excessive preoccupation with them actually blocks the much more fruitful free associations of our unconscious mind upon which we must mainly depend for imaginative intuitive thinking. The nonlogical (that is, not based on logic) is not necessarily illogical, and it represents the most effective approach to the discovery of the logically unpredictable.

For these reasons, creative biologic thought is much more an art than a true science. Accordingly, we shall have only a few words to say about what little use we can make of formal logic (p. 266). We shall emphasize much more the semi-intuitive logic, the construction of fruitful theories from idea-units that cannot be sharply defined, and the astonishingly naïve fallacies (p. 294) that have, in fact, corrupted and continue to corrupt the thinking of even the greatest biologists.

These fallacies, transparent as they are in retrospect, remain the most constant and dangerous causes of error in everyday laboratory practice. Of course, they are due to errors in formal logic, but these errors, once pointed out, are obvious to everyone. The difficult thing is not to understand but to see them. To avoid these fallacies, we do not need to know more about logic, but about the psychology of research. We must learn not to develop psychologic blocks—blind spots that prevent us from seeing a problem in its proper perspective if we have approached it from the wrong point of view. I believe that by analyzing not just imaginary examples, but many fallacies that have actually been committed by biologists, we develop an instinctive alertness for analogous situations that face us in our daily work. This way we shall learn much more about the art of biologic thought than through any systematic study of the abstract canons of formal logic. But suffice it here to outline the problem; we shall need a whole chapter for our detailed analysis of "How to Think" (p. 263).

Memory and Experience

"My memory is extensive, yet hazy: it suffices to make me cautious by vaguely telling me that I have observed or read something opposed to the conclusion which I am drawing, or on the other hand in favour of it; and after a time I can generally recollect where to search for my authority. So poor in one sense is my memory, that I have never been able to remember for more than a few days a single date or a line of poetry."

[Charles Darwin [26]]

"Experience is the name everyone gives to his mistakes."

[Oscar Wilde]

Memory (as distinct from the act of recollection or recall from memory) is the totality of what has been learned. It is a store of facts whose wealth depends mainly upon experience and, hence, to a great extent upon age. An important aspect of this store is that we can recall memories from it into consciousness, through conscious or unconscious associative mechanisms.

The part played by memory in creative thinking has already been discussed in connection with imagination, intuition, and logic, all of which work with recollected data. But, given a certain innate talent for acquiring facts through observation, the creation of usable experience will depend upon our ability to memorize them (in the brain or in notes) and to retrieve them at will. The young man who is full of dreams and imagination but has yet spent little time in the lab, tends to underrate the value of experience. The senior scientist easily falls into the opposite error, sometimes to a point where his repetitious emphasis upon the value of experience exasperates his junior colleagues who, of necessity, at least in this one respect, cannot equal him.

But, in addition to storing data, memory does something to them; they seem to mature in storage. A night's sleep and, even better, years of experience mellow our facts as aging mellows wine. When first perceived, some aspects of an observation are exaggerated, others underemphasized; but in the great mixer of the unconscious, idea hits upon idea again and again, until the rough edges are polished away and each unit fits in at its proper level. An observation made long ago and half forgotten, or one unconsciously repressed because of its unpleasantness, comes to the fore; while the novelty of the latest and the glamor of the most welcome findings wear off.

Unfortunately, with age we accumulate not only facts but also prejudices, and in general (not always), as knowledge increases, originality and intuitiveness diminish. Too much information interferes with an independent freshness of aspect. As we shall see, in research some things are done better by the young, others by the old (p. 113).

Concentration

The power of consciously directing attention toward a single object is essential for abstract thinking and for the use of memory.

We have seen that the factors most likely to interfere with concentration are interruptions and boredom. Any incidental noise or motion around us can interrupt a train of thought, but, even in the absence of any such external interference, our mind tends to wander if we make little progress in our analysis and become bored by our ineffectual effort.

I remember that, when I was a young medical student in Prague, I attached so much importance to the power of concentration that I often deliberately studied on street cars or in noisy coffeehouses as a form of training. This kind of exercise is quite useful, because the art of concentration can be improved by practice. Yet, perfection is never attained. Hence, nowadays I take, and encourage my associates to take, elaborate precautions against deviations.

While I am thinking about a problem that necessitates great concentration, I put out a DO NOT DISTURB sign on my door and ask the switchboard operator to disconnect my phone. If there is too much noise on the corridors, I even use ear plugs. These precautions take care of most interruptions; but, much to my dismay, the inevitable, unexpected emergency still breaks through my carefully constructed barricades. That is why I like to work early in the morning, when there is nobody around.

It is somewhat more difficult to overcome deviation of attention by internal factors. In this connection it helps to have some sort of skeleton that guides our thoughts as previously explained (p. 63). A list of the main points to be considered, or a tentative schematic drawing of puzzling interrelations, helps to keep the mind on a single track.

Abstraction

"My power to follow a long and purely abstract train of thought is very limited; and therefore I could never have succeeded with metaphysics or mathematics."   [Charles Darwin [26]]

Abstraction is the gift of neglecting the irrelevant for the isolation of the essential; the faculty of imaginatively selecting the common characteristics of things, usually with the aid of symbolic thinking. Abstract thought is particularly essential in mathematics (including statistics), logic, and all generalizing or integrating activity.

Disregard of the irrelevant presupposes a definition of what we consider relevant to our topic. For example, in thinking about ovarian hormones we must first define these by their distinctive properties before we can say of any particular substance whether it belongs. In biology, precise definitions are not easy to formulate. It is said that: "the hormones that come from the ovary are ovarian hormones." On this basis, estradiol and progesterone would belong to this category. However, these same substances are also secreted by the placenta, and they can even be synthesized in the laboratory. When they thus originate outside the ovary, are they still ovarian hormones? And how about the androgens? These are testicular hormones, yet small amounts of them are normally produced by the ovary. Are androgens also ovarian hormones? And if so, what about the androgens produced by the testis? Ovarian hormones could also be characterized by their typical action upon the female sex organs. However, certain synthetic compounds, not even chemically related to the natural hormones of the ovary, exert similar actions upon the female genitalia.

These simple examples illustrate a very general difficulty about abstract thinking in biology: the units of biologic thought are ill-defined and overlapping. The same hormone could be regarded as a hormone of the ovary, the placenta, or the testis and man-made drugs can so closely imitate the natural hormones of the ovary that it would seem arbitrary to place them in a separate category. It is here that a symbol which does not actually occur in reality must replace real objects as a yardstick of relevance. This symbol—e.g., the concept of a hormone, characteristic only of the ovary—exists only in our mind, and its value depends on how close it comes to the quintessence of the group it represents.

But these difficulties are by no means limited to biology or even to science in general. They are constantly encountered in everyday life. Who is a Canadian? One who was born in this country, even though to foreign parents who happened to be here in transit at the time? And what about the foreign-born infant who, at the age of a few weeks, was brought to Canada and never saw another land. Is he Canadian even if he never took out naturalization papers? Should the letter of the citizenship law, the ethnic background, or the home address be considered relevant?

In all these instances we must construct artificial symbols out of the features that we consider most important. For example, we may say that an ovarian hormone is one made by the ovary, and that a Canadian is a person who lives in Canada. These symbols retain their value as abstract yardsticks for classification even if, in reality, there is no group that quite corresponds to them. Estradiol is an ovarian hormone even if the same substance can originate elsewhere, and a Canadian does not lose his nationality by spending a week end in New York. Later, we shall have more to say about the theory and practice of idea-unit formation in biology (p. 268); here I merely want to emphasize its inherent limitations.

In mathematics, an entirely different situation exists. Two is two and there is no two that does not fit perfectly into this concept. This precision is intellectually very satisfying, and countless efforts have been made to analyze biologic problems on a mathematical basis. Undoubtedly, mathematics, and particularly biologic statistics, have their applications in the life-sciences (p. 258).

It would be impossible to imagine modern neurophysiology, biochemistry, and biophysics without a strictly quantitative approach. Some of the greatest advances in the study of life have been made recently with the highly intricate and accurately measurable procedures of molecular biology. To me, however, it seems that, dazed by these spectacular advances, undue emphasis is being placed now upon the feasibility of, and the need for, reducing all biologic phenomena to mathematical equations.

Many a gifted young biologist has just no talent or taste for the mathematical approach. He should not be discouraged on this account. A gift for mathematics is undoubtedly of value, especially in biologic research that yields accurately measurable end points. But, as a rule, the ingredients of biologic reactions are far too variable to be thus analyzed; besides, you first have to discover a field before you can calculate the behavior of its ingredients. By the mathematical approach it is hardly possible to discover new cell-types or biologic phenomena such as evolution, immunity, the microbial cause of a disease, or the antibiotic action of a mold. The great discoveries of Darwin, Harvey, Virchow, Ramon y Cajal, Cannon, Sherrington, Pavlov, Ehrlich, Fleming, Koch, Richet, Medawar and Burnett, Waksman, and so many others were all made, thanks to genius of another kind.

In view of current tendencies, I think it is well to state these facts clearly. Abstract symbolic thinking is indispensable for all forms of classification and generalization in biology, but it often need not, and usually cannot, be carried to the point of a purely mathematical analysis.

Ethics

By ethics we mean the principles which govern our conduct. Under this heading we shall discuss: honesty with self, achieved by introspection and self-examination. Mental self-discipline, that is, control over the mind to the end of effective action, and physical self-discipline, the enforcement of a healthful way of life are also relevant, but these aspects of conduct will be dealt with later (p. 135).

HONESTY WITH SELF

"Not by my sins wilt Thou judge me, but by the work of my hands."
[Robert William Service]

"Since when was genius found respectable?"
[Elizabeth Barrett Browning]

"Resolve to be thyself; and know, that he who finds himself, loses his misery."   [Matthew Arnold]

Scientists as a group have good reason to worry about their ethics, their conduct toward work and people. Great enthusiasm and the ambition to achieve excellence in any field are so consuming as to leave little behind but a highly specialized, goal-directed machine of a man. It is only natural for the scientist to ask himself from time to time whether his conduct is properly adjusted to the goal and, more important still, whether the goal is worthwhile.

Having engaged in such introspection and self-examination every time I made an entry in these Notes, I now find that arranging and editing them acts as a kind of Great Catharsis by purifying and putting order into my thoughts. In preparation for this work

I have read the biographies and diaries of other scientists, books which gave me much pleasure many years ago. It gives me perspective and tranquility to note that our worries and foibles are apparently quite common and natural. I rather like to hope that if these Notes fall into the hands of a young scientist, the feeling may be transmitted.

In all my life, I have known only two men who purposely falsified their scientific results, and they were mentally unbalanced. Of course, illness in any form can occur in all professions. It happens too often, however, that a scientist, especially a young one, gets so carried away by his enthusiasm that he sees only what he wants to see. We must be on the alert against this. "The most beautiful theory can be destroyed by a single ugly fact"—the art is to know how to accept this. In my own work I usually found that, if the theory was really beautiful, its destruction was not a defeat but a victory. It led to a still more fruitful theory without doing any harm to the tangible facts uncovered by the obsolete one.

In general, scientists try to be scrupulously honest with themselves regarding their work; they may not be quite so eager to examine the real reasons for their behavior toward society. This is deplorable, for no one can live in peace with himself unless he sees and approves his own motives—and, after all, the analysis might show that we need not be ashamed.

Most scientists are also strictly honest with themselves in claiming credit for their discoveries. The trouble is that, having worked hard on a certain question, they tend to overrate the importance of their own contributions in comparison with those of others. Temperamental scientists—and alas, most of them fall into this group —may become bitter if the world does not see things as they do. This is a pity; it can lead to endless aggressive polemics which destroy objectivity and kill the scientific spirit. It is well to reexamine one's mind from time to time for any trace of this evil pest; it has an insidious way of hiding behind the venerable mask of "a sense of justice."

Scientists are extremely truthful about science, but I am less sure of scientists' ethical standards in other respects. I wouldn't put it past some of them to cheat a little on their tax returns, smuggle the odd box of cigars across the border, or flirt with their neighbor's wife—that is, when they are not too busy. Of course, most of us would not go that far but, in all frankness, I must admit to occasional qualms of conscience because of the laxity with which I tend to view my duties as a citizen, administrator, examiner, committee man, member of editorial boards, fellow of scientific societies, and filler-out of questionnaires. Mind you, it is not that I deny my responsibilities in these respects. I just don't seem to succeed in working up the energy to do much about them. To justify my neglect I try to convince myself that more good can be done in re-search—but, of course, I can see through this excuse. Yet, sitting here in the lab all day, I feel so hopelessly incompetent in appraising the real issues behind the newspaper comments on our political parties that I like all of them equally well. I realize that somebody must administer my Institute, run the scientific societies, examine students, judge applications for grants, and correct manuscripts sub-mitted to journals for publication. I know that the University could not be run without committees, and questionnaires are printed to be filled out. If everybody would take my attitude, we would get into a terrible mess—but fortunately, not everybody does.

This may seem like a very egotistic attitude, and perhaps it is. But I suspect that many people prefer to do these things rather than live my life and I trust that my neglect of these tasks is no great loss. The usual argument, "if everybody did the same thing," is not really a very good one. I could not even sit down on my chair if I worried about what would happen if everybody wanted to sit on it at the same time. Fortunately, we all have different talents and predilections, and it may not be such a bad thing for everyone to say that he wants to do only what he is most competent to do. Probably this way of thinking is due to a deformation of my in-tellect by the single-mindedness of its purpose, but let me charitably think of it as an unavoidable professional disease. We are talking about honesty, and perhaps this whole argument is not very honest —but I honestly think it is.

Perhaps the most serious ethical problem met by the scientist is concerned with the consequences of his work. Whenever a medical investigator proposes a new drug, he worries about its possible dangers which no one can foresee; still, we have to take risks. Few people would prefer not to profit by the advances of modern medi-cine; and yet, despite the greatest care, the possible toxic side effects of new drugs can never be foreseen—and all drugs were new at first.

We biologists, fortunately, do not have the tremendous ethical problems of this kind met by the physicists. Still, in the concluding passage of his Nobel prize address, Pierre Curie said with confidence:

"One may also imagine . . . , that in criminal hands radium might become very dangerous, and here we may ask ourselves if humanity has anything to gain by learning the secrets of Nature, if it is ripe enough to profit by them or if this knowledge is not harmful. The example of Nobel's discoveries is characteristic: powerful explosives have permitted men to perform admirable work. They are also a terrible means of destruction in the hands of the great criminals who lead the peoples towards war.

"I am among those who think, with Nobel, that humanity will obtain more good than evil from the new discoveries."   [Eve Curie [24]]

I hope that the immortal French physicist was right. Unfortunately, those who use discoveries do not always have the wisdom of those who make them. But in any event, I think it would be below the dignity of Homo sapiens if he had to buy his survival at the price of self-imposed ignorance. Surely man's salvation should be sought not in the maintenance of darkness but in the creation of still more light by the untiring development and propagation of culture and knowledge.

Contact with Nature

By contact with Nature I mean the establishment of a close relationship with the natural phenomena we wish to study: how to take them in and see them clearly, how to influence them or even evoke them at will, and how to interpret their meaning. The practical aspects of observation, technique and evaluation will be discussed at length later (pp. 199–262); here, we shall merely outline the importance of these talents as basic traits in the mental structure of the scientist.

OBSERVATION.   Observation is the passive aspect of our contact with Nature. We don't do anything to her; we just watch. It is usually the first step of an investigation, since we have to see something before we can take it apart for further study. This much everybody knows, but there are a few fine points about observation that may be worth discussing: its constituent parts; the difference between seeing and discovering; the extraordinary importance of what I like to call "peripheral vision," and the role of meticulousness in the evaluation of data.

Actually, the term "observation" comprises three essentially distinct activities: noticing, recognizing, and measuring. By "noticing" I mean just seeing that a thing is there. "Recognizing" implies that we perceive it as something previously known or not known—in other words, we tie it in with our memories; while "measuring" implies a quantitative assessment of its qualities.

If I walk down the street and absent-mindedly get out of somebody's way, I have noticed him; if I see it is John, I have recognized him; and if I establish that his height is five foot eleven, I have measured him. The same distinctions hold true in the scientific observation of a cell, a biologic reaction, or a chemical compound; but much confusion has arisen because scientists often fail to distinguish between these three aspects of observation. You can't help seeing something that comes into your visual field, but that doesn't mean that you recognized and discovered it. Scientists have an equal chance to see things; it depends more or less upon the hazard of just what comes before you. But, as Pasteur said, *"Dans les champs de l'observation, le hasard ne favorise que les esprits préparés."* ("In the field of observation, chance favors only the prepared minds.")

It is perhaps the scientist's greatest asset to recognize the importance of the things he sees. That is why he needs erudition; his memory must be enriched by having seen—or read—much, and he must be greatly talented in connecting the newly observed with the particular memories relevant to it. Only in this way can he actually discover something.

Now, about this *"peripheral vision."* Horace Walpole coined the word "serendipity" on the basis of an old Ceylonese fairy tale about "The Three Princes of Serendip" who were always discovering, by accident or sagacity, things which they were not in quest of. How did they do it? To my mind, the answer is "peripheral vision": the ability not only to look straight at what you want to see, but also to watch continually, through the corner of your eye, for the unexpected. I believe this to be one of the greatest gifts a scientist can have. Usually, we concentrate so much upon what we intend to examine that other things cannot reach our consciousness, even if they are far more important. This is particularly true of things so different from the commonplace that they seem improbable. Yet, only the improbable is really worthy of attention! If the unexpected is nevertheless found to be true, the observation usually represents a great step forward.

It is notoriously difficult to observe facts if we are looking only *at* them and not *for* them, particularly if the facts present themselves as a complete surprise and if we are distracted at the time by emotion. To illustrate this, W. H. George reports the following instructive story:

"At a congress on psychology at Göttingen, during one of the meetings, a man suddenly rushed into the room chased by another with a revolver. After a scuffle in the middle of the room a shot was fired and both men rushed out again about twenty seconds after having entered.

Immediately the chairman asked those present to write down an account of what they had seen. Although the observers did not know it at the time, the incident had been previously arranged, rehearsed and photographed. Of the forty reports presented, only one had less than 20 per cent mistakes about the principal facts, 14 had from 20 to 40 per cent mistakes, and 25 had more than 40 per cent mistakes. The most noteworthy feature was that in over half the accounts, 10 per cent or more of the details were pure inventions. This poor record was obtained in spite of favourable circumstances, for the whole incident was short and sufficiently striking to arrest attention, the details were immediately written down by people accustomed to scientific observation and no one was himself involved. Experiments of this nature are commonly conducted by psychologists and nearly always produce results of a similar type."   [Beveridge [11]]

It is especially noteworthy that errors in observation are not limited to missing the seemingly obvious but are often due to pure invention of detail. There are innumerable examples of optical illusions, of being misled by distraction of attention (magicians' tricks) and by change of reference standards (lukewarm appears cold after we experience heat, but hot after cold; gray appears almost white after we look at black, but dark after we look at white). Errors in observation are frequently made owing to bias by immediately preceding impressions. For example, a normal adrenal may seem very small if we observe it immediately after having looked at several unusually large adrenals.

Besides, we tend to see only those things that we are prepared to observe. In viewing an experiment on a dog, the antivivisectionist will note only that the animal is well anesthetized. The dog lovers will observe the breed, and scientists of diverse specialties will note different scientific details.

Pasteur had the most extraordinary gift for seeing the unexpected. His researches on fowl cholera were interrupted by the summer vacations, and when he resumed work, nearly all the germ cultures proved to be sterile. He attempted to revive the microbes by injection into fowls, but the birds were not affected. He was about to give up when he had the inspiration of reinoculating the test fowls with a potent fresh culture. His colleague Duclaux [31] relates:

"To the surprise of all, and perhaps even of Pasteur, who was not expecting such success, nearly all these (pretreated) fowls withstood the inoculation, although fresh fowls succumbed after the usual incubation period. . . . This resulted in the discovery of the principle of immunisation with attenuated pathogens."

On another occasion, Pasteur was surprised to note that the germ of anthrax can be isolated from the soil where sheep, dead from this disease, were buried twelve years before. He wondered how the germs could resist so long and then produce epidemics at intervals of several years. Once, walking through the fields, he noticed a patch of earth differing in color from the rest and asked the farmer about it. He was told that sheep, dead of anthrax, had been buried there one year earlier.

"Pasteur, who always examined things closely, noticed on the surface of the soil a large number of worm castings. The idea then came to him that in their repeated travelling from the depth to the surface, the worms carried to the surface the earth rich in humus around the carcase, and with it the anthrax spores it contained. Pasteur never stopped at ideas but passed straight to the experiment. This justified his forecast. Earth contained in a worm, inoculated into a guinea-pig produced anthrax."

[Emile Roux, quoted by Beveridge [11]]

No amount of reasoning in his office could have led Pasteur to this discovery without a personal observation in the field.

In my own work I have often had occasion to see how blind we are to the totally unexpected. In 1941, I was working on the effect upon the sex organs of the then recently synthesized ovarian hormone, progesterone. For this purpose, I injected rats subcutaneously with this compound daily, and focused attention upon expected changes in the sex organs. After a few weeks, I handed the work over to a technician who had just then joined our laboratory, but, much to my surprise, the next day she reported that all the animals had died. Since I had given the same amount of progesterone for many days before without any trouble, I thought that she must have made some mistake in preparing her solution and merely told her to repeat the experiment more carefully. Next day the girl came to see me greatly perturbed: despite every precaution the animals died after the first injection. I could not imagine what might have gone wrong, so I asked her to inject another group of rats, this time in my presence.

It turned out that, being unacquainted with our techniques, she injected the hormone intraperitoneally because in her previous job (in a bacteriological lab) this was the customary procedure. I did not think that the route of administration would make much difference, but while I was telling her so all the rats fell asleep, just as if they had received a strong anesthetic, and eventually they died. Now, this was very odd. Progesterone had never been shown to have any toxic effects, and no steroid hormone—indeed no hormone of any kind—had ever produced anesthesia. So I repeated the experiment, using smaller doses of progesterone. The animals again fell asleep, but under these conditions they woke up within a couple of hours and were then perfectly all right.

Here, we were dealing with a true hormonal anesthesia, with sleep induced by a natural product of an endocrine gland. Apparently, this phenomenon had been missed before, because following the usual subcutaneous injection, the absorption of progesterone is too slow to reach anesthetically acting blood levels. However, when the inexperienced technician injected the compound her way, it was rapidly absorbed from the large peritoneal surface. Yet she did not notice anesthesia because after injection there was no reason for her to watch the animals until injection time next day, and by then they were already dead. Even if she had examined them soon after injection, it is doubtful whether she would have ascribed their immobility before death to a true anesthesia. After I had described these observations, several experienced authors challenged my interpretation, attributing the immobility of the animals merely to "shock." Yet we now know that steroid hormones can produce anesthesia not only in animals but also in man. Indeed, hydroxydione, a close derivative of progesterone, is in clinical use at present as the anesthetic of choice for certain surgical operations.

The more we rely on complex instruments, the more the faculty of observation tends to atrophy. It is well to train the young scientist to acquire the habit of carefully observing the clinical behavior of his animals and of making meticulous autopsies with special emphasis upon "peripheral vision" by the systematic search for changes that are not expected.

Apart from their position in the periphery of our visual field, important things may escape attention because irrelevancies blur the picture. The talent to see likeness in the midst of difference—and, more important still, difference in the midst of likeness—is the basis of all classification. We shall have much more to say about this later (pp. 228–255).

Finally, a word about *meticulousness:* painstaking attention to detail. Everybody agrees upon the importance of this qualification, not only in scientific research, but in all walks of life. According to Cannon [16], "Willingness to take infinite pains and to regard carefully minute details, is an essential element of the research spirit," and Thomas Carlyle says that genius itself is merely "... the transcendent capacity for taking trouble first of all."

Meticulousness prevents ideas from smudging each other's contours. It is needed in all aspects of research work: in evaluating both thoughts and observations. Yet, the greater a man's élan of imagination and the greater his ardor to complete a visionary picture, the more he is tempted to disdain minutiae. Only the greatest minds are impatient enough to reach out avidly far into the unknown, and yet, patient enough to check all along the way that they are still on the right course.

TECHNICAL SKILL

"...This study renders men acute, inquisitive, dexterous, prompt in attack, ready in defence, full of resources...."　　　　　[Edmund Burke]

Close contact with Nature, either through passive observation or the active modification of her manifestations, presupposes a great deal of technical skill and resourcefulness.

I think a young man, during his formative years, should learn techniques without any immediate application in mind, for two reasons: he finds out what he can and likes to do with his hands, and he builds up a stock of skills which will be handy when a good idea unexpectedly creates a need for them.

The many tricks in surgery which I learned as a medical student from my father were of great use to me later. Then, as a demonstrator in the pathology department at the University of Prague, I had ample opportunity to learn histologic techniques. Still later, I became so convinced that the basis of all modern medical research is chemistry that I took my second doctorate in this subject. When I now look back upon the time devoted to learning all these techniques, it seems to me well spent although many of them I never actually used in research.

I happen to be a morphologist and an experimental surgeon by inclination. Although, before embarking on a definite research career, I spent much more time in learning the techniques of synthetic chemistry, this is the aspect of my training that I use least. Yet I do not regret those years in the chemistry lab. They gave me a certain feeling for the possibilities and limitations of this science as viewed against the background of my inclinations.

I still think of chemistry as one of the most valuable tools for medical and other biologic research, but it is not biology. I like life itself as manifested by form and motion—things I can appreciate directly with my senses. A biologic reaction that I can see with my naked eye, a cell that I can observe under the microscope—these mean much more to me than a colorimetric reaction indicating the blood level in an invisible compound. I like the techniques of experimental surgery because of the preciseness of the information they furnish. Pharmacology also provides techniques that block the functions of certain nerves or of the kidney, but it always remains doubtful whether they abolish them completely and selectively, without interfering with any other organ. The situation is much clearer if you cut the nerve or remove the kidney. (Parenthetically, it must be admitted that I also like experimental surgery just for its craftsmanship: I have often tried to solve a tricky surgical problem in animal experiments without any immediate application in mind, merely to see whether it could be done. If so, useful applications usually presented themselves spontaneously, sooner or later.)

In pharmacology and physiology I prefer to experiment in vivo on the whole animal, rather than on isolated organs or even on animals extensively mutilated by various "sensitizing and desensitizing procedures." In this connection I remember a meeting at which a young scientist held forth for thirty minutes on observations showing that, if a cat is anesthetized, tied down on a board, given atropine (to block the vagus nerve), and hepatectomized (to eliminate liver function), the administration of a certain drug causes defecation, urination, and a wagging motion of the tail. When the paper was opened for discussion, the only question asked was: "What else could the cat have done under the circumstances?"

Conditions are still more artificial when the whole body is removed except for one organ that we examine separately in the test tube, that is, in vitro. Of course, certain very important metabolic problems can be studied in no other way and those whose interests lie in this direction must work in vitro. But the less a technique disturbs life the more I like it.

In general, I am also disinclined to use complex new techniques soon after they have been discovered. Now that the electronmicroscope and the radioisotope methods are available, their application to countless problems is sure to yield publishable, new, and often useful information. The young man in search of a topic is well advised to profit by these opportunities. But those who have already acquired experience in other techniques and have found their chosen field of interest should not be dazzled either by the novelty or the intricacy of new approaches. The latest techniques usually improve with time, and can then be used to greater advantage for studies in which the idea is new rather than the instrument.

Of all techniques I like morphology best, because a single observation gives me so many kinds of information. If, in an experiment on calciphylaxis, we determine the calcium content of a skin specimen, we get a single end point. We can say, for example, that this piece of skin contains 1.25 mg. of calcium. Histologic examination of this skin specimen cannot duplicate such precision regarding the total calcium content; it can furnish only a rough estimate. But just think of all the additional information it gives us. Using appropriate stains, we can see precisely where the calcium granules are, within or outside the cell; in addition, we see all the other structural elements of the skin which provide us with countless end points, not to speak of the interrelations between all these points, which are likewise clearly before us. No one interested in biologic correlations can remain indifferent to these advantages.

Another attraction of surgical and histologic procedures is that possible technical errors are easily checked. This is of great help especially in large-scale correlative work. Usually the director of research does not determine the calcium content of the skin himself; what he actually sees is the figure of 1.25 mg. on a piece of paper. Was the determination well done? The histologic slide may be spoiled by bad technique, but artifacts become obvious under the investigator's microscope. No technical error can make a cancer cell look benign or transfer the calcium deposit from one cell to another. The experimental surgeon, even if he did not do the operation himself, can easily check the completeness of a nerve transection or organ removal on the autopsy table. It is not possible to achieve equal precision in the verification of a drug-induced blockade of an organ's function.

I do feel, however, that after an investigator reaches a certain stage of maturity, he should no longer go on learning more and more of the established techniques to compare their merits—or just to have them on hand in case he might want to use one of them for something. Instead, he should develop his own methods. It is characteristic of almost all the great biologists that they ingeniously founded the special technology of their particular subject. Lavoisier had to make himself the balances, thermometers, and calorimeters that he used. Pasteur proved to be an extraordinarily resourceful inventor of bacteriologic techniques, many of which are still in use today. The same is true of so many prominent investigators that it would be redundant to list more examples. The birth of a new science requires the midwifery of a new technology.

EVALUATION OF THE OBSERVED

"What is the first business of one who studies philosophy? To part with self-conceit. For it is impossible for any one to begin to learn what he thinks that he already knows."　　　　　　　　　　　　　[Epictetus]

"I ... followed a golden rule, namely, that whenever a published fact, a new observation or thought came across me, which was opposed to my general results, to make a memorandum of it without fail and at once; for I had found by experience that such facts and thoughts were far more apt to escape from the memory than favourable ones. Owing to this habit, very few objections were raised against my views which I had not at least noticed and attempted to answer."   [Charles Darwin [26]]

The gift of shedding all forms of blinding prejudice is the first prerequisite for the objective, honest assessment of the observed facts. We have seen how much scientific research leans on previous experience which builds up prejudices (p. 43), but we must learn to control prejudice. A sound judgment in the appraisal, rating and interpretation of data depends largely upon an ability to view what is before us without fixed ideas, and upon our willingness to change our views when new evidence requires it, without surpassing, by unwarranted extrapolation, the inferences that can be drawn from what we see.

According to Cannon [16], President Eliot of Harvard told the story that, when he entered a crowded New York restaurant, he handed his hat to the colored doorman. As he came out he was astonished to see the doorman promptly pick his hat out of the hundreds there and hand it to him. In his surprise he asked, "How did you know that was my hat?" "I didn't know it was yo' hat, suh," was the answer. "Why, then," asked Mr. Eliot, "did you hand it to me?" Very courteously the doorman replied, "Because when you came in you handed it to me, suh." This precise limitation of inference pleased the president.

One of the worst diseases of the scientific mind is the tendency to see what we want to see; in our lab we have come to call this "corruptive optimism." I remember a graduate student who set out to prove that drug A was more fatal than drug B. He treated two groups of ten rats with each of these drugs: five died in the group treated with A and six in the other. Yet, he saw confirmation of his view in this experiment because he talked himself into believing that he could see some incidental morbid lesion, unconnected with the treatment, in every rat that, according to his expectations, shouldn't have died. This happened to be a very intelligent student who subsequently developed into an objective, reliable investigator and is becoming quite well-known today. Yet as a beginner this is how he saw things. Unfortunately, many other men I knew never matured much beyond this stage.

Since, in science, we are constantly running into things quite contrary to everyday experience, shedding our prejudices is no easy matter. When you clearly see the sun constantly rising and setting on the evidently immobile horizon, it takes quite a bit of flexibility to accept, when first faced with the evidence, that it is not the sun that turns around the earth but vice versa—or indeed, that the whole problem is merely a matter of relativity.

3. What Should Be Done?

The Choice of a Problem

We have already spoken about the balance which must be struck between curiosity and applicability, in the choice of scientific problems (p. 10). It is in the things he considers important that the scientist differs most from people in other walks of life, and it is in this same respect that the great scientist differs most from the average investigator. As far as I can see, the over-all intellectual capacities of an outstanding jurist, businessman, financier or statesman are very much the same as those of a great scientist. The only essential difference between them is the choice of the problems that they consider worthy of their attention. The things that interest the scientist are not man-made. Their significance does not depend upon man-made laws or social conventions that can be changed by man. Hence, their value is perennial though often difficult to see.

To solve a complex legal or political problem, to acquire great wealth, to furnish livelihoods for many people, to build a much needed dam or bridge are all activities whose value is immediately obvious to everyone. The same could not be said of efforts designed to identify the pigments in a butterfly's wing or the forces that direct the course of a distant star. It takes a special kind of curiosity and a great detachment from accepted worldly values to pursue such apparently impractical aims. And yet, in such pursuits lies the strength of the scientist, no matter how trivial they may seem to most people. He does not consider them impractical because, in his mind, the satisfaction of his curiosity and the potentially great future applicability of any natural law outweigh all other considerations. Because of this intense interest in things quite outside the preoccupations of the average person, scientists are often considered peculiar and eccentric by their contemporaries. This attitude changes later—

though sometimes only centuries later—when the general and often highly practical implications of the discoveries become evident.

The choice between one subject and another continues to be the most important and the most difficult task of the scientist throughout his life. He is always at the crossroads, forced to select from many avenues leading into the unknown. And his problem is not—as one might think—to decide whether the road is good or bad; there is merit in solving any unsolved problem. The question is always whether it is better to go this way or that, because everything is done at a price—at the price of not doing something else while one question engages our attention.

We shall have to consider this problem of selection particularly in relation to certain pitfalls in the anticipatory appraisal of still unsolved questions, since it is only before their solution that they are of scientific interest.

What Is a Discovery?

Was America discovered by the Indians who were here from time immemorial, by the Norsemen who came in the tenth century, or by Christopher Columbus who arrived in 1492? Is it still being discovered, now, every day, by anyone who drills a new oil well or finds another deposit of uranium on this continent? It depends upon the particular aspect of America and upon the extent of exploration to which you attach the greatest importance. Discovery is always a matter of viewpoint and degree. Whenever we single out an individual as the discoverer of anything, we merely mean that for us he discovered it more than anybody else.

The historian of any exploration is faced with these confusing facts. Usually, the subject of the discovery has been suspected and even more or less fleetingly seen from many angles by many people long before it was "actually discovered." For practical purposes, it is unimportant who made a scientific discovery, as long as we can enjoy its fruits. In this sense, it matters little who discovered America as long as we have been given the use of the country. But it does matter, if we want to share the thrill of following the unrolling of a true adventure story or to profit by the practical lessons that can be learned from it. And a great deal can be learned from it. For one thing, the history of an exploration can teach us just what constitutes an important discovery not only for the professional explorer in his scientific studies but for anyone in his daily life.

Take again the discovery of America. Obviously, we consider Columbus to be the discoverer only because he, more than anyone else, was responsible for giving us—by "us" I mean the non-Indians —a new continent. The Indians would certainly not look upon him as the discoverer of America. From their point of view, his arrival was the date on which the white man was discovered.

Those isolated groups of Norsemen who came during the tenth century had the great merit of getting here long before any other European. But although they unwittingly discovered America for themselves, they played no part in discovering it for the rest of us. Their exploits were completely forgotten, because they failed to establish a workable and permanent connection between the New World and the Old. That is why they did not do us, today's inhabitants of America, any good. The Norsemen did not help Columbus either because, when he planned his trip centuries later, neither he nor anyone in his surroundings knew anything about those earlier voyages. We have learned about them only quite recently, long after America became part of the civilized world. Columbus had to plan his trip without profiting from previous experiences.

The important difference between the discovery of America by the Indians, by the Norsemen, and by Columbus is only that Columbus succeeded in attaching the American continent to the rest of the world.

It is not to see something first, but to establish solid connections between the previously known and the hitherto unknown that constitutes the essence of scientific discovery. It is this process of tying together which can best promote true understanding and real progress.

The relativity of discovery has impressed many a scientist. For instance, the great American bacteriologist Hans Zinsser [92] said, "So often, in the history of medicine, scientific discovery has merely served to clarify and subject to purposeful control facts that had long been empirically observed and practically utilized."

This kind of consideration is not without practical value. It happens too often that a young scientist is discouraged from continuing a promising investigation because he feels that "this was known anyway."

What Do We Mean by "Known"?

A thing seen, but not recognized as to its importance and connections with other things, is not known. Just because somebody has seen, ages ago, that one of his microbe cultures was killed by accidental contamination with a mold (concluding only that he must make another culture because this one is no good anymore), he has not discovered antibiotics. Even if he has described this observation in a footnote, honestly registering it as a regrettable sloppiness in his technique, he has contributed nothing to our knowledge. It would have been most unfortunate if modern bacteriologists had given up research on this subject because they stumbled upon his paper and concluded that the subject "is already known." As we shall see in discussing Gley's work on insulin (p. 91), whoever sees a thing and fails to note its importance has most clearly shown his incapacity to discover it, because he had the best chance and yet failed.

Even if an observation is fully described in the literature with all its implications and hence is "known" in the conventional sense, it is well to ask "known to whom"? An important observation, published only in an extinct, inaccessible journal and in a little known language, may actually be known to no living person. Such a fact may be well worth rediscovering, with of course, proper mention of the original publication. These extreme cases are unusual, but it is astonishing how many useful observations, published in little-read journals, slip past the notice of those who should know them.

A few years ago, Dr. Serge Renaud, at this Institute discovered that for the histochemical detection of calcium in tissues, fixation in alcohol-formol is far superior to the customary neutral formalin. He then found that this fact had been properly described in the old German literature, long ago; yet pathologists throughout the world still commonly use neutral formalin for this purpose. Hence, I strongly encouraged Dr. Renaud to publish his observations (of course, citing the earlier literature), and I am sure many investigators are glad he did so.

Seeing vs. Discovering

Several times we have touched upon the essential difference between seeing and discovering (pp. 77, 88). Let us illustrate this important point now by analyzing the story of insulin as related to me by Banting. The discovery itself has already been mentioned as an example of an intuitive flash (p. 48).

In 1889, the German physiologists Minkowski and von Mering surgically removed the pancreas from dogs and thereby produced diabetes, but they did not realize that the disease resulted from a lack of insulin. Their finding did not stimulate much progress until 1921, when Sir Frederick Banting and C. H. Best extracted insulin from the pancreas, showing that, with this hormone, it was possible to treat not only experimental diabetes but also that which spontaneously occurs in man.

It is interesting to note that many earlier workers (Hédon, Zuelzer, Rennie and Frazer, Scott) obtained suggestive results with pancreatic extracts but ascribed the hypoglycemic reactions to the "toxicity" of their preparations. In France, the well-known physiologist, E. Gley, had performed experiments very similar to those of Banting, but sixteen years earlier. He even described them in a private communication which he deposited in a sealed envelope, with the Société de Biologie de Paris, in February, 1905. Gley injected oil into the pancreatic duct and thus caused the gland to sclerose (Claude Bernard's method). He noted that such dogs do not become diabetic and that intravenous injection of extracts of these sclerosed glands diminishes the glycosuria of pancreatectomized dogs. Only in 1922, after Banting's publication, did Gley give permission to open this sealed letter. It fully supported his claim to have first found insulin.

Subsequently a great deal was written about the moral aspects of such a priority claim. In any event, Gley received little credit and at an international symposium on diabetes he violently protested against the injustice of this. Old Professor Minkowski was in the chair and stopped the embarrassing scene with the mild but knowing remark: "I understand just how you feel, I was also very disappointed not to have discovered insulin, when I realized how close I had come to it."

Obviously, Gley did not recognize the importance of what he saw; otherwise he would not have been satisfied to deposit his findings under seal. In fact, it would have been criminal to do so had he realized he would thereby have become responsible for the deaths of the thousands who succumbed from diabetes for want of insulin during the intervening years. None of Gley's subsequent work was comparable in importance to the discovery of insulin. Why had he put the subject aside, if not because he failed to understand its significance? It is easy to deposit private communications about things we are not sure of, then unseal them if and when somebody else proves that we were on the right track. To my mind, Gley not only failed to discover insulin but he also proved that he could not do so. Although he saw it by chance, he still did not discover it.

There are many similar instances in the medical literature. An important observation is made, but the discoverer is somewhat uncertain about it or fails to realize its implications. Hence, he makes only incidental reference to the chief point or even omits mention of it. In such cases, the "discoverer" deserves less credit than he who, not having been accidentally confronted with the fact, had no opportunity to give such evident proof of his inaptitude to evaluate it. If a scientist makes no important observation he deserves no credit, yet, at least he can blame it on lack of chance. But if a significant fact comes his way and he still does not see its importance, he can blame only himself. The element of chance, in medical discoveries, is overrated in any case. "Chance is a lady who smiles only upon those who know how to appreciate her artful charms; these connoisseurs she rarely neglects—the secret of the game is art appreciation" [H. Selye [66]].

Contrary to common opinion, Edward Jenner was far from being the first to inoculate people with cowpox to protect them against smallpox; William Harvey was not the first to recognize the circulation of the blood; Darwin was not the first to suggest evolution, and Pasteur was not the first to formulate the germ theory. Carbolic acid was used as a wound antiseptic before Lister's time. But these were the men who really developed these ideas to a point where they became useful.

Importance of the Problem vs. Likelihood of Its Solution

Do not confuse the importance of your goal or the refinement of your tools with the significance of your work. It is the accomplishment, not merely the aims and tools, that should be admirable. Few of us would not prefer to find a cure for cancer, to success in whatever medical research we do; all of us admire the complex structure of electronic computers, electron microscopes and X-ray spectrometers. But the choice of cancer research as a subject, or of complicated machinery as a tool, does not in itself imply great foresight or guarantee success. Unfortunately, many a young scientist and even some subsidizing agencies tend to forget this.

FORMULATION OF QUESTIONS. Two major lines of thought lead to the formulation of research projects, *the practical and the impractical questions*. In relation to the action of an agent upon a target, a practical question is: "What would happen if I did this?" We may ask ourselves what would happen to an animal if we removed its adrenals? A practical question in connection with static observations would be: "What is this like?" We may ask, "How are the nerves distributed in the adrenal medulla?" Another practical question concerns quantitation: "How much of this agent is needed to elicit such and such a result?" We may ask, "How much ACTH is required to produce a 20 per cent increase in adrenal weight?" All these practical questions can be logically designed to answer a specific problem and so formulated as to yield a feasible experimental plan. Here, the solution is rarely an aim in itself; it is part of a larger project. For example, the specific questions just mentioned are all concerned with the better understanding of the adrenal gland.

The impractical problems are actually not projects at all, but wishes. They are expressed by such statements as, "I wish I knew more about the adrenals," or "I wish I could find a cure for cancer." Curiosity in such matters is a justifiable and necessary motivation for research, but it is quite useless as a plan unless it can be reduced to practical questions. Many a young man who has decided to work on cancer, the basic mechanisms of enzyme actions, or perhaps even the nature of life, feels very superior to colleagues having more limited objectives and deems himself justified in asking for special consideration. He forgets that the mere choice of a great field requires no particular talent, nor does it give any assurance of success. There must be a reasonable balance between the importance of our problem and the likelihood of our solving it; otherwise the result is only lifelong frustration. Most of the "misunderstood geniuses" are people who do not realize this.

The beginner usually finds it particularly difficult to choose a problem that is important and yet within his reach. Here, consultation with his teacher is especially useful. Since most students work best on ideas suggested by themselves, the tactful director of research should try to lead his pupil to propose a fruitful experiment and then let the student feel that the idea was his. In any event, the beginner should at first choose subjects within the field of the senior investigators in the laboratory. Only thus can he benefit from their guidance and true interest, at the same time obtaining a real understanding of what the experienced scientists are doing. It is also important that the research student should start with a problem in which he has a good chance of succeeding, for success is as stimulating as frustration is paralyzing.

In my own work I usually give preference to topics that present themselves spontaneously from accidental observations made in the lab, because then I am sure to have all the technical prerequisites for producing the phemonenon that is to be investigated. I also recommend to my students that, as far as possible, they should thus follow the line of least resistance. Of course, any student who has real talent usually experiences no great difficulty in finding a suitable problem after a while. "If he has not in the course of his studies noticed gaps in knowledge, or inconsistencies, or has not developed some ideas of his own, it does not augur well for his future as a research worker" [W. I. B. Beveridge [11]].

THE PROBLEM COMES BEFORE THE TECHNIQUE. Excessive preoccupation with the practical aspects of investigation, without any thought for the basic problems is fruitless. The gadgeteer who is overly impressed with the possibilities of technical perfection may eventually devise methods and instruments of extraordinary precision without ever contributing any fundamental new knowledge. We must *look for techniques that fit the problem and not for problems that fit the technique.*

This point has been symbolized in my mind since the very beginning of my career by the attitude of a young colleague who had spent a great deal of time in developing a really admirable procedure for the accurate determination of fecal iron in the rat. He had no inclination to do any experimental work on animals himself, but he continually accosted people on the campus with the question, "Do you happen to have any experiments going in which very accurate iron determinations on rat excrements would be particularly useful?" He was very disappointed if you said no, but if you said yes, he arrived cheerfully next day in your lab with his little pots to collect the material. Eventually, the man became a well-known campus character because of this habit; unfortunately, he never became well-known for any other activity.

Simplicity vs. Complexity

BALANCED PERSPECTIVE. In science, as in everything else, we need perspective to single out the important points in the general picture. "To look at his picture as a whole, a painter requires distance; and to judge of the total scientific achievement of any age, the standpoint of a succeeding age is desirable" [John Tyndall].

The man who specializes in the metabolism of sodium gradually but unfailingly becomes convinced that this element is the most important one in the body. He notes that sodium is present in every organ, that a severe change in blood sodium alters the metabolism of all other compounds; in fact, life itself is impossible without sodium. He knows very well that the same could be said about calcium, potassium, or even water, but somehow his great preoccupation with sodium represses such considerations. This attitude is ridiculous, but from a practical point of view very useful—if kept under reasonable control. The human brain can think of only one subject at a time, and if we want to survey the part this one thing plays in the various manifestations of life, it helps to look at it as if it were the center of everything. Of course, it isn't; life has no single central axis—no more than any of the wheels in your wrist watch could be singled out as the central pivot of the whole mechanism. Life depends as much on sodium as on potassium, on cells as on intercellular substance, on the brain as on the spinal cord, on the adrenals as on the parathyroids.

Yet, there are less important parts; life can go on without nails, hair, and even the loss of an eye or a limb does not mean death. The physiology of the mammary gland is an important subject, but babies can be raised quite well on the bottle. Consciously or unconsciously, all these considerations influence us in our choice of an important research problem. What handicaps our vision most in this assessment is that the closest things appear to be the largest. Whatever I happen to be working on at the moment seems to me most interesting and meaningful. Any related published or personally observed fact immediately attracts my attention because I can best see its significance in connection with other things that are fresh in my memory. This one-sided sensitization is what we need to profit by chance observations. It is the kind of preparation that helps us to see the unexpected—even if it happens to turn up in the periphery of our visual field—and to interpret the observed facts correctly against the background of our relevant knowledge. That is why it is best not to change subjects too often, since, other things being equal, we should profit from our specialized experience.

On the other hand, in working consistently along the same lines, we eventually come to a point of diminishing returns; after the essentials are well established, let others work out the details. There are enough collectors of minutiae and too few coordinators of broad subjects. The difficulty is to see the point of diminishing returns when we reach it. The greatest gift is the ability to skim the cream of everything that comes your way. To do this well, avoid overspecialization; maintain a certain distance to recognize those points occupying pivotal positions in the whole picture. Try not to learn many facts about a few subjects, but a few important facts about many subjects. That is why the scientist who wants to do correlative work should keep himself up-to-date—at least on the fundamentals, the things that eventually get into textbooks—on as many subjects as he can cover. When we come to speak about the techniques for the coordination of knowledge (p. 228), we shall have more to say about the "mass reading" needed to skim the cream of published data.

SIMPLE VS. COMPLEX TOOLS.   Beginners are often discouraged by the thought that, because through so many centuries so many outstanding minds have explored the salient problems of medicine, presumably most of the important pivotal points have already been discovered. In talking to my students I hear this view expressed again and again. They are also convinced that, to make really interesting discoveries today, one would need large sums of money, modern laboratories equipped with all kinds of complicated, expensive machinery, and preferably a large staff of highly trained assistants. Yet, "even large pieces of laboratory equipment—wind tunnels, electronic computers, and cyclotrons—bring dangers and should be feared. They represent large investments and can exert pressure on scientists to work on problems which use the monsters, and thus promise some return on the investment" [A. Schild [61]]. The means of learning become ends in themselves.

Young men tend to believe that the times have gone when it was possible to make an immortal medical discovery simply by looking at a hitherto unexplored part of the human body.

Take the adrenals which have played such a prominent role in my work on stress: the most important fact about them is that they exist. Without knowing this, we could have discovered nothing else about them. Well, this basic fact was revealed in 1563 by Bartolommeo Eustacchio, physician to Cardinal della Rovere who, because of his connections in high places, managed to get permission to perform dissections in Rome. After that it was easy; merely by prodding about in the fat around the upper pole of the kidneys, he could not help discovering the adrenals. Apparently, there was nothing to it.

I think it is very wrong to look at things this way. First, it must have taken insatiable scientific curiosity to overcome the prejudices of the sixteenth century sufficiently to ask for, and use, permission for the dissection of a human body. Second, it required great perspicacity to recognize that the inconspicuous little piece of whitish tissue, embedded in fat of almost the same color, is a separate organ, worthy of description. We must always measure the importance of a discovery against the background of the times in which it was made. We should not envy the ancient anatomists for having been able to make a great discovery with simple means, any more than we should complain that our research tools are primitive in comparison with those of coming centuries.

It will be recalled that the signs upon which the whole stress concept (p. 51) was based were: adrenocortical enlargement, thymicolymphatic involution, and intestinal ulcers. Then came the realization that this syndrome is triphasic, with the initial appearance of marked acute manifestations (alarm reaction), their subsequent disappearance (stage of resistance) and finally, a breakdown in the organism, with complete loss of resistance (stage of exhaustion). These were the facts upon which the first note on "A Syndrome Produced by Diverse Nocuous Agents" was based. All this is easily seen with the naked eye. Actually, a pair of scissors with which to open my rats was the only instrument I had used up to that time, and the production of stress by toxic substances certainly necessitated no complicated apparatus either. The stress reaction or "general adaptation syndrome" could have been discovered during the Middle Ages, if not earlier. Its recognition did not depend on the development of any complicated pieces of apparatus or new techniques of observation—nor even upon much training, ingenuity, or intelligence, as far as that goes—but merely on an unbiased state of mind, a fresh point of view.

Only the future will tell us just how much the stress concept can contribute to promoting the understanding of disease and the relief of human suffering. But if in these respects it should prove of some value, let the beginners draw encouragement from the fact that it was found without any of the luxuries of modern laboratories, indeed even without much knowledge or experience. Fortunately, it is not so much what we do not know that handicaps our research, but what we think we know, although it is false. Lack of equipment, or even lack of knowledge, is much less of a handicap in original research than an overabundance of useless materials or useless (and sometimes false) information which clutters up our laboratories and brains.

I think any young man at the beginning of his career—whether he wants to become a scientist, an artist, a businessman, or an engineer—should keep in mind that he needs but his eyes to see a whole forest. It is only for the detection of some minute detail in a single cell of one tree within this forest that he requires a microscope. As long as you are young, look for the mere outlines of big things with your fresh, untrained, and unprejudiced mind; when you are older you may no longer be able "to see the forest for the trees." But cheer up, by that time you will have the money to buy fancy tools and to hire assistants who know how to exploit the details with them.

BIG THINGS CAN BE SEEN WITHOUT MAGNIFICATION.   There are two ways of detecting something that nobody else can see: one is to aim at the finest detail by getting as close as possible with the best available analyzing instruments; the second is to look at things from a new angle where they show hitherto unexposed facets. The former requires money and experience, the latter presupposes neither; indeed, it is actually aided by simplicity, the lack of prejudice, and the absence of those established habits of thinking which tend to develop after long years of work. Both roads are passable; but, if you can, take the second.

You could never learn what a mouse is like by carefully examining each of its cells separately under the electron microscope any more than you could appreciate the beauty of a cathedral through the chemical analysis of each stone that went into its construction. It would be very useful to know the exact structure of parathyroid hormone, but the chemist would not even have an inducement to start work along these lines had it not been shown first, by simple removal of the parathyroids and the injection of impure parathyroid extracts, that the gland is of vital importance.

It may be unnecessary to belabor this point so much, but simplicity of technique and approach was the key to whatever success I have had; hence, these pages seem to me the most important in my Notes. Don't let complex machinery dazzle you; do not talk about "investigation in depth"; remember that big things can be seen without magnification, and that the greatest laws are the simplest.

Of course, you can go only so far with simple observations. The correlations between the parts of living beings are highly complex and their study involves complexities, though not as much in analysis as in synthesis. To prove the structure of a complex chemical compound, it does not suffice to break it down into elements; we must also be able to build it up from its parts. It is the same with biologic phenomena. We can learn a certain amount by dissecting living matter into ever smaller particles, but there is an even greater lesson in putting these together again.

In any event, keep in mind that no matter how gifted the individual may be, the enormous mass of mediocre investigators will still beat him in making chance observations by the assiduous repetitive use of existing tools and ideas. Only for the coordination of many facts into what we call understanding is it necessary to mix them all in a single brain.

Complexities of Matter versus Complexities of Causation

In the life sciences it is the fashion today to examine the complexities of living matter with ever-increasing accuracy. This involves the chemical and physical analysis of biologic structures under normal and morbid conditions, using procedures and instruments of great precision. It is surprising how little attention is given, on the other hand, to complexities in the causation of these structural characteristics. In other words, we concentrate so much upon the target that we neglect the agent.

In examining an organ, no chemist would be satisfied to determine just one or two constituents; no morphologist would be content to identify only one or two cell types. We realize that all living matter consists of an integrated system of chemical and structural building blocks, the meaning of which can be understood only when we see them in their natural habitat. A modern biochemist would not dream of limiting a study concerning the effect of cortisone on the metabolism of glycogen (a complex sugar) in the liver, merely to glycogen determinations. He would feel that these could reveal very little unless he simultaneously explored the enzymes participating in the synthesis and degradation of glycogen, precursors, and metabolites of glycogen, energy-yielding substances, etc. On the other hand, he would be quite prepared to accept the cortisone he injects as "the agent." At most, he might see to it that his animals receive the same standard diet or are fasted during the experiment. It is true that some biologists do not limit themselves to the study of a single causative factor; they may go as far as to explore the simultaneous effect of two or three. For example, in this study they may explore the effect of cortisone plus desoxycorticosterone, or perhaps even adrenalectomy plus cortisone plus desoxycorticosterone—but they rarely go any further.

It seems to me that, in the analysis of causation, contemporary biology is far behind its own progress in the analysis of matter by chemical and physical means. My associates and I have spent many years in demonstrating that, depending upon a great multitude of "conditioning factors," the same agent may have diametrically opposite effects, qualitatively different effects, or no effect at all. These conditioning factors are just as important, and just as subject to analysis, as the chemical or structural components of living matter.

To illustrate this point, let me take an example from a recent study on the relationship between stress (p. 51) and calciphylaxis

(p. 241). We had previously established that exposure to any kind of stressful situation can prevent the abnormal tissue calcification otherwise induced by calciphylaxis. Now, since the hormones of the adrenal cortex play an important defensive role in stress, we wanted to know whether perhaps an increased production of these substances might be responsible for the prevention of calciphylaxis by stress. To explore the role of the adrenals, we had to use intact animals and compare their response with that of rats deprived of their adrenals, the only organ that can make cortical hormones during stress. Furthermore, we had to study the effect of artificial treatment with injected cortical hormones of the two major classes, cortisone (a glucocorticoid) and desoxycorticosterone (a mineralocorticoid) given either singly or in combination.

To produce the calciphylactic syndrome in which we were interested, we had to give dihydrotachysterol (a calciphylactic sensitizer), ferric dextran (a calciphylactic challenger), and polymyxin (a mast-cell discharger). Of course, some groups of animals had to receive only one, and others various combinations of these agents but, to simplify matters, let us speak here only of the group that received the full treatment. Here, "the agent" was:

1. Adrenalectomy, 1st day plus
2. Cortisol, 400 μg. per day hypodermically, starting 1st day plus
3. Desoxycorticosterone, 3 mg. hypodermically, per day, starting 1st day plus
4. Dihydrotachysterol, 1 mg. by mouth, once on 5th day plus
5. Iron, 1 mg. chelated (in the form of ferric dextran) with
6. Dextran, once intravenously, on 8th day plus
7. Polymyxin, 1 mg. hypodermically, once on 8th day.

Of course, numerous preliminary experiments were necessary to determine such things as the most suitable species, weight and sex of animals, or the best route of administration and dosage of all compounds used. The timing of each treatment likewise proved to be of decisive importance; for example, by giving the challenger (here, iron dextran) on a different day, we either obtain no calcification or a qualitatively different distribution of calcium deposits. Yet, if the same treatment is given, the changes are predictable.

Nothing is arbitrary in this arrangement: the iron must be complexed with dextran and be injected on the 8th day intravenously, the dihydrotachysterol must be given 3 days earlier and by mouth, etc. Each of these facts had to be established separately, by appropriate experimental series. It is to perform this kind of correlative work that we use about 1000–1400 rats per week and need our huge documentation service for planning. But in this manner we have learned a great deal about the factors necessary for the fixation of calcium in various organs.

Well, for those whose mind is such that it can be satisfied only by complicated investigations, I hope this is complicated enough. Yet, all the complication lies in synthesizing the causative situation; the target area has hardly been examined in any of these calciphylaxis experiments. Inspection with the naked eye or the loupe is sufficient to see the distribution of the white, calcified spots. Occasionally, we have verified the presence of calcium phosphate, iron, or discharged mast cells in the affected parts by simple histochemical techniques, but that was all. It is obvious that detailed chemical analyses, electron-microscopic studies, investigations with radioisotopes, X-ray diffraction analyses of the crystals, and many other investigations, will furnish additional information. The fact that we did not do more along these lines has been deplored by even the most enthusiastic reviewers of my book *Calciphylaxis* ([74]), but this complaint in itself shows that, once we know that there is such a thing as calciphylaxis, further "exploration in depth" readily suggests itself. In our group, we have no experts in any of the complex techniques recommended by the reviewers; so why not leave this work to those already qualified to undertake it? We are better prepared to analyze the underlying complex pathogenic situations; if we now tried to acquire the training necessary to explore the target-organ changes in great detail, we could not continue the work we have learned to do.

I believe that those of us who are especially interested in causation should use the simplest and most characteristic target-organ change as an indicator; for our purpose, the mere inspection of the easily visible, white, calcific deposits sufficed. This kind of research is very complex indeed; but the complication is neither in purchased equipment nor in the techniques developed by others, but in the synthesis of the pathogenic situations. We have to develop our own techniques for putting together the complex systems that Nature can use to perform specific tasks.

The Prognosis of Importance

DISCOVERY VS. DEVELOPMENT. We have said before that only the kind of research usually designated as "basic" is true discovery. What follows is development. The former is basic, or fundamental, precisely because all other types of research develop from it; it strikes us as impractical and the work involved as haphazard, because wholly original observations cannot be planned in advance. To do so, the observation would have to be anticipated on the basis of previously known facts, hence, it could not be wholly original. That is why most of the completely new leads are accidental findings made by men with the rare talent of noticing the totally unexpected. These discoveries subsequently form the basis of all premeditated research—the kind I call development.

It may be argued that any attempt at the early appraisal of basic research must be foredoomed, since the unexpected cannot be anticipated. To some extent this is true. Of course, there is no reliable yardstick with which to compare the relative importance of basic-research projects, but I believe it possible to formulate certain principles which can serve as general directives. Think of them not as rigid measurements, but rather as a kind of course in science appreciation, helping us to recognize and enjoy creative scientific thought.

To my mind, it is characteristic of great basic discoveries that they possess, to a high degree and simultaneously, three qualities: they are not only true but very true and in a very special sense; they are generalizable, and they are surprising in the light of what was known at the time of the discovery.

The discovery must be true.   It may seem redundant to say that the newly discovered facts must be true. However, in science, things are not true or false; they can be true only within a certain frame of reference and within certain statistically determinable limits which tell us the likelihood of the same observation repeating itself in the future if we try to reproduce it again. The degree of this probability naturally influences the importance of the discovery.

Even if an observation is very true in the sense that it has a small standard error (a great probability of being reproducible), it must also be true in that it is interpreted in its proper perspective. Otherwise, the finding may be misleading because of the inferences drawn from it. Not long ago, a chemist tried to make a compound that would diminish appetite and cause loss of weight. After years of study, he succeeded in producing a drug that conformed to his theory concerning the structure this kind of substance should have. He then tested the compound on rats, cats, dogs and monkeys. As he expected, all the animals ate very little and lost weight. In a paper describing his findings, he explained why he thought a drug of such chemical structure would act in this manner. In the conventional sense, his findings were true. In my sense they were false. We know that almost any damaging substance will diminish appetite, and his substance was damaging. The author neither admitted nor denied this. He did not even specifically recommend his drug for human use. Still, his paper implied applicability; hence, his finding was untrue by implication. Had he realized that his compound decreased appetite only because of its damaging effects, he would not have bothered to write a paper about it. Few scientists knowingly publish untruths, but many scientific papers contain such untruths by implication.

Yet, even if a finding is true by all standards, it may not be important. I recently read a paper describing the mean weights of the internal organs of laboratory rats. The author's facts were correct; he had killed hundreds of animals to build up a highly significant series. But the resulting information was of limited importance, being neither generalizable nor surprising. It is not generalizable, because we can deduce no general laws from it. Nor is the information surprising, because it was evident at the start that the mean weights could be determined by measurement. This sort of work not only fails to qualify as "basic research" but it has not even been practically applied to anything. The best you can say for it is that it might be applicable by somebody needing these figures as a standard of comparison for original investigation, but then his would be the basic research. Scientific literature abounds in such reports. The authors customarily protect themselves by stating self-righteously that they draw no conclusions from their observations. But this is not good enough; facts from which no conclusions can be drawn are hardly worth knowing.

A similarly unimaginative primitive type of research is called "screening." A clinician may screen a number of cortisone derivatives, more or less at random, to see which is the most active in patients with rheumatic diseases. Again, all this is development suggested by previously known facts; it is not original, creative research.

We are guided in such work by deductive reasoning, which helps us foretell certain things about an individual case from a previously established generalization. If most cortisonelike compounds are effective against rheumatism, any newly prepared member of this group looks promising. But the deduction itself cannot be generalized. The work may be of immediate practical importance, leading us perhaps to the ideal antirheumatic compound; but, in the highest sense, it is sterile, because once such a substance is found, the observation is complete in itself, offering little likelihood of further discoveries.

Unfortunately, this drab kind of research is the easiest to finance, because its plan and applicability to practical problems can be precisely described in a routine application for funds.

The discovery must be generalizable. Other observations lend themselves to inductive reasoning, the formulation of general laws from individual observations. But this feature does not suffice either. To illustrate, it was shown that the first ten hormones that could be prepared in pure form were all white. From this, we could generalize. We could foretell, with a high degree of probability, that the next five hormones to be synthesized would also be white. So they were. But what of it? Who cares what color future hormone preparations will be?

Here, then, was an observation both true and generalizable, but lacking the third essential quality of important basic research, the quality of surprise; that is, the unexpectedness of the discovery at the time of making it. Most body constituents are white when purified; it is not surprising that hormones should be white.

The discovery must be surprising. I recall my astonishment on learning in medical school that certain pathologic growths in the human ovary, the so-called "dermoids," may contain teeth and hair. A medical curiosity, but not generalizable—at least not at present. All we can say now is that occasionally, even without fertilization, an egg in the human ovary may develop into a monster consisting mainly of hair and teeth. This much has been known ever since the seventeenth-century German physician, Scultetus, gave the first complete description of what he called *"morbus pilaris mirabilis,"* the astonishing hair malady. Martin Luther referred to it as the "Offspring of the Devil."

For centuries, physicians and laymen alike have been fascinated by this anomaly. But it opened up no new vistas of research. The reason is, I think, that the observation was made too early. Even today we are not yet equipped to evaluate it. It is like a strange island remote from the charted areas of human knowledge. Perhaps later—when we know more about fertilization, about reproduction without fertilization, and about the "organizers" that direct the formation of human structures—the "Offspring of the Devil" will become an angel guiding us to the solution of Nature's mysteries. But merely being aware of the oddity avails us nothing. Scultetus saw, but he did not discover.

The discovery must be true, generalizable and surprising at the same time. The outstanding feature of truly great discoveries is that they are not only true (in the special sense in which our views divert) but highly generalizable and surprising at the time they are made. This holds true, for example, of Mendel's discovery of the law of genetics, Richet's and Pirquet's discovery of allergy, or the finding by Fleming, Florey and Chain that molds have antibiotic effects.

4. When Should It Be Done?

The success of a research project depends largely on its timing in history, the scientist's lifetime and even the time of day. A conscious analysis of proper timing may help considerably in making our work profitable and pleasant.

When During History?

"When discoveries are made before their time they are almost certain to be ignored or meet with opposition which is too strong to be overcome, so in most instances they may as well not have been made."

[W. I. B. Beveridge [11]]

It is often said of a scientist that his period was not ripe for him. This may be so, but I wonder whether the whole blame should be put upon the period. To my mind, scientific genius should be able to appraise the feasibility of a project from this point of view also. It is futile to plan work for which we do not yet have proper techniques, or to expound theories for which mankind is totally unprepared, unless we can develop the needed techniques ourselves, or explain the concepts in terms understandable to, at least, the elite of our contemporaries. The work of those who disregard these points is easily forgotten and lost forever; it will have to be rediscovered by others at the proper time. In practice, the pathetic figure of the frustrated, misunderstood genius comes dangerously close to that of the fully understood crackpot; both expound impractical ideas that create only chaos.

In any event, anyone who has an idea that seems to be far ahead of his time should concentrate on techniques which might prove his point, rather than waste a lifetime in the frustrating effort of convincing others by argument. Research can be useful to mankind and satisfactory to the scientist only if it is performed at a time when it is feasible and meets with the interest and understanding of others. The atomic theory of matter as expressed by Democritus in pre-Socratic Greece was premature and hence, at the time, sterile because there were no practical means of proving or disproving it. Later, in the Middle Ages, when it became possible to substantiate the existence of chemical elements, the alchemists tried to make gold, guided by the hope that one element may be transformed into another. Recently, this concept proved to be correct; yet the alchemists were justly regarded as eccentric dreamers, since, at their time, the idea was nothing but a hope. All dreams have a grain of truth in them; genius consists in recognizing those dreams from which this grain is extractable. Those who, hundreds of years ago, dreamed about the possibility of travel to the moon, cannot claim the credit for modern astrophysical research. Even if it should become possible in the future to prolong man's life by several hundred years, a contemporary physician cannot be regarded as a great prophet just for saying so now.

The situation is somewhat different if the dream is not merely a commonplace wish, but the intuition of some fertilizing hidden truth which would not occur to others. If this truth—although not immediately subject to research—is sufficiently close to the knowledge of the period it may stimulate others to develop appropriate techniques. In its first stage, when formulated by Fracastorius, the idea of contagion by invisibly small living organisms was not a practical theory for research, because there were no microscopes or any other means of verifying it. Yet, this intriguing thought smoldered on until the time of Pasteur and Koch and probably contributed an impulse for the subsequent development of microbiology. During this second stage, it was the idea of submicroscopic infective organisms that proved to be impractical, but it undoubtedly contributed the stimulus to look for viruses during the third stage when methods of ultrafiltration and electronmicroscopy became available.

There are imperceptible transitions between the mere wish for the obviously desirable (the wholly impractical dream) and the intuitive hunch of something that is far from obvious but has some chance of stimulating feasible research at the time when it is expressed— or, at least, when it is not yet forgotten.

Mendel's discovery of the basic principles of genetics was ignored for thirty-five years after it had been not only read before a scientific society but even published. According to Fisher [36], each successive generation seems to have noted in Mendel's original paper

only what it expected to find, ignoring the rest. Mendel's contemporaries saw merely a repetition of the by then well-known
hybridization experiments. The next generation realized the importance of his findings concerning the mechanism of inheritance but
failed to appreciate them fully because they seemed to be in contradiction with the then particularly much discussed theory of evolution. Let me add that Fisher, the famous statistician, re-examined
Mendel's results and claimed that when subjected to modern
statistical treatment, the conclusions of the father of genetics showed
unmistakable evidence of being biased in favor of the expected results.

Let us illustrate the difficulty of choosing the right time for a
research project by an important contemporary problem of endocrinology. There is a great interest nowadays in the metabolism of
hormones. We want to know what they are made from, how they are
stored, at what rate they are secreted into the blood, and how
quickly they are destroyed again after they have performed their
function. All these problems are of great theoretic interest; and much
attention has been given to them of late, especially in connection with
the metabolism of ACTH, the adrenotrophic pituitary hormone that
plays a key role in stress reactions.

During the past years, I saw several institutes where intensive
work is in progress along these lines. Both the accurate determination of ACTH and the mathematical analysis of the data require
expert teamwork with intricate machinery and techniques. However, the basic principle of all these investigations is easy to explain
by the "bathtub analogy." If we measure the initial and final water
content of a tub as well as the amount "secreted" through the outflow, it is easy to compute the rate of inflow during a given period.
It would appear, therefore that, if in a rat you determined the ACTH
content of the pituitary and of the blood before, during, and after
exposing the animal to stress, you could calculate the rate at which
ACTH is synthesized in this gland during the general adaptation
syndrome. The inflow of the precursors, from which ACTH is made,
cannot be measured directly, but it should be possible to compute
ACTH synthesis from such measurements.

Unfortunately, in practice things are not that simple. Even in
the analogy of the bathtub, the calculations would be misleading if
some of the water were lost by spilling or evaporation, without
running through the outflow. In the case of the pituitary, the situation is still more complicated because countless factors can vitiate
the calculation. ACTH might be held in the pituitary in a masked

form which escapes detection. The ACTH content of the gland could be affected by the simultaneous presence in the pituitary of synergistic and antagonistic hormones. Part of the synthesized ACTH might be locally destroyed before it ever reaches the blood. Similar factors might affect the ACTH determinations in the blood, and thereby simulate variations in ACTH content. In view of these considerations, studies made on the bathtub principle, can reveal only variations in the concentration of detectable ACTH present in the pituitary and blood at the moment of observation.

Now, even this much information is valuable. Those who engage in such work are pioneers in hormone metabolism. We are indebted to them, because someone must take the first step and more meaningful metabolic studies cannot be performed until we shall have more perfect techniques. The question is only whether this kind of information warrants the extraordinary effort required to obtain it, or whether it would be better to wait until we have succeeded in devising a more reliable technical procedure.

I must admit that, even if there were a way of determining it, I would not be terribly curious to know exactly how much ACTH is produced by the rat's pituitary during stress. I was much more interested to learn that there is such a thing as ACTH in the first place, and that much of it—though not an exactly measurable amount—is secreted during stress. In any case, even the idea for the complicated metabolic work just mentioned could not have been conceived before these basic facts had become known—and their discovery was comparatively easy.

I am still full of admiration for my former teacher, Professor J. B. Collip, who discovered that ACTH is a special hormone. At that time, the adrenocorticotrophic, or ACTH, effect was considered to be merely one property of other hormones present in the crude pituitary extracts then available. There were technical difficulties, but it was possible to overcome them before starting with the major study. First, ACTH had to be chemically separated from other hormones (gonadotrophic, thyrotrophic, somatotrophic) that contaminated the crude pituitary extracts. This work showed that a fraction can be prepared which stimulates only the adrenal cortex and nothing else. But this was still not enough proof because by that time we had found that all stressors (including many organ extracts) can stimulate the adrenal cortex. Their action is the same as that of injected ACTH because they increase the ACTH production of the test animal's pituitary.

Now, a simple method had to be developed for the removal of

the pituitary, a technique suitable for large-scale experimentation with many fractions of extracts. Using such a method, it could be shown that in animals which have no pituitary (and consequently cannot secrete ACTH), only the ACTH-containing extracts produce adrenal stimulation. Thereby, the existence of a special adrenal-stimulating pituitary hormone was definitely established. This test —based on the production by an extract of adrenocortical stimulation in the absence of pituitary tissue—is still the standard method for the assay of ACTH now, three decades after we first described it.[21] The surgical procedure, upon which this test is based, takes two minutes and requires nothing but the simplest instruments.

I may be prejudiced in favor of simplicity, but it is this type of consideration that led me to formulate what has become the motto of our lab: "Do not confuse the importance of your goal nor the refinement of your tools with the significance of your work."

I am constantly guided by considerations of proper timing in my own work. No biologic research is ever finished. Every new observation poses new problems and usually we come to a point where further work along the same line would not be efficient—no matter how interested we are in the problem—simply because the time is not ripe for it. For example, I believe that our work showing that, depending upon circumstances, stress can either produce or prevent cardiac necroses, may well turn out to be the most important and practically applicable result of all our stress research. Yet, as much as I was interested in this work, I decided to abandon it, at least temporarily, when I realized that, with my training and facilities, I could not add much more. There came a time when I felt that subsequent real progress must depend upon clinical and biochemical investigation.

The problem seemed so important to me that I even considered changing my whole career and returning to clinical or biochemical work to see the problem through to the stage of practical application. However, I decided against this course, because I felt that we had described the experimental basis for this work sufficiently for competent specialists to carry it further. We published numerous articles in well-read reputable journals and gave detailed synopses of the entire field in the form of two monographs [H. Selye [71, 73]] which make the literature easily available to others. A certain period of incubation was then necessary until the significance and the potentialities of these observations became more generally recognized. I hoped (as events showed, not without reason) that clinicians and biochemists, who already possess the special qualifications that I lack, would then carry the problem onward much more easily than I could. In the meantime, our group could turn its attention to other subjects which we were better equipped to investigate.

We pursued the same policy with regard to earlier general stress research. We have done virtually nothing either about the clinical applications or about the fundamental biochemistry of stress and the stress hormones. Yet, after the basic principles had been described and a certain period of maturation had elapsed, the problem developed, and still continues to develop, very effectively without our intervention. This gave us the chance to turn our attention to calciphylaxis. Here, I feel there is still a great deal we can do with our particular training and facilities, but I have every intention of dropping the subject whenever I believe that we have not much more to contribute.

All any one scientist can do is to carry a problem a few steps further than his predecessors; then he must be willing to yield place and hand it over to others who already have—or in a few years, decades, or perhaps centuries, will have—the techniques needed to make significant further advances. An observation well established is equally true whenever and wherever it is made, but it is not equally useful. Its theoretic evaluation and practical application are largely dependent upon the contemporary status of knowledge in related fields.

When During Our Life?

Creativity often manifests itself in cycles [Ernest Jones [44]]. There is no doubt that peak productivity cannot be maintained uninterruptedly throughout life, but I doubt that periodicity is often as regular as biographers try to see it. It is understandable that after a breakthrough which opens a new field in science, important publications will follow in rapid succession; then, once this problem is exhausted, there comes a lull while enough material is gathered to prepare for another major advance. The periods of productivity are usually—and quite understandably—associated with great excitement; the lulls, with depression. Hence, creative periodicity has been interpreted as a kind of manic-depressive phenomenon. I should find it very difficult to verify, however, whether here the excitement and the depression are respectively the causes or the consequences of cycles in productivity.

In my own work, periodicity has been very obvious but I can detect no regularity in the length of the cycles. Whenever I hit upon something new that supplies me with interesting things to do, I stick to it until I get the feeling that, with my particular background and competence, I am unlikely to get very much further. Then I drop the subject, at least for a while. Since I have been in a continuous state of manic excitement about science throughout my life, I have never been able to take a rest after exhausting a topic. I have merely changed the subject. First I worked on sex hormones and lactation, then on stress, after that came anaphylactoid inflammation, steroid anesthesia, inflammation, the endocrine kidney, and right now I am fascinated by the possibilities offered by the newly discovered phenomenon of calciphylaxis. Changing the subject offered me as much rest from the previous task as I needed—and it was much more fun.

From all this I can derive only one lesson concerning the proper timing of research during a lifetime: while a subject is going well, stick to it; when things begin to become routine and you feel that you are getting into a rut, don't get depressed about it; just change your subject. There is always something else to do whose novelty will be stimulating.

A great deal has been written about the best age for creative scientific thought. It is difficult to generalize. Evarist Galois (1811–1832) developed a new theory of algebraic equations, which was presented to the Academy of Sciences in Paris, when he was a sixteen-year-old high school boy. At nineteen, he published his classical work on the basis of which he became accepted as one of the greatest mathematical geniuses of all times. However, such precocity occurs almost exclusively among mathematicians, musicians, painters, and poets. It can hardly be expected in medicine, physics, or chemistry where experience and erudition are indispensable.

Yet, even in this respect there are exceptions. Banting discovered insulin in his early twenties, and Laennec invented auscultation at twenty-five. Augustus Waller was a first-year university student when he began his studies on the "Wallerian degeneration" that takes place in nerve fibers separated from the nucleus. When the great physiologist and physicist Hermann von Helmholtz published his findings on the enzymatic activity of yeast, when Paul Langerhans discovered pancreatic islets which produce insulin, when Paul Ehrlich discovered the mast cell, they were all still in medical school.

Self-analysis is somewhat difficult here, because few of us are sufficiently objective to realize that nothing we have done is really important enough to serve as an example. Besides, toward the end of our career, we may lose objectivity to a point where even our latest pet observation assumes disproportionate significance. I was twenty-eight when I described the stress syndrome and fifty-five when I stumbled upon calciphylaxis; yet, right now, I like both subjects equally well.

In any event, important early discoveries in medicine are often single accomplishments, never again followed by any subsequent indication of talent. In some cases, however, they furnish enthusiasm and research material for the rest of the discoverer's life, so that he can continue to do first-rate work even without introducing fundamentally new concepts.

Richet [59] says that in experimental medicine "great intellectual productivity begins on the average at the age of twenty-five, but this peak is closer to thirty-five in other sciences. Besides, there are so many exceptions that I do not dare to formulate a rule. In any event, it is very rare that a great mathematician has not yet given some proof of his genius at twenty-five and that a great biologist has done nothing of value before he reached thirty-five".... "In general, inventivity decreases rapidly with age. This is sad, but it is true nevertheless. As soon as one has passed fifty, one has almost no new ideas; one only repeats oneself...."

Fortunately, not all of us realize this.

YOUTH AND MATURITY. Certain investigations can be done better by young, others by older scientists. It is easier to take an unprejudiced, fresh attitude when you don't know too much as yet, and are still uninhibited by ingrained habits of thought. It is easier to perform repetitious, boring tasks when you have not yet done them too often. It is easier to stand at the lab bench or surgical operating table for many hours if your feet are not yet worn out by too many decades of use. An entirely new original idea comes usually (not always) during the early years of scientific activity and can then be carried more readily through the strenuous initial stages of proof (p. 70).

On the other hand, all these advantages are outweighed by experience and influence when it comes to the complex task of coordinating and developing a broad field. Here, the most important assets are those that mature with age: the practice of observation, familiarity with many techniques, extensive knowledge of the literature, and leadership mellowed by an acquired understanding of the needs of coworkers. This kind of large-scale work usually also necessitates considerable physical facilities, many coworkers and substantial funds. Its progress is accelerated if the basic concept and its proponent have already gained a certain acceptance throughout the world. Others are then more likely to listen and to take up specific aspects that require their specialized knowledge.

All these assets come with time and, hence, leadership in correlative studies on broad fields is better undertaken by older, experienced scientists. However, such projects also furnish excellent opportunities for the training of younger members within a team. No matter how gifted a young man is, he cannot sit down and force himself to discover an original new fact. He has to start out by doing something that gives him a chance to observe and think. Inspiration comes while we are engaged in such activities; it cannot be summoned by sheer will power. Therefore, I recommend that young men start as members of a larger team, but, in addition, they should always carry out some original experiments of their own on any subject that seems worthwhile to them.

The great tragedy of age is overspecialization with enforced distraction of attention from the selected field. The association of these two factors results in the most paralyzing poison for senior scientists. As time goes on, research men become increasingly proficient in their specialty, but as I said elsewhere (p. 37), our whole society conspires to destroy them with the fruits of their success. They are given highly honorific representative tasks; they must administer the large institutions that took them so long to build up; they are requested to spend their time appraising the (often very mediocre) research of younger colleagues who are candidates for degrees, prizes or grants; they are invited to speak or write about their past accomplishments. They may even have acquired enough personal wealth and property that looking after it begins to take up a good deal of their time. All this prevents the scientist from thinking about the specialized research work that really interests him and that he is trained to do.

One of the most efficient ways for the granting agencies to help science today would be to devise plans which relieve our experienced senior specialists of administrative tasks that are now forced upon them, either as honors or as moral duties that cannot be refused.

THE PERIOD OF SEVERANCE. The transition from guided to independent research is a difficult period in the beginner's life. Up to this point he has worked in a team or separately, but always under the supervision of a senior. Although he may have participated very actively, not only in the technical execution of the work but also in its planning, he has failed to realize how much his whole thinking has been guided. Now he is horrified because he just cannot think of anything original by himself; everything that occurs to him is suggested by what he has previously been doing under supervision.

In the lab we call this the period of severance (or more conversationally, "navel-cord-cutting time"). It can be very painful. A young scientist who has been full of self-confidence, now suddenly panics. In this condition he will desperately try any experiment that comes into his head, as long as it is *his* and not based on any advice received from others. Of course, the mere desire to prove himself is no proper motive for basic research, and these hectic efforts usually lead nowhere.

Next comes the "period of the scapegoats." Since the beginner is unwilling to assume responsibility for failure, he begins to look for excuses: he doesn't receive enough material assistance; his family responsibilities take up too much of his time; his kindness is being exploited by his colleagues; his training is inadequate; he is just not interested enough in labs and rats, he should have gone into clinical medicine; he has too many administrative and teaching duties. Worst of all, his chief and colleagues show no enthusiasm for his work. Eventually, he may feel completely misunderstood, persecuted and frustrated to the point of admitting defeat. Many a young scientist gives up the career that he worked for so assiduously, at this critical time just when it was going to start.

If the frustrated beginner does not give up, he finds ways to postpone the evil day when he will have to reach some conclusion about his competence and future course. He may do this by indefinitely prolonging the period of his apprenticeship, by taking additional courses, learning more and more techniques, doing more and more preparatory reading, perhaps applying for a traveling fellowship to see other places, or even collecting additional diplomas. All these plans have nice, clear-cut end points, symbolizing some definite accomplishment. A course followed, a technique learned, a diploma obtained—all mean progress. Even assuming responsibility for some routine teaching or helping in administration is a welcome justification for the time spent. Besides, these activities may lead to promotions which bear reassuring, tangible testimony of advancement.

But watch out, young man. Inexorably time marches on! You may spend your whole life in preparation for that blissful moment when you will finally be fully prepared for the important basic research that you really want to do. The perfect conditions always seem to be just around the corner, but you may never get there; unless you take care, you may go to seed in several ways, all equally horrible. You may become so deeply involved in routine teaching and administration that you accept the role of martyrdom: "Somebody has to do these things." You may become a big boss through excellence in grantsmanship or politics and eventually talk yourself into believing that, thanks to your "vision and leadership," you can do science by hiring brains. You may even concede defeat and go into general practice.

When I spoke about scientific techniques, I said: Look for techniques that fit your problem and not for problems that fit your technique. Now, in speaking about your whole career, my recommendation is very similar: Don't try to guide your scientific and private life to fit your still unproven research talents, but let your talents express themselves first and then adjust the rest of your life as best you can to suit their demands. I think this can be done by remaining a productive, respected, and self-respecting associate of a teacher or team until you hit upon something that is worth pursuing independently. But then let no promise of advancement or exaggerated sense of duty stand in your way. Go off on your own as fast as you can.

ON YOUR OWN.   Once you are independent, I have but three recommendations regarding timing:

1. *Try it "in the test tube" before you try it on a large scale.*
2. *Give your experiments a logical order of precedence.*
3. *Strike hard while the iron is hot.*

(1) When we want to prove a fact, we naturally like to get the proof as soon as possible, and this can be done only by large-scale experimentation. However, just as the chemist will try a reaction first in the test tube before he does it on a large scale, so the biologist should use only a few animals in preliminary experiments before proceeding with a statistically significant series. Strict observance of this simple rule, even at times when curiosity makes us impatient, can save an enormous amount of time in the long run.

(2) The order of precedence in experimentation is also very important. There is no point in exploring the action of three agents given simultaneously before determining the effect of one or two administered separately. There is no point in trying to find out whether a biologic reaction can be produced in five or six different species before you have definitely shown that it can occur in at least one. When we come to "The Design of Experiments" (p. 224), we shall have much more to say about the order of precedence in experimentation; here, I merely want to mention it as a significant consideration in timing.

(3) It rarely pays to change your subject as long as it continues to yield interesting results easily. When I was working on time-consuming projects—such as stress, steroid anesthesia, the ana-phylactoid reaction or calciphylaxis—I was often tempted to drop the topic under investigation and follow the seductive novelty of some unexpected sideline. I always tried to resist such temptation and rarely have had cause to regret it. When you have labored on a subject for long, and harvest time arrives, it is best to go on with the harvesting for which you are fully prepared, rather than to start sowing seeds in a new field.

When During the Day?

Even during the course of a single day, there is a right and a wrong time for this or that. People differ very much as to their alertness in the morning or evening hours, but our daily program should make allowances for such individual variations.

I for one feel rested, fresh, and optimistic about everything in the morning and get increasingly more tired and pessimistic as the day wears on. If I have to do something that needs much energy and concentration (such as the writing of these Notes) I do it early in the morning, before the staff comes in and my self-confidence wears out. Other occupations require less personal effort, but more assistance. Hence, most of my work that depends upon associates in the lab or office is done during regular working hours between 9:00 A.M. and 5:00 P.M. After that, when I have neither staff nor energy left to help me along, I usually spend the last hour or two of my day at the microscope. Studying sections does not require much energy, self-confidence, or concentration of thought; nor do I need anyone to assist me. For some reason, this most passive form of occupation—like the passive reading of others' books that keeps me amused after dinner—has a relaxing effect upon me after a busy day.

A TYPICAL DAY. If I am to be the guinea pig in this analysis of a scientist's timetable, I might as well add a brief description of one of my typical days. I picked at random January 26, 1963, to make some notes.

4:30 A.M. Becoming partially conscious. Thirty minutes of conversation (about calciphylaxis) between my conscious and unconscious self.

5:00 A.M. Return to complete consciousness. Explosive severance from bed. Exercise (chest expander, sit-ups, push-ups, stationary bicycle). Shave. Ice-cold bath. Kiss wife and children goodby. (They all mutter incomprehensible sounds without regaining consciousness.) Make and eat breakfast in kitchen.

6:00 A.M. Limp two blocks through thick snow to garage and drive to Institute. (Just remembered this is my birthday. The 56th!)

6:20 A.M. Two minutes of chummy grumbling (politics, weather) with night watchman in porter's lodge. Repair to office. Light first pipe.

6:30 A.M. Dictate, on tape: first rough text for forthcoming book *Mast Cells;* then these notes (based on yesterday's events).

8:30 A.M. Mrs. Staub, Chief of Secretariat, arrives—comfortingly radiating energy as usual—to discuss agenda for the day: proofreading a manuscript; organization of European lecture tour; correspondence; preparation of author index for mast cell book; checks to be made out for car repairs and children's schools.

8:40 A.M. Dictation for *Mast Cells.*

9:00 A.M. Noise in corridor; entire staff arrives. Mail brought in (opened) by Miss St. Aubin. She has already separated from my folder all items to be answered by mimeographed form letters (to patients who do not know that I don't practice, high school students who want impossible help with essays on stress, inventors who want to sell cancer cures), or by other members of the staff (administrator, librarian, grants officer, editorial secretaries, assistant in charge of postgraduate students, purchasing agent). As always, I answer my own personal and scientific mail immediately, although, as far as possible, merely by reference to previously prepared sample letters (acceptance or refusal of lecture invitations, arrangements for visits to our Institute, etc.).

9:30 A.M. Lab rounds. For me, this is the most important part of the day. Assistants and I go through all labs to watch progress of experiments, particularly the clinical behavior of experimental animals, and to discuss possible need for changes in treatment.

10:30 A.M. Autopsy conference. Entire graduate staff gathers in autopsy room. To save time, the animals are already partly prepared for autopsy. (Each group is placed with its protocol; wherever comparatively inaccessible parts have to be examined, these are already partly dissected, etc.) Assisted by the chiefs of the two main laboratory units (Dr. Giulio Gabbiani, 7th floor; Dr. Beatriz Tuchweber, 8th floor), I perform all autopsies with binocular loupe and head lamp, pointing out interesting details to the others. Slides of instructive specimens from previous autopsies are exhibited for discussion at three microscopes in autopsy room. Last minute check of plans for all experiments to be started today. Discussion of two note-worthy papers on stress that recently came to the attention of staff members. Consideration of qualifications of one Italian and one Indian physician who applied for postgraduate fellowships. (I wish people would not look over my shoulder when I'm making confi-dential entries in my notebook during autopsy conferences. By now the staff is so international that I have to write Hungarian text in the Russian alphabet for privacy and this is difficult.)

12:15 P.M. Back to office for brief discussion with Mr. Mercier, administrator of the Institute (on hiring of a new assistant librarian, structural changes in surgery, purchase of an ultraviolet lamp, raises in certain salaries).

12:30 P.M. It being a sunny day, I repair to "Florida" (Lab. R724) for lunch (pea soup, cold cuts, coffee, grapes) which I take basking in the sun (stripped to the waist, the rest of me being carefully wrapped in an electric blanket against the bitter cold). After lunch, reading (still in glorious sun) of yesterday's (not so glorious) dictation on *Mast Cells.*

1:15 P.M. Back to office for cigar (Upmann's) and reading of Dr. René Veilleux' thesis on "La Réaction Anaphylactoïde Calcifiante."

4:00 P.M. Study of day's histology in my office. Selection of some instructive slides for tomorrow's autopsy conference. Six representa-tive slides are taken to illustrate points in a paper on calciphylaxis that I dictated yesterday. Certain regions are marked for photog-raphy (by Miss Barath) and their legends dictated at microscope. Other slides are sent (to Mr. Nielsen) for additional special stains.

6:00 P.M. Mrs. Staub comes in to report about phone calls, mes-sages, and the day's secretarial work. She delivers copy transcribed from my tapes.

6:15 P.M. Reading of copy just received.

6:40 P.M. Drive home.

6:55 P.M. Fifteen minutes of exercise on stationary bicycle while children report about school and play.

7:10 P.M. Dinner. During soup and meat course we play "Geog-raphy." (I mention the names of cities, children have to identify in which country they are.) Again, Michel has trouble with Teguci-galpa! Marie keeps the scores. Jeanot, having most points, gets all the glory and the ten cents foreseen for the winner. According to house rules, this game must stop when dessert is served to let Mommy talk. Mommy talks.

7:40 P.M. We repair to bedroom for distribution of daily prizes:

best report about school and play (ten cents), first place in "Geography" (ten cents), consolation prizes to the others (candy). Drawing imaginary, improbable looking animals.

8:00 P.M. Kids out. Reading *Il Gattopardo* by Lampedusa.

9:30 P.M. Lights out. Another fifteen minutes of half-conscious floating in the world of calciphylaxis. Then sleep . . . sleep . . . sleep . . .

ATYPICAL DAYS.

Every Tuesday we have a round-table discussion of library problems with the codifiers who peruse and index the world literature. Usually 15–30 minutes.

Every Thursday we hold a round-table "Staff Conference," at which each graduate has ten minutes for a concise progress report, followed by five minutes discussion. The chairman (Dr. P. Prioreschi), very strict about timing, forces the speakers to prepare their remarks carefully. Excellent training for participation in congresses, also helps to keep all of us interested in everyone else's work.

Depending on volume of work, once or twice a week we hold a "Protocol Conference" with my closest associates. Here, all protocols of experiments terminated since the last conference are more leisurely discussed than is possible within the framework of the concise progress reports presented at the Staff Conferences.

Visiting scientists and groups (usually students or members of scientific societies meeting in town) are shown through Institute by assistants who undertake this task in rotation. Afterward I meet the visitors briefly in my office.

My assistants and I frequently leave town to participate in congresses or to give lectures. We also give a few lectures (no more than ten per annum) to our medical students, but none of us participates in administrative or committee work.

5. Where Should It Be Done?

Basic research needs a favorable climate. This somewhat intangible factor depends upon public understanding for science within the nation at large, upon favorable relations with associates within the scientific community and upon the available physical facilities. All these points must be taken into consideration in selecting an academic home.

Public Understanding

"Without public understanding of science in a democracy, neither democracy nor science can hope to survive."

[Parliament of Science, Washington, D.C.]

"The future and the good fortune of humanity depend upon science. Woe to our human societies if they have not understood this evident truth."

[Charles Richet [59]]

"The problems of science do not present themselves in the same way to all men. The Negro or the Jew views the same world in a different way from the German scientist." (B. Rust, Hitler's Minister of Education at the dedication of the Physical Institute of the University of Heidelberg.)

[Quoted by Walter Cannon [16]]

In his eloquent plea for the establishment of a better climate, a better public understanding for basic research, Charles Richet pointed out in 1923 that fifty years earlier no one could have foreseen the telephone, the telegraph, aviation, vaccination, serotherapy, and the synthesis of the numerous useful drugs then available. We might now add that no one could have foreseen in Richet's time the development of television, antibiotics, or artificial satellites. If basic research must lean upon practical results for self-justification, we could add quite a few accomplishments to this list. Unfortunately, there is an equally impressive debit side to this ledger; nuclear warfare is also a child of basic research and it alone—without mentioning war gases, microbial warfare, and the many other horrors of destruction—if let loose on mankind could outweigh all the practical achievements that can be credited to scientific investigation.

It is precisely because the fruits of science can be as poisonous as they can be sweet, that public understanding of their power is indispensable. It must be realized that the most characteristic practical outcome of basic research is neither good nor bad. It is power—power over the elements, over disease, over man. It can be used for good or bad, depending upon what, through his leaders and representatives, man does with it. And knowing that he may not always be able to control it, man fears power. Science also destroys many of his cherished, accustomed ways of thinking. It shatters the false deities born of prejudice and superstition. Hence, throughout the centuries mankind has ruthlessly persecuted and attacked some of its most eminent scientists.

The great Galileo was exiled from his home and had to wander from city to city, until, thrown into prison, he was asked to disclaim his discoveries as despicable errors. Descartes, after also being exiled, was forced to lead a hazardous existence as soldier, physician, philosopher, and physicist until he died in a foreign land. Vesalius had to live a vagabond's life, being severely penalized for imaginary crimes and eventually dying of hunger. Copernicus did not dare publish his great discoveries, and it was only on the day of his death that he finally saw them in print. Kepler, though pensioned by his emperor, lived in misery because he never received his pension.

Let no one think that this kind of persecution could happen only in the dark Middle Ages; it can happen in a highly cultured, modern state right now. It happened a short time ago in Hitler's Germany. The science of Albert Einstein, Otto Loewi, Otto Warburg, and many others among the nations' and the world's greatest minds was labeled Jewish and, hence, unacceptable. All these men had to flee their country in shame, because now even more easily than in the Middle Ages, a rabble rouser who gets command of mass communication media, can debase public thinking within a few months, so that the mob rises in blind rage against the greatest representatives of its own national culture; it burns churches, paintings and books that it cannot even appreciate. It is to prevent such abuses and to learn how to employ the power derived from science that we must create a better public understanding of basic research.

Some people have naïvely suggested that the best way to prevent the potentially dangerous consequences of the power gained by research, is to stop investigation. This is not only undesirable but quite impossible. No nation would like to take the first step in outlawing basic research; besides, enforced ignorance is hardly an elevating or even a useful ethical principle for man. It was science that put an end to the epidemics of pestilence and malnutrition that devastated entire nations during the Middle Ages. We must surely not seek our salvation in closing our eyes to truth, but in learning how not to be blinded by its light. If we abolish science, we might as well prohibit writing and speaking also, for they can be equally dangerous. Even art can be used for rabble-rousing propaganda. Without science and art, mankind would have no other outlet for its energy but war and the struggle for money.

The only acceptable solution to this problem is the creation of a better understanding of the good or bad that science can do. A glance at the national budget of any "civilized" country today will show that all our societies are built around two activities: war and commerce. Must this be so? Could we not gradually shift over to a civilization built around science and the arts? Of course, preparation for war against other nations provides innumerable livelihoods. But could not preparation for war against Nature do the same? If all the talent and manpower now used for the creation of destructive machinery and destructive armies, were employed on a full-scale attack against Nature, we might find that the construction of the required machines and teams provides as many livelihoods; the result might be the prolongation of human life, the cure of cancer, the improvement of food production and, most important of all, the return of purpose into man's life. Not everyone has the talent or inclination to become a scientist or artist, but the society I envisage would need commerce and industry just as much as our present one, and whoever has any kind of constructive talent would have a chance to develop it.

We can no longer afford to allow scientific genius to remain idle for want of money. Nor can we afford to concentrate all our attention upon the physical sciences alone, just because of Sputnik. Nuclear war may or may not come, but the war against disease and death from "natural causes" is on right now.

However, the problem goes beyond the mere provision of financial aid to our scientific elite. To adapt ourselves to the spirit of this century we must reassess our whole philosophy and our sense of values. Just as the Stone Age, the Bronze Age and the Iron Age were characterized by the use of stone, bronze and iron, so our era will undoubtedly go down in history as the Age of Basic Research. Man has gained unprecedented power through the investigation of natural laws. This power can lead us to the brightest chapter in human history—or to the final chapter.

Why fight each other? Why not fight Nature? Why should men attack men in bitter competition for jobs? Why should nations attempt to exterminate other nations in a struggle for power? Nature is our most powerful enemy; she can also be our most helpful servant.

If man must always fight—as, undoubtedly, fight he must—let him measure his strength against the one adversary who is a worthy match for the strongest among us; one powerful enough to put up a challenging fight and rich enough to provide priceless loot, as long as man shall live on this earth.

There are two kinds of people in this world; those who create wealth and those who fight over the spoils. The former are undoubtedly the happier. Wealth is the by-product of their passion. It should be possible to develop a civilization centered around the creation of new wealth, rather than the fight for the wealth of others.

Until recently, most of us engaged in basic research saw no reason to explain our work or our motives to the public. We felt that there was something vulgar in discussing our peculiar problems with people not fully prepared to appreciate all the fine technical points, and that it would be an immodest bid for attention. We felt that the singular world of basic research could be understood only by those living in it. Any attempt to explain it in lay language seemed hopeless and even childish—as futile and naïve as to expound the current problems of the American automobile industry to an African chieftain who had never seen either America or an automobile. This attitude must change. Whether he likes it or not, the scientist must occasionally find time to leave the isolation of his laboratory and try to stimulate public understanding of what he is doing, for he is the only one who can do this.

Of course, the creation of a new social order such as I envisage would take a long time—if, indeed, it can be accomplished at all before the present one destroys us. In any event, it would take a Messianic figure to convince the public to support this novel platform rather than one or the other of the well-worn and virtually identical programs of our political parties. I, myself, certainly possess none of the missionary qualifications needed for this task. The best I can do is to add my voice to that of the many scientists beginning to realize that they should take a little time to explain themselves and their science to the public.

Let us get back to earth, then, and try to spell out in more precise terms what kind of climate favors basic research under existing conditions.

The Climate for Creative Work

Creative minds develop best where there is genuine respect for creativity. Such a receptive climate depends on many factors. The community at large must be prepared to appreciate creative effort, because its attitude starts to take effect at school age when the child is guided toward whatever teacher and parents admire. Later, throughout life, motivation for creative work continues to be stimulated by the appreciation shown for it by girl friend, wife, family, and the general public. In a society which pays only lip service to culture, but actually covets physical perfection, leisure, and the status symbols of wealth much more, few potentially creative minds will develop their gifts for anything but these commonly accepted aims. Where the girl friend admires only the rich boy, the baseball player, and the crooner, the arts and sciences will make few recruits. Where it is obvious from conversation at every party that, despite all the transparent pretences, actually everyone longs only for luxurious homes, jewelry, furs, cars, and the like, where even scientific and artistic accomplishments are gauged in terms of the money they could fetch, there only the most independent minds will be able to resist the temptation to accept the commonplace ideals of the herd.

In this respect, there is still much room for improvement even in the most advanced countries. It is almost unbelievable that, as late as 1925, a science teacher was prosecuted in Tennessee at the notorious "Monkey Trials" for teaching evolution. Even today, in many states, various societies devoted to interference with vaccination and vivisection continue to handicap progress. If science and culture are to flourish, we must reassess our values. It is characteristic of our times that recently, Miss Christine Keeler, a lady of easy virtue, was offered a night club job in London at a weekly salary of about $15,000, mainly because she created a sex-espionage scandal by carrying on affairs simultaneously with the British Minister of War and the Soviet attaché in London. As Mr. Harold Wilson, the Leader of the Opposition in Great Britain, said, "There is something utterly nauseating about the system of society which pays a harlot twenty-five times as much as it pays its Prime Minister."

The great periods in the history of the arts and sciences coincided with a genuine appreciation by the people at large, and particularly by the most influential ruling classes, of music, painting, literature, and learning. In order to flourish, science must be rooted in a society that respects knowledge, and many a scientist has to leave his homeland to find such a climate.

Merit, and merit alone, must count in the selection of people for creative careers. In corrupt societies, where candidates for scientific work are chosen largely on the basis of political patronage, connections, wealth, race, or religion, too many excellent prospects are eliminated from the start. It is true that some especially strong individuals will assert themselves under any conditions. It is equally evident, however, that the son of a hunter in some small village of Uganda, or of an Eskimo in the polar regions, has no chance of becoming a great physicist if he has never even heard of physics. But we need not go so far. Right here in Canada and the neighboring United States, I should say that the vast majority of people with great genius for science are eliminated during early childhood because nothing that they hear or see at home, at school, or through the mass communication media, is likely to make them look upon a scientific career as something desirable and within reach. Unlike children in primitive countries, our children are taught to respect science, but they think of scientists as abstract figures who grow in textbooks, not in their own neighborhood. The son of the dirt farmer on the prairies may think of himself as a future big-league baseball player, general, millionaire, or even the Superman of the comic strips, but he is unlikely to contemplate seriously the possibility of becoming a great philosopher, mathematician, physicist, or biologist.

There is no reason to believe that the genetic background of any race or nation has much to do with the predisposition for scientific eminence, but the mental and even the physical climate does play a role. In general, northern nations (northern Europe, North America) are more honest than their southern neighbors in offering opportunity on the basis of merit alone, but they are also less passionate in their desire for creation. The current decline of medical research in certain countries can be traced to the now prevalent patronage system, in which a young man cannot get ahead in science unless he has the full support of his chief. This support does not always depend on merit alone but to a large extent upon various bureaucratic (senseless exams, number of publications, seniority), political, and social considerations.

It is my impression that the highest incidence of scientific genius occurs among people who come to the United States from academically corrupt regions of Europe. North America still does not breed genius well, but the finished product, whether home-made or imported, gets a fair chance on the basis of merit rather than ancestry, wealth, political views, or an ability to please the chief. The early hardships suffered by immigrants are no disadvantage; hardships help them to appreciate new possibilities and give them stamina and endurance while their "luckier" homebred colleagues, who never knew real difficulty, do not try hard enough.

Plutarch reports that: "Anacharsis, coming to Athens, knocked at Solon's door and told him that he, being a stranger, was come to be his guest, and contract a friendship with him; and Solon replying, 'It is better to make friends at home,' Anacharsis replied, 'Then you that are at home make friendship with me.'"

There is little xenophobia in America; she treats her immigrants well, and has been richly rewarded by their gratitude for acceptance into the community. The Statue of Liberty, which welcomes immigrants to the New World, bears the inscription:

> "Give me your tired, your poor,
> Your huddled masses yearning to breathe free,
> The wretched refuse of your teeming shore,
> Send these, the homeless, tempest-tossed, to me:
> I lift my lamp beside the golden door."

Through this door entered Albert Einstein, Otto Loewi, Albert Szent-Györgyi, Leo Szilard, Enrico Fermi, Edward Teller, Werner von Braun, Arturo Toscanini, Igor Stravinsky, Béla Bartók, Thomas Mann, and so many other great representatives of science and art. They came to the New World looking for refuge and anxious to deserve it. Through this door came many a younger man who did not have prestige to bring along, but was quite determined to show that, given a fair chance, he would be no discredit to his adopted country. I entered through this same door in transit to Canada on the *President Harding* in 1931 and know the feeling.

Now, I have been serious for quite a while and although I emigrated from my native land more than three decades ago, I am still far too Viennese by temperament to stand the threatening specter of pomposity for more than a few pages. So let me finish this section on the suitable climate for research, by relating an incident that happened to me through lack of public understanding for my work. It was a devastatingly tragic experience at the time, but now, so many years later, I think I can tell it without shedding a tear.

THE HANDICAP OF INTERNATIONAL BORDERS. It happened during the reign of His Most Gracious Majesty King George VI, that I was desperately looking for the urine of patients suffering from periarteritis nodosa. I suspected that this disease might be due to a derangement in the adaptive activity of the adrenals and associated with an increased corticoid excretion. Now, I wanted to verify this hypothesis, but at that time the disease was not yet very well known and probably not often diagnosed. In any event, we could not find a single case either in Montreal or in the vicinity; eventually I located two cases in Burlington, Vermont, just across the border. Because of the war, we were on a strict austerity program, and it was considered unpatriotic to import valuable materials from the United States, but, pushed by curiosity, I decided to proceed anyway. Suitable arrangements were made for shipment of the urine in sealed containers by plane so that it might arrive fresh. One of my associates was to meet the plane and I was waiting in my lab ready to extract the specimen before any decomposition could set in.

During this vigil I received a desperate phone call from my assistant at the airport informing me that the Royal Customs men could not pass urine. I wanted to know why and learned that the item was simply not listed in His Majesty's Customs Book, either as duty-free or as dutiable; hence, it could not pass. Irritated by this silly red tape, I asked our dean to write an official letter to the highest customs authorities of the land, explaining that, in basic research, we sometimes need items which might impress people as odd, but we need them, just the same. The customs officials of a cultured nation should know more about the needs of a university engaged in basic research.

This strongly worded letter, coming from a dean of McGill University, worked. Only a few days later we received an answer informing us that, of course, the federal authorities had foreseen such cases; it was only the inexperienced customs official at the airport who didn't know where to look for this item in the book. It was listed there clearly as duty-free, since it was manifestly comprised by the category described as "used personal articles."

Now this was fine, but by then I knew the shipment had decomposed anyway, so I did not collect. During the following days, we received more and more urgent telephone calls from the airport, begging us to remove the merchandise which apparently had become somewhat offensive. I didn't budge, because by that time I had lost interest. Finally, the postman brought a printed statement; evidently such cases had also been foreseen, or there would not have been such a form to fit the occasion. Only the number of my shipment was inscribed in handwriting and the printed text read as follows: "Unless within five (5) days after receipt of this notice you collect the merchandise mentioned above, the shipment will be opened and contents sold at public auction."

I must admit I failed to follow the case further and, to this day, I do not know who the happy winner was. But I do believe that my tragic experience clearly indicates the need for better public understanding of the nature and special requirements of basic research.

Earliest Influences

We could not discuss the climate for creative work without saying a few words about the influences of early childhood experiences. Here again, as I have done so often before, let me volunteer as a guinea pig.

I have often tried to reconstruct when and why I decided to go in for medical research as a career and what were the earliest factors that influenced the particular course my work has taken. However, after so many years it is no longer easy to be very sure of these things. We tend to remember not the earliest events themselves but the pictures of our necessarily idealized reminiscences of them as they were formulated again and again; in other words, we remember the recollections of the recollections. By now, there are too many intermediate points with possible distortions at every stage.

Still, as far as I can remember, what influenced me most were undoubtedly the standards set by my family: the admiration for real excellence, for peak accomplishments of all kinds; the disdain of mediocrity and quitters that constantly reflected itself in the actions and conversations of my parents.

Other factors affected my later development in a more subtle way. The fact that we were well-to-do failed to provide me with the security of capital, for our entire fortune disappeared in the collapse of the Austro-Hungarian Empire. Yet I cannot claim to be a self-made man; indirectly, the family fortune did help. Since money was never an important problem during my youth, I developed a certain indifference to it and to those occupations that make the acquisition of wealth their main purpose. My parents also let me travel quite widely at an age when one is still receptive to the cultures and social manners of different peoples and readily learns their languages.

I never really had a nationality of my own or, if you prefer, I had so many of them! My father was Hungarian and the intense Magyar

nationalism of my teachers at Komárom had a telling effect. But my
mother was Austrian and so was I by birth, having first seen the
light of day in a Viennese obstetrical clinic. Then, after 1918 our
home town was ceded to Czechoslovakia, and at the age of eleven
I acquired citizenship in this newly formed country without even
changing my domicile. But from the time of my arrival in 1931, I
have felt an increasing attachment to Canada, the one country that
I chose of my own volition and where my wife and all my children
were born.

All this seems to be quite unrelated to science, but I am convinced that the somewhat cosmopolitan attitude thus acquired
helped to prepare me for research because it taught me open-minded
flexibility; it showed me how the same problem (social, political,
economic, linguistic) can be effectively resolved by different races
through altogether dissimilar approaches. This open-mindedness for
the unaccustomed comes in handy in the lab.

Selection of medicine as a career required little originality. Since
my father, grandfather and great-grandfather were all physicians,
it was taken for granted that I would carry on the family tradition
into its fourth generation. My father owned a flourishing private
surgical clinic in Komárom (a small town on the Danube about
halfway between Vienna and Budapest), and, being the only son,
I was expected to take over in time.

I did very poorly in the "classical gymnasium" of the Benedictine
Fathers where I received my training up to the age of seventeen.
Then, the following year I suddenly moved to the head of my class
at the University of Prague, remaining at this position until graduation in medicine. The fact is that I just could not work up any enthusiasm for the bookish learning we received at the "gymnasium"
in Komárom; the subjects did not seem real and, oddly perhaps,
I hated biology most. There was practically no lab work, the teacher
himself was not interested, and doing well would have implied
memorizing page after page of—for me, and I suspect even for him—
quite meaningless text.

At this stage I did well only in philosophy and gymnastics. I tried
to point out with facetious pride to my disgusted parents that this
was after all the proof of *mens sana in corpore sano* (a healthy mind
in a healthy body), the great Roman ideal. But actually I did well
in philosophy only because our philosophy teacher—a truly great
man with whom I still keep up an animated correspondence—happened to like and know his subject. Ironically, I excelled in gymnastics because I tended to be a fat, flabby kid and could not

stand the razzing I got for it; so I decided to beat my miserable soft body into shape until I could lick anybody in the class—and eventually I did.

Now, in my own defense I must state that scholastic standing is not a good guide to a student's ability to do research. Paul Ehrlich got through his final examinations in medicine only because his professors had the good sense to give recognition to his special talents, and Einstein flunked the entrance examination at the Polytechnical School. Charles Nicolle [50], the great French bacteriologist, said that inventive genius cannot store knowledge and that inventiveness may actually be killed by teaching fixed ideas and by too much erudition. Still, being a bad student certainly does not augur well for future success in science and when I first announced my intention to go in for basic research as a career everybody was greatly perturbed. Under the circumstances it was hardly surprising that my parents would have preferred me to take over the very lucrative "Selye Surgical Clinic"—a career open to an only son without the need for competition—rather than risk failure in the then badly underpaid career of basic research.

As regards persistence and stamina—two most valuable qualifications for basic research—it was my father who helped me most. He was a kind-hearted and rather sentimental man, but he had been a military surgeon in the army of His Majesty the Emperor of Austria and King of Hungary for more than a quarter of a century, and he could not stand a quitter. I can still clearly remember an event that must have occurred when I was about nine, and which I believe had a permanent influence upon my later life. Father bought me a beautiful jet black Arab pony. I loved this horse as only a nine-year-old boy can love a beast, but it had one curious and most objectionable habit: from time to time, for no reason that anyone could see, it would jump into the air on all four feet simultaneously and say—or perhaps I should say neigh—"Kweech." Indeed, for this reason it was christened "Kweechka." The performance was very amusing to watch, but I fell off the horse every time she kweeched and one day I broke my arm on hitting the ground. My father watched this occurrence with seeming equanimity, then quietly took me to surgery and put my arm in plaster. But as soon as he had finished he ordered me right back on Kweechka (although I was quite reluctant to mount her just then), "because," he said, "if you don't mount her now you will always be afraid of her." I couldn't prove it but I think my resistance to quitting whatever I think I should do is largely due to the self-confidence derived from riding Kweechka with a fractured arm freshly encased in plaster.

After I had become a medical student, I even received technical direction from my father. He let me assist him with minor surgical operations and helped me to perform the innumerable experiments on frogs and chickens that I undertook—much to my mother's dismay—in our basement. I am still outraged that, despite several pompous letters in which I tried to convince the city fathers of Komárom that the future of medicine depended upon my obtaining the unclaimed dogs from the pound for experiment, they didn't even bother to reply. Still, I did manage to get some rats and the first paper demonstrating the effect of vitamin D upon blood coagulation was published from my basement laboratory during a summer vacation from medical school.

But perhaps the most fundamental extraneous influence was the constant change in my surroundings and the repeated loss of every material possession as a result of two world wars. The uncertainty and relative insignificance of personal ownership was most strongly impressed upon me during early childhood by my father, after he had lost all his savings and military rank in the disintegration of the thousand-year-old monarchies of Austria and Hungary, which certainly seemed to be quite perennial. He told me then that the one safe investment was in myself. "The only thing that is really yours," he said, "is what you can learn. Nobody can take that away from you without taking your life, and if you have to die it doesn't much matter what else you lose." It is curious that this precept made such a deep impression on me, despite my extreme youth, but the lesson stood me in good stead ever since.

Earliest impressions have a great formative influence and I was very fortunate in the kind of guidance and assistance I received as a child. My only regret is that, having had such a sheltered youth, having received so much help during my formative years, I can never convince myself that I could have accomplished anything worthwhile unaided. I continue to look with envious admiration at every self-made man, and shudder to think what would have become of me had I been the son of poor uneducated parents.

Physical Facilities

Extensive physical facilities, such as ample space, complex machinery, and the like, are indispensable only for certain types of research; they are rarely of decisive importance for biologists. In any event, this problem need not be discussed at length here, since scientists are usually quite aware of the physical facilities they require.

I should like to place more emphasis upon two aspects of the workshop that are often badly neglected: order and beauty. Too many of the labs that I have seen are hopelessly drab and disorderly if not dirty. Old jars that collect dust and contain unidentifiable specimens, dismantled pieces of useless apparatus, and the like are just as out of place in the lab as old rags or broken bits of furniture would be in the living room. The scientist's main task is to bring order into apparent confusion. He is certainly not helped in his effort by the presence of disorder in his lab and on his desk.

A research department should not be turned into a museum of art or a picture gallery, but there is no reason to make a sharp distinction between the home and the lab (where he spends most of his waking hours) regarding the need of any cultured person to surround himself with objects that have no other utilitarian purpose but to please him. A beautiful growing plant, a bowl of colorful fish, a pleasing statuette, an artistically bound volume of a cherished classic, the portrait of a great scientist whom we admire, some bric-a-brac that we picked up on a trip and that brings back pleasant memories—these can be distributed here and there throughout the labs and offices. These objects do a lot to create a stimulating and personal atmosphere around us, at a very low cost in money and effort.

6. How to Behave

"Respect all such as sing when all alone!" [Robert Browning]

"The research worker is sometimes a difficult person because he has no great confidence in his opinions, yet he also is sceptical of others' views. This characteristic can be inconvenient in everyday life.... Discoverers are often men with little experience or skill in human relations, and less trouble would have arisen had they been more diplomatic. The fact that Harvey succeeded eventually in having his discovery recognised, and that Semmelweis failed, may be explained on this basis. Semmelweis showed no tact at all, but Harvey dedicated his book to King Charles drawing the parallel between the King and realm, and the heart and body."

[Beveridge [11]]

A sincere, well-balanced, and understanding attitude toward ourselves and others is the key to happiness and success in any walk of life. The scientific career is no exception. The starting point for the construction of our personal code of ethics must be *Gnothi Seauton* (Know Thyself), the motto engraved on the temple of Delphi and which Socrates has made his own. We must, above all, learn to act in harmony with ourselves. But man is singularly shy about looking at himself with cool objectivity; he is ashamed of seeing his most intimate parts naked. Yet neither our minds nor our bodies are of our own creation. Who are we to set ourselves up as judges and to condemn, as unfit to look at, certain organs or certain mental reactions with which Nature has endowed us? The scientist wants truth no matter what it shows. He cannot remain content in living by conventional rules and prejudices merely because his modesty prevents him from analyzing them. And yet, here, our inhibitions are so deeply engrained that it takes great self-control and much time to overcome them. In this respect, we can learn a great deal from having lived with ourselves and with others for a

134

long time under varying conditions, and from having cast many an indiscreet look behind the curtain of propriety.

If these Notes are to be of any use to others as an example of a scientist's life, or to me as a catharsis, they must give an unretouched, true picture of my experience. That is why I am determined to say as frankly as I can what I have come to accept as a proper code of conduct for myself and my associates. But, to start with, let me reemphasize that scientists are—and to be original must be—individualists. They are different from other people and from each other. Do not expect from me a generally applicable code of conduct; each scientist must develop his own. All that any of us can do is to teach by example how one person, who tried hard, developed a pattern of behavior which suited him.

"The only reasonable way to educate is to act as an example—if one can't help it, a deterring example."   [Albert Einstein [32, 33]]

PERSONAL CONDUCT

Self-Discipline

"I learned that scholarship is a calling and a consecration, not a job. I learned a fierce hatred of all bluff and intellectual pretense, as well as a pride in not being baffled by any problem which I could possibly solve. These are worth a price in suffering, yet I would ask this price to be exacted of no man who has not the strength to stand up to it physically and morally. This price cannot be paid by a weakling, and it can kill."
[Norbert Wiener [89]]

In general, the true scientist leads a rather monastic life, secluded from worldly concerns and wholly devoted to his work. He needs an ironclad self-discipline to concentrate all his faculties upon a complex task (an experiment, a train of thought, a manuscript) that requires prolonged undivided attention. Experience has shown him that creative activity cannot be performed in leisurely small instalments; the intuitive coordination of many factors into a harmonious whole is done in one session or not at all. The artist can draw an elegant curve in one stroke, but he could not do it slowly, bit by bit. The jet can race rapidly through the sky, but if it tried to slow down beyond a certain point it would crash. Traveling at a nice comfortable pace, our mind can also succeed only in pedestrian efforts.

The greatest self-control is needed by the scientist for the persistent effort required to create and develop an entirely new field. It may take a lifetime to finish even the outlines and to present a coherent picture sufficiently meaningful to others that they may use and perfect it. In such extensive projects the need for urgency stems again from the fact that correlations on a broad scale depend upon the mixing of much information in a single brain—and, hence, in a single lifetime. Millions of industrious bricklayers do not equal one great architect. In laying the foundations for a great new scientific concept, neither the mass of plodders nor even leisurely bit-work by the gifted few can equal the sacred fire of one possessed by an idea and in full possession of himself while he struggles with it. The weakling likes to use the philosopher's doubts about free will as an excuse for lack of self-control. The question is not whether we do or do not have free will in the philosopher's sense; in practice, freedom of volition is a matter of degree. We have complete control over the decision to close or not to close the window. Our will is less free to prescribe with success a daily, uninterrupted, fourteen-hour work period if need be—and when it comes to a whole lifetime of assiduous activity, few wills prove strong enough to be obeyed.

Fortunately, will power can be trained. We must develop the habit of maximal effort. History has shown again and again that rich cultures degenerate when the population loses this habit for the lack of any compulsive need to work hard.

Our North American culture has just arrived at this dangerous point; our future will depend on the way we meet it. The threat to our civilization is not only the atomic bomb but internal rot. The young man of today knows that if he fails at one job, he can easily find another; he is so preoccupied with his struggle for a high living standard that he never questions its value. He comes to think only about the short cuts to comfort and security, forgetting that leisure in itself is not a satisfying aim in life. The real dangers are that wealth deprives us of the incentive for peak accomplishment and that he who can no longer respect his own purpose decays.

In our Western civilization, a youth will participate in sports, and in some schools (not many) he is encouraged to maximal effort in learning. But beyond the age of twenty-five or thirty, if he is any good he "has arrived" in a sedentary career. He falls into the habit of using a car instead of walking, of relying upon mechanized assistance in everything, never wearing himself out to the limit; inevitably there sets in a disuse atrophy of self-control and of the power of concentration.

Effort as such in any field has a general invigorating influence that increases the potential of peak accomplishments in other fields as well. It is useful to do muscular work, to deprive oneself of food, to withstand pain unflinchingly, because all of these efforts teach us self-discipline. The real value of the Greek Olympics, the fasting of the fakir, or the dueling in the German student fraternities is not to be found in the reasons for which man usually exposes himself to such ordeals, but in the fact that the required effort gives us the power of self-control and endurance in entirely unrelated fields also. Those who acquire the habit of maximal physical effort will also be able to do mental work despite fatigue, disturbing noises or headache. They will acquire the will and the stamina to accomplish the unusual. They will acquire determination and the thirst for purpose.

The danger in developing self-discipline lies in mistaking means for ends. As in so many other useful activities, we develop conditioned reflexes which make us confuse things that are good for something with things that are good in themselves. For the professional athlete, the development of physical prowess is an aim in itself. The circus "artist," who learns to swallow a sword or to stick needles through his hands unflinchingly, is proud of his accomplishments for their own sake; but the scientist must not forget that, to him, self-discipline is only one of the qualifications needed for peak accomplishment in his chosen field. It may be well to study a complicated text on a noisy streetcar as a means for the development of our ability to concentrate, but I would certainly not recommend the habitual selection of the most uncomfortable surroundings for intellectual work. Neither the Spartan ideal of extreme austerity and self-denial nor the Epicurean striving for a high living standard is conducive to fruitful scientific research. The purpose of the scientist is discovery; he must never forget this. He should permit himself every comfort and even luxury, but not for their own sake, only as a means to save his energies for an even greater unrelenting drive toward excellence in science.

I like to live an "Epicurean-Spartan" life. I allow myself every comfort in office, lab, and home that will increase my capacity to do research and enjoy a life that to me has meaning and purpose—but no more. My rooms at the Institute and at home are comfortably furnished, air-conditioned and soundproofed. No matter what their price, I am very fussy about using the simplest and best available instruments for research. I do not vacation in Sunny Florida because that would take me away from my work for too long, but I do bask in the sun, even if to make this possible I have had to create my own "Florida" right here in Lab R724 at the Institute. We do not have much sun in winter Montreal, but whenever we do, I spend my lunch hour in a comfortable chair before an open window and imbibe all the solar energy I can get. I cannot afford to waste much time and my meal takes only ten minutes, so I have installed a dictating machine in "Florida" and I work there in the sun for an hour or two on nice days. It is perhaps somewhat unusual to consult with a shirtless director, and new assistants often look startled when I first call them in for a noontime research conference, but they get used to it and eventually come to enjoy the sun themselves. It does them good. Much more good than to see me perfectly tailored or even in academic robes. We also seem to accomplish more in these pleasant and comfortable surroundings than in a smoky office, and we are not likely to be interrupted. In "Florida" there is no telephone and the door is always locked.

Resistance to Frustration

In research, frustrations are much more common than successes. It is hard to accept that the beautiful experiment cannot be performed because of insuperable technical difficulties and that our joy in the all-embracing theory was short lived, hence premature, because newly discovered facts are incompatible with our view. The strength to accept failure is one of the most valuable assets of the successful scientist, for, in the long run, this strength will lead to one or two successes among the many failures and then perseverance will have been worthwhile.

The life of an investigator is immensely rewarding but has its own particular irritating frustrations. He must learn how to face them, so let us first take a look at the most common among them [apart from irritating criticisms which are considered separately (p. 148)].

"TO SEE THAT NOTHING CAN BE KNOWN"

"Alas! I have explored
Philosophy, and Law, and Medicine,
And over deep Divinity have pored;
Studying with ardent and laborious zeal;
And here I am at last, a very fool,
With useless learning cursed,
No wiser than at first!
Here am I—boast and wonder of the school;

Magister, Doctor, and I lead
These ten years past, my pupils' creed;
Winding, by dexterous words, with ease,
Their opinions as I please.
And now to see that nothing can be known!
That knowledge cuts me to the bone."

[*Faust, Goethe, tr. by J. Anster* [38]]

Fortunate (and naïve) is the experimentalist who never experienced the frustrating cruelty of this thought. Of course, each point depends upon all others in the limitless network of our ideas, but you will be spreading things pretty thin if you try to learn it all in one lifetime. Is it not better to admit in all humility that the human brain cannot encompass everything needed for complete understanding and to stick to one central theme, instead of dissipating energy in sterilizing compulsive thoroughness? Knowing a lot does not make a scientist of you any more than memorizing words can turn you into a novelist. It would be difficult to achieve eminence in letters without an adequate vocabulary, but I am sure that even the greatest talent for creative writing would be extinguished by memorizing the 450,000 entries in Webster's *New International Dictionary of the English Language,* or by consciously analyzing the grammatical correctness of every sentence. If we want to pursue our aim, unencumbered by useless ballast, *we must know not only what to learn but also what not to learn.* Things that are of immense importance to the statistician, logician, or philosopher of science may merely be impediments to the progress of the experimentalist in the daily pursuit of his laboratory work. Nothing that has any bearing upon research—mathematics, philosophy, logic, psychology, even the mere technique of managing people in a team or abstract cards in a file—is irrelevant for an experimental physician; but, in general, he must know only where to find information on these paramedical subjects if and when he feels the need for it.

Though Nature is eternal and infinite, each student of Nature can meet her only during the very short span of his own life and with the limited capacities of his own person. Brevity and simplicity are, therefore, not merely incidental features but the very essence of science.

When, as a medical student, I first visited the library of our department of biochemistry, I found all the shelves of one huge wall completely filled with the innumerable volumes of Abderhalden's *Handbook of Biological Methods* and Beilstein's *Handbook of Organic Chemistry.* It took me a long time to recover from this sight.

Never before had I so clearly realized my own limitations. Every volume that I happened to look up contained important information for one who, like myself, wanted to study biochemical problems. Yet, I could see at a glance, that, even if I lived to be a hundred, I could never master it all. I have since been reminded of this experience whenever I saw the bewildered eyes of a graduate student on first entering my library which now contains more than half a million entries.

Many a talented young man must have been permanently frightened away from research as a result of such frustrating experiences. The only way I managed to overcome my feeling of inferiority was by telling myself, *"If others can do it, I can do it."* Actually, I had no basis for this "optimism by analogy," but it worked. It restored my self-confidence. In fact, I still use it whenever I realize my hopeless inadequacy for a task—which happens quite often.

In collecting material for this book, for instance, I was gradually led to read more and more abstruse and voluminous dissertations on psychologic, philosophic, and statistical problems whose very existence I had never before suspected. Then, it suddenly dawned on me that, to determine what is worth putting into my book, I had only to replace the principle, "If they can do it I can do it" by the question, "What do those know who can do it?" Surely, the scientists who proved their worth in experimental medicine would be my best guides. Why should we let philosophers, logicians, or mathematicians tell us what we must know for the successful pursuit of experimental medicine? Why not be guided by what successful experimental physicians actually do? I have had occasion to discuss these problems with many of the most outstanding scientists of our time. I know pretty well how much paramedical knowledge they were able to use. I also know what problems were met in directing my own research and that of my pupils. This knowledge, I believe, will serve as a more practical guide for the selection of what one should or should not read than will the armchair philosophy of scholars who, though well versed in their own disciplines, have never engaged in medical research.

THE EXPERIMENT THAT CANNOT BE REPEATED. It does not happen often, but to my taste too often, that a result is obtained regularly in every animal of a large group—and never again. This experience is very frustrating. Usually the contradiction starts us off on a long series of experiments in which we try to reconstruct the results obtained the first time, but to no avail. If we have performed the first experiment ourselves, we torture our memory in trying to remember some detail of technique that might have been introduced unnoticed, but we cannot think of any. If the experiment was originally performed by technicians, we torture the technicians with our questions: "Are you *sure* you injected subcutaneously?" "How was the solution prepared that first time?" "What was the time interval between individual injections?" Finally comes the desperate exclamation: "But there must be a difference because it did work the first time in every animal. The results were undoubtedly of high statistical significance. Think! Think!" But no one can think of any difference between the experiment that worked and the one that didn't. So we repeat and repeat and repeat again, randomly changing this or that factor, but all in vain. This is really frustrating!

Often it is only years later, in connection with some altogether different experiment, that we discover accidentally the factor that caused so much frustration. This may be, and in my experience often has been, the most unexpected thing: for example, one of the many manifestations of what we shall come to know as the "Cage Factor" (p. 320), that is, any accidental disturbance affecting one cage only. Of course, the more often we find the cause that made the experiment unrepeatable, the more likely we are to solve such frustrating problems in the future, and the discovery of these interfering factors often calls our attention to phenomena which are even more important than those we originally set out to explore.

Still, the frustration of continual failure may induce in a young man what H. A. Harris calls "lab neurosis." He becomes irritable, aggressive, depressed, and discouraged; eventually, he may give up the research career. A good protective measure is to follow up several projects at the same time, since one at a time of these may go well (or at least give the encouraging impression of going well). For the same reason, it is useful to have some ancillary occupation —such as clinical work, administration, or teaching—which will help to produce a feeling of useful accomplishment.

SHAMEFUL FRUSTRATIONS. There are other frustrations that are more irritating because we are especially annoyed to be annoyed by them. That delay in getting to the next rung on the career ladder, or our impotence in solving administrative problems that we should not really take to heart are not only frustrating in themselves, but the fact that we are troubled by them humiliates us.

I know many a scientist who became a mental wreck and developed a serious inferiority complex just because he did not obtain a certain prize or medal which he felt he deserved, or because he was not elected to some honorary society. In such instances, the mere formal recognition of accomplishment becomes in itself a final aim, and this wholly artificial purpose destroys the true natural motives of the scientist. I have several highly distinguished and successful colleagues who, for some reason or another, were not elected to Fellowship in the Royal Society of Canada and consequently came to regard themselves as complete failures. Every time I wanted to consult them on some scientific matter they would bring up this one painful subject. Again and again they would try, not recoiling before even the most humiliating intercessions to obtain this honor. Finally, they gave up research in disgust, although they had all the qualifications necessary for earning even greater distinction by continued investigative work.

As I have said elsewhere, contrary to many of my more reserved colleagues, I fully admit that the approval of others, as expressed by recognition and honors of all kinds, is an important incentive for most, if not all of us. Justifiable or not, it is there. But this thirst for approval certainly should not become the ultimate aim of life. No real scientist would want the coveted distinction at the price of becoming a petty politician whose whole energy is consumed by string-pulling to the point where he has no strength left for research.

A young scientist can save himself a lot of unnecessary frustration in the course of his career if he thinks about these problems unabashed. There can be only one president of a society, one chairman in a department, but the other members may be just as good or even better, and anyone who must be "the fairest in the land" can, in the intimacy of his own soul, think that he is—even if others do not see him that way. This attitude does him a lot of good and it does not hurt anybody so long as he makes no case of it.

To paraphrase the famous quotation attributed to Cato the Elder (p. 13): It is better if people ask why isn't he the head of the department than why is he.

Modesty

"Modesty is a fault of which scientists are virtually free. And this is very fortunate. Where would we be if the scientist would begin to doubt his own intelligence? His timidity would paralyze all progress. He must have faith not only in science but in his own science. He must not believe himself infallible but when he experiments or reasons he must have an intangible confidence in his intellectual strength." [Charles Richet 59]

"To tend towards infallibility without pretending to possess it."
[Malebranche, quoted by Charles Richet 59]

What the scientist really needs is a kind of megalomania tempered by humility. He must have enough self-confidence to reach for the stars and yet enough humility to realize, without disappointment, that he will never reach them. Unfortunately, this megalomania —and the firm determination to try to reach the stars anyway or die in the attempt—can poison the life of the scientist and, even more so, that of his associates.

Some scientists develop such a morbid craving for applause, that they spend most of their life immodestly trying to attract attention to their own accomplishments. This is not only an ineffectual but also a most repulsive effort to assure one's standing in society. The only related form of conduct which is even more repugnant, to me at least, is the premeditated display of modesty. True modesty remains quietly hidden inside; it is never so immodest as to draw attention to itself. Really great men are too honest to simulate modesty as a social asset and too humble to exhibit their heartfelt modesty in public. Though proud of their work, they are careful not to exaggerate its importance; they are far too interested in its substance to divert attention to their own contribution by making an obtrusive show of modesty.

Time to Think

No matter how active a scientist may be, no matter how eager to do things in the lab, he must set aside ample time for contemplation. This seems obvious, and yet, so many research men are driven by an uncontrollable compulsion to be continually active that they have no time to plan their experiments properly, and to digest what they have seen. The typical eager beaver—usually a younger man —overestimates the value of doing things; in fact, he may not feel that he is working while he sits still, merely immersed in thoughts or even just dreams. This is a great mistake. We have seen that some of the best ideas originate in dreams or daydreams and we can save many hours of plodding routine work by a single good idea.

But nothing is worse in the course of meditation than having to drop the thread of your thoughts just when you are about to formulate a concept. That is why, whenever I want to concentrate on something, I take refuge in my office behind the DO NOT DISTURB sign and disconnected telephones. It took a long time to make this barricade effective. There was always some unexpected emergency —an experiment which would be spoiled without my immediate intercession, an urgent long-distance call, the unannounced visit of some important personage—and I was forced to admit that in such cases an exception must be made. However, eventually, these exceptions became the rule and I never had an uninterrupted hour for myself. Then, it occurred to me that I am sometimes absent for a whole week on a lecture tour, yet the lab seems to function quite normally; it ought to be possible to run it without me for a few hours a day, even if I am in town. On the strength of this reasoning I put my foot down and now, when it says DO NOT DISTURB on my door, nobody, but nobody can enter—except Mrs. Staub, in case of mortal danger. (Of course, I must admit, sometimes my protective system does get fouled up. I remember—how could I forget it!—the time when a new switchboard girl was initiated in the art of convincing people who want to talk to me about "personal matters" to put their problem in writing. The number of such calls and the extreme loquaciousness of some callers has made this defensive measure mandatory in the majority of cases. Still, the system can be too rigidly applied; my wife did not feel happy at all when, upon asking for me on the phone, she was told to put her problem in the form of a letter. Next day, the operator explained that she did not catch the name, but I wonder how often similar oddities occur without ever coming to my attention.)

Let others who hesitate to use such drastic means for protection profit by my experience: the lab runs perfectly despite my periodic retreats. The assistants learn to make their own decisions in emergencies (in fact, it turns out that real emergencies are exceptional) and the long-distance caller calls again (indeed, usually what he wanted was not so urgent anyway). Even the distinguished visitor is not offended because he knows he should have made an appointment, and the secretary only tells him that I am "not here" (she doesn't tell him that I am *there*, behind a closed door). In any case, there can be no implication of an offensive indifference to him in particular, since I am not even notified of his arrival.

Now, of course, there remains a possibility that my distinguished caller may want to make an appointment for next day. But we are prepared for this too. We recognize three classes of visitors:

1. *Very interesting people.* I am always delighted to see them, so they create no problem.

2. *Moderately interesting people.* They—like any interested visi-

tor—are first taken on a trip through the Institute by one of the assistants in rotation. This gives them a good idea of our current subjects and the way we work. Then, I receive them in my office and they stay for varying periods of time, depending on whether they just wanted to shake hands, take a photograph, get a book autographed or actually had some questions to discuss. Sometimes they turn out to be much more interesting than expected, but this is rare. Much more often they turn out to be less interesting than anticipated, and then the problem is how to end the interview without being offensive. This is where "Operation Nightingale" goes into effect to bring prompt relief to the sufferer. I cannot reveal the actual procedure for obvious reasons, but its principle is this: I call Mrs. Staub on the intercom and ask her if she has finished the manuscript for Dr. Nightingale. That is the secret signal. She says no, but it will be ready in a few minutes. Of course, she knows there is no manuscript; in fact, there is no Dr. Nightingale. My question means only that two minutes after being asked she must rush into my office, exclaiming excitedly that I am urgently wanted in the lab. Now, this statement is a bit of an exaggeration, one might almost say a white lie, but I am almost always more or less usable for consultation in the lab, and, in any event, it terminates the interview pleasantly. Few, if any, visitors would suspect the causal connection between my interest in Dr. Nightingale's manuscript and the arising of an emergency in the lab.

3. *Bores and crackpots.* I seem to exercise a particular attraction for bores and crackpots of all kinds. Some want to sell me insurance or cancer cures; others offer, free of charge, their body for dissection or research plans to make me famous. These have to be diagnosed (an unusually large number of them are bearded, but the criterion is not pathognomonic), thanked for the kindness, and removed by my secretary without creating a disturbance.

I apologize for having expatiated at such length about the need for time to think and the techniques that we use to obtain it; but I believe that most of my colleagues will agree, this is a point of cardinal importance and no effort is too great to arrive at a satisfactory solution.

Parascientific Interests

Of these I can say little except from hearsay. I am interested in very few things that are totally unrelated to science, or perhaps it's just that I see everything in the same light as I see science. I have never been able to make any clear-cut distinction between my private and academic life. This may also account for my singular obtuseness to the pleasures of private ownership. It doesn't make any difference to me whether a car, a book, or a piece of furniture belongs to me or not, as long as I have the use of it. Walking through gardens, museums, or picture galleries, I have never had the feeling that I would like to own them, when I am allowed to visit them anyway—without worries about their upkeep and administration.

Until quite recently, I personally owned our Institute's library. I had bought its nucleus for hard-earned cash, from Mrs. Biedl, my former chief's widow, when I was still a postgraduate student. Then, for many years I had to pay the expenses (a stenographer's salary, stationery, reprint boxes, stamps for reprint requests) out of my meager salary. But when this seed began to grow into a huge documentation service, and it became obvious that it would be easier to finance if it belonged to the University, I just donated it to our school. Not out of any magnanimity, but because owning a library is meaningless to me. I would not have sold it any more than I would sell my family album, and, in any case, I have always shared and will continue to share the use of these books and reprints with my colleagues.

I mention these points because I believe I am somewhat unusual in the degree of my one-sidedness. But to me, everything is Nature. My family, coworkers, experimental animals and books—be they scientific monographs, philosophic treatises, novels or volumes of poetry—the whole world we live in, including myself, are to me but different aspects of the same Nature in and around me. Science is the study and enjoyment of Nature. I experience my body, my mind, my surroundings, and my actions as a coordinated whole. It would be equally correct to say that I have no private life or that all my life is private. To me, there is no difference between work and play—only various ways to play the same game.

If all this sounds quite inarticulate, it is not because of any shyness to speak about such intimate matters. In these Notes I want to discuss everything I know about science and about scientists, including myself, in the frankest possible terms. But I just cannot express this particular feeling in more generally meaningful, understandable terms, perhaps because it is here that I differ most fundamentally from the great majority of people that I have ever met.

I know that the public—especially the American public—expects a scientist to be a sociable "nice guy," a good mixer, who is "just like anybody else." But is this really obligatory? It is so terribly difficult to reconcile with the scientist's proverbial single-mindedness of purpose (p. 32). Biographies of scientists usually assure us that their . . .

"subjects are very approachable human beings as well as trained and often highly creative people. But do we want our scientists to waste their time in approachability? Do we really care that they have wholesome hobbies and the mandatory five healthy children? Are they not worth more to us if they're as crusty as Newton, as odd as Pascal, as remote as Willard Gibbs? Shouldn't they be let alone so that they can do their work instead of being compelled to placate us with that ole fishin' pole? I am not convinced that the common run of us really prefer geniality to genius."

[Clifton Fadiman]

INTERPERSONAL CONDUCT

"In order that people may be happy in their work, these three things are needed: They must be for it: They must not do too much of it: And they must have a sense of success in it." [John Ruskin]

"They do not love that do not show their love." [William Shakespeare]

The art of communicating with people through the free and considerate interchange of thought and feeling is a great asset to any scientist. This gift depends primarily upon an understanding of our own motives and those of others—an understanding that is essential in the organization of teams which nowadays play an ever increasing role in research. We must learn not only how to convince others but also how to master the more difficult art of listening to argument without prejudice.

Thorough familiarity with the prototypes of personalities as they manifest themselves in ourselves and in our associates (p. 21) promotes efficiency and harmony in any scientific institution. We must learn to live with a healthy balance between natural egotism and compassionate altruism, self-certainty and modesty, encouraging praise and corrective criticism. We must gain reasonable control over vanity and a resistance to flattery. We must avoid secretiveness, which invariably leads to uneasiness and tension in a lab. We must make a sincere effort to understand foreign customs and languages, since science is essentially international and suffers enormously from all forms of clannishness and isolationism.

True fellowship is best established through the policy of "give and take." Compatibility must be based on a sympathetic understanding of the difficulties of others, together with a readiness to show gratitude and appreciation to satisfy their need for approval.

There are certain particularly irritating qualities which can easily poison the life of a young investigator by making him obnoxious to his colleagues. Among these are: lack of consideration for coworkers; an attitude of superiority, manifested by the tendency to minimize the contributions of his associates and to attach undue importance to the smallest of his own observations; secretiveness about his results, which deprives him not only of the pleasure of sharing but also of valuable criticism; "creditomania," the habitual compulsion to say—or more frequently, to imply—that he has seen or said this before; bluffing, about the extent of his erudition, about the enthusiastic reception of his work by others, or even about the weight of proof he has behind his assertions.

Effective interpersonal relations depend largely upon the proper argumentation. Convincing is the gift of satisfying by argument or proof. It is a kind of salesmanship and showmanship which, in science, must always depend only upon the clear exposition of tenets by words or demonstrable objects, without any special pleading. A scientist who is overenthusiastic about his work, or overanxious to save face before his audience, must be especially careful to avoid the use of arguments or the quotation of authority merely because they appear to support his tenet.

Interpersonal relations are also of paramount importance in the organization of teamwork. All men are primarily guided by their emotions, and many of the basic emotional needs and qualifications of the most humble attendant are essentially the same as those of senior scientists. Only the manner of expressing instinctive drives is modified by intellect and learning. Therefore, whatever I shall have to say of one group is largely applicable to all others as well.

Criticizing and Being Criticized

"Is it so bad, then, to be misunderstood? Pythagoras was misunderstood, and Socrates, and Jesus, and Luther, and Copernicus, and Galileo, and Newton, and every pure and wise spirit that ever took flesh. To be great is to be misunderstood."   [Ralph Waldo Emerson]

"Men reject their prophets and slay them, but they love their martyrs and honor those whom they have slain."   [Fyodor Dostoevsky]

"Our [Wallace and Darwin] joint productions excited very little attention, and the only published notice of them which I can remember was by Professor Haughton of Dublin, whose verdict was that all that was new in them was false, and what was true was old."   [Charles Darwin [26]]

"There is only one thing in the world worse than being talked about, and that is not being talked about." [Oscar Wilde]

"Though the boys throw stones at frogs in sport, yet the frogs do not die in sport but in earnest." [Plutarch]

The development of a balanced critical attitude is one of the most essential prerequisites for success in any walk of life. The scientist needs critical judgment not only in assessing his own work and that of others but also in objectively evaluating the debate that will undoubtedly confront him if he accomplishes anything unusual. It is not easy to profit from sharp, aggressive criticism because our emotions tend to get in the way, but the art must be learned. The common statement "I don't care what anybody says" is almost invariably untrue. Probably, I should not even have said "almost" because I do not know of a single person who does not care what anybody says. Is this pretense necessary? If a person is quite certain he is right (which is rarely the case among intelligent people), he should stick to his guns no matter how much he is criticized. Strong people can do this; but no one is indifferent to censure.

CRITICISM OF THE INNOVATOR. Louis Pasteur met with tremendous opposition from medical men because he was a chemist and yet dared to suggest innovations to physicians. Even today many M.D.'s exhibit a condescending attitude toward Ph.D.'s whose research is related to medicine. This clannishness can make it very difficult for a biochemist or psychologist to obtain access to clinical material. In selecting his place of work, a Ph.D. is well advised to make certain that he will not meet opposition in this respect.

Of course, even the M.D. degree offers no protection against the skepticism and hostility with which most revolutionary doctrines are faced at the beginning. Here, the only remedy is to realize that this is unavoidable, and to make the best of it. We must learn not to disregard criticism merely because its aggressive tone irritates us and, yet, not to be affected by unjustified attacks. To say much about criticism will make me seem hypersensitive to it—perhaps I am. But I think we all are (though few admit it) and combating this weakness is indispensable for success. Here, we can learn much from past experience, so let us see first how others thought about it.

In his autobiography, Cannon [16] devoted an entire chapter to debate about his work. It is a remarkably instructive and inspiring dissertation, especially for those who knew the author personally.

Although Cannon did not specifically refer to his own reactions, the intimate feelings of the much criticized Father of Homeostasis come through to the reader as he mildly comments, "Any aspersions, any slurs cast upon the skill or ability or the personal uprightness of the man whose work is being corrected are sure to stir resentment."

Cannon consoled himself with the thought that original scientists have always been the victims of vicious criticisms, often even by highly competent colleagues. He pointed out, for instance, what happened to one of his distinguished predecessors among the professors of physiology at Harvard. When Oliver Wendell Holmes Sr. was still a very young physician, he presented evidence that childbed fever "is so far contagious as to be frequently carried from patient to patient by physicians and nurses." J. W. Meigs, a prominent and much older Philadelphia obstetrician, contemptuously commented on this foolish suggestion of "some scribbler," and declared that he was not impressed by the opinions of "very young gentlemen." Instead of weighing the evidence, Meigs righteously declared, "I prefer to attribute cases of childbed fever to accident or Providence, of which I can form a conception, rather than to a contagion, of which I cannot form any clear idea." This must have sounded very cautious and proper at the time. But the fact is that young Holmes was right and old Meigs was wrong. Ignaz Philipp Semmelweis, the Hungarian obstetrician who subsequently proved the contagious nature of this disease, saved the lives of countless mothers by prescribing antisepsis in the delivery room. Yet, even this great benefactor of humanity was violently attacked and ridiculed by his peers, so much so that he eventually became mentally deranged and committed suicide.

Experience is certainly a great asset but we must not lean too heavily upon authority. Even the greatest physicians may, especially as they grow older, become quite blind to new concepts. The great German pathologist Virchow rejected Semmelweis' doctrine about the causation of puerperal fever by "cadaveric material"; he claimed that the weather played the decisive role, because the highest incidence of the disease was in the winter. Semmelweis tried to convince him that this seasonal peak occurred because the midwifery students performed most of their autopsies during the winter semester, but the Father of Pathology remained unconvinced. Virchow also rejected the evidence submitted to him by young Robert Koch that the little rod he saw under the microscope (now known as the Koch bacillus) could be the cause of tuberculosis. Those in authority must be especially careful in evaluating the work of a beginner because their opinions are taken very seriously.

The great Walter Cannon himself was my first critic. I can still vividly remember his reaction when—just after having completed my initial experiments on stress—I talked to him about them. We discussed stress twice: first, briefly, when I visited his laboratory in Boston, and again a few years later in more leisurely fashion, in the Faculty Club of McGill University, just after he had delivered a remarkable lecture to our students. I felt quite frustrated at not being able to convince the Great Old Man of the important role played by the pituitary and the adrenal cortex in my stress syndrome. He gave me excellent reasons why he did not think these glands could help resistance and adaptation in general, and even why it would seem unlikely that a "general adaptation syndrome" could exist. But there was no trace of aggressiveness in his criticisms, no sting that could have blurred my vision to the point of refusing to listen. His comments only sharpened my eye for the limitations in the part played by the pituitary-adrenal axis during stress. They helped me, among other things, by inspiring the experiments with which we established that certain stress-manifestations could still be produced in the absence of this gland system.

Of course, even the most objective scientist is not infallible. One of the greatest physicists of all times, Michael Faraday, said, "That I may be largely wrong I am free to admit—who can be right altogether in physical science, which is essentially progressive and corrective?" This is, of course, even more true in a less precise science, such as medicine. A detached analytic debate helps to point out and correct errors; criticism must always remain objective. It should be offered in the friendly tone which behooves colleagues in the same field of learning, who want to promote science by mutual constructive advice. Above all, debate must, as far as our human limitations permit, not be directed by considerations of personal prestige. The question is not, *"Who* is right?" but, *"What* is right?" An old Hebrew proverb maintains that "The envy of scholars will increase wisdom." Even debate inspired by jealousy can stimulate research, but it is less efficient and certainly less pleasant than cooperation.

Great progress can be made only by ideas which are very different from those generally accepted at the time. Unfortunately, it is not only literally true that the more someone sticks out his neck above the masses, the more he is likely to attract the eyes of snipers. "The new truth," says Jacques Barzun [8], "invariably sounds crazy, and crazier in proportion to its greatness. It would be idiocy to keep recounting the stories of Copernicus, Galileo, and Pasteur, and forget that the next time the innovator will seem as hopelessly wrong and perverse as these men seemed."

A new concept in biology, such as Darwin's theory of evolution, is almost certain to provoke what Huxley called a "public war dance." When Pasteur proclaimed that infectious diseases were due to germs, when Pirquet and Richet discovered allergy, the literature was full of biting, hostile remarks, in which those who did not have the originality of creating—or even understanding—new concepts in medicine tried to compensate by displaying their wit.

In his biography of Freud, Ernest Jones [44] points out that the psychiatrist Walther Spielmeyer had, at first, denounced the use of psychoanalysis as "mental masturbation." Indeed, by 1910 the mere mention of Freud's theories was enough to start Professor Wilhelm Weygandt—then chairman of a medical congress in Hamburg—banging his fist and shouting, "This is not a topic for discussion at a scientific meeting; it is a matter for the police."

The most irritating criticisms are usually inspired by lack of understanding, by the desire to exhibit wit or by the jealousy of those who have not themselves accomplished much. It is annoying for a man, who has worked assiduously for many years on clarifying a subject and then has written a detailed monograph about it, to see all his labors brushed aside with some flippant witticism. It is especially irritating if the critic is some unknown author, obviously unfamiliar with the field, who happened to receive the book for review and, shielded by the traditional immunity of the book review column, derives narcissistic pleasure from attacking a giant. It is even more vexing if the critic merely expresses general disappointment, without mentioning any faults in particular—or uses the journal space for the presentation of an opposite but purely hypothetical concept which he could not get published otherwise.

Such petty attacks are annoying, but few mature authors or readers take them to heart. Besides, this kind of cheap, detrimental review is sure to be compensated by an equal number of similarly insignificant, favorable reviews in which the same work is glorified far beyond its merit by equally incompetent but excessively benevolent reviewers. Experience has shown that every noteworthy discovery or original publication and, particularly, every major treatise on a new subject will unfailingly elicit a crop of such unjustified and worthless, favorable and unfavorable reviews. We need not give them too much attention.

Parenthetically, it may be remarked that the exhibitionists of wit may select the most unexpected features of an investigation as a platform for their oratorical talents. At a colloquium on stress, arranged in London during the mid-fifties when research in this field was particularly active throughout the world, I was asked to prepare a list of subjects for discussion. Thinking that it would be most instructive to review the weakest points in the stress concept, I carefully compiled a complete inventory of them. This list was circulated to the invited guests, but without mentioning that I had prepared it. The impression created was that the concept consisted only of debatable points, and that the object of the colloquium was to annihilate me. Only when the discussion was well under way did I begin to realize this, and I experienced the rather uncomfortable feeling of having been unconsciously maneuvered into the position of enforced, public hara-kiri.

At this point, one of the participants got up and delivered a lengthy and biting oration on all the weak points in the stress theory, flaws to which, said he, my attention had been called "by those who had prepared the program." But he expressed particular concern over the hundreds, nay thousands, of publications that had encumbered the medical literature of all countries as a result of my description of the general adaptation syndrome. "Those of us," he exclaimed in a tone of desperation, "who are responsible for clinical work, cannot possibly keep up-to-date with this avalanche of stress literature! How can we be expected to teach the subject to our students?"

I was somewhat taken aback, having been unprepared to justify the excessive interest created by the stress concept. All I managed to say was that "I fully agree. Those of us who do not have the time to learn about stress should not be asked to teach the subject to students." It was immediately obvious from the reaction of my listeners that this recommendation struck them as being, on the whole, rather reasonable.

Petty dialectics of this kind are annoying, mainly because they waste time and force us to participate in squabbles whose very tone is incompatible with the dignity of science. I don't mind sarcasm in private conversation (or even in these informal Notes) but I do think it is in bad taste during scientific debate.

The first rule of good criticism is objectivity. "You can spot the bad critic when he starts by discussing the poet and not the poem" [Ezra Pound].

Beveridge [11] is very eloquent on this subject. New ideas, he says, are usually met by the "attack-escape" reaction. Attack may be limited to mild forms of ridicule or to systematic scientific criticism, while escape usually consists in an effort to forget the problem so that we may not need to cope with it. The reason for the attack may be quite irrational—as exhibited by the crowd that attacked the first man who carried an umbrella in London—but the scientist usually tries to rationalize it, giving reasons for what is only an automatic reaction of rejection against the novelty. If we observe ourselves objectively, we shall often find that we have begun to argue against a new idea even before it has been completely stated.

J. J. Waterston wrote a paper in 1845 on the molecular theory of gases in which he clearly anticipated much of the work of Joule, Clausius and Maxwell. However, the referee of the Royal Society, to whom the manuscript was sent said: "The paper is nothing but nonsense." Waterston was deeply disappointed and eventually abandoned research. His work was forgotten until its rediscovery forty-five years later. Trotter [84], who related this story, remarked that many discoveries must have thus been smothered at birth, and many discoverers who lacked the energy of defending their novel point of view are frustrated and subsequently lost to science.

After Jenner had introduced vaccination with cowpox against smallpox "all sorts of dire results were prophesied, including 'cow-mania' and 'ox-faced children' (one was actually exhibited!)...."

"Jenner's discovery has its element of irony which so often lends additional interest to scientific anecdotes. Modern investigators believe that the strains of vaccinia now used throughout the world for many years are not cowpox but have derived from smallpox. Their origin is obscure, but it seems that in the early days cowpox and smallpox got mixed up and an attenuated strain of smallpox developed and was mistakenly used for cowpox."   [W. I. B. Beveridge [11]]

Beveridge [11] also describes the extraordinary ridicule which greeted Röntgen's first announcement of the discovery of X-rays, yet the great physicist J. J. Thompson was quite prepared to accept the report as true. Similarly, Becquerel's discovery that uranium salts emitted radiations seemed quite acceptable to Lord Rayleigh but not to most other physicists. "Thompson and Rayleigh had minds that were not enslaved by current orthodox views."

This tendency is illustrated by many more examples in "The Construction of Theories" (p. 277). Very few fundamentally new ideas manage to bypass the heresy stage. Among the really outstanding discoveries, only procedures which have immediate and important practical application are relatively immune to violent criticism from the outset. To this group belong the discovery that insulin cures diabetes (Banting and Best); that penicillin (Fleming, Florey, and Chain), streptomycin (Waksman), and the sulfonamides (Domagk) have marked antibacterial effects; that antihistamines can suppress allergies (Halpern); that ACTH and cortisone are useful in combating arthritis (Hench and Kendall). All these are undoubtedly great discoveries, but they represent simple statements of new facts, not theories which could conflict with established medical thought. Accordingly, they stimulated only minor debates, mostly about limitations of their usefulness and about damaging side effects.

On the other hand, broad biologic concepts, such as the theory of evolution (Darwin), the microbial causation of disease (Pasteur, Koch), the role of allergy in the causation of morbid lesions (Pirquet and Richet), or psychoanalysis (Freud), are sure to provoke bitter attacks because they irritate. Some people do not like to be descendants of monkeys; others resent their actions being sexually motivated; even the idea of a serious disease apparently caused by innocuous little animalcules or allergens was at first so strange as to offend common sense.

The progress of science is considerably delayed by such prejudices and we must look out for them when the next new idea strikes us as heretic. We have to judge each observation, each concept, on its own merit without paying too much attention to what we were accustomed to think and, above all, without attacking the proponent instead of his views. Let us remember that "A man gazing on the stars is proverbially at the mercy of the puddles on the road" [Alexander Smith]. Let us not be the puddles. The great innovator has his hands full struggling with his problem, and we must not add to this difficulty by unwarranted attack.

How to offer criticism. Reasonable criticism is welcome if presented in proper terms; it calls attention to certain aspects the innovator may have overlooked and gives direction to his research. Indeed, an investigator who arouses a great controversy and has the conviction to face it is stimulated by the general interest shown in his concept even if not all of his tenets are immediately acceptable to everyone. Insignificant ideas are not attacked; they are ignored. A great controversy shows, at least, that its creator need not worry about having produced nothing but an inconsequential platitude. "They say a reasonable number of fleas is good fer a dog—keeps him from broodin' over bein' a dog" [Edward Noyes Westcott].

One of the most vexing problems for the advanced pupil in the laboratory is criticism of his work by his teacher. The chief of a lab is responsible for the work of his associates (even if his name does not appear on their papers), and this fact may create delicate problems if a fundamental disagreement arises.

The young man is full of enthusiasm for his brain child, which is as it should be for without enthusiasm he could not get anywhere. But this same enthusiasm can create unbelievable blind spots for anything that is contrary to a cherished idea. The senior, on the other hand, having burnt his fingers more often, is usually more cautious; if he is reasonable, he also realizes that he may be over-cautious and hesitates to be dogmatic. Yet it is up to him to protect his student against making blunders, and this gives rise to a situation which I for one find very difficult.

Certain types of errors—a misspelled word or bad grammar and redundancy in a manuscript, insufficient controls or faulty technique in experimentation—are rarely the cause of disagreement. But what do you do when a man wants to make generalizations on what seems to you (but, alas, not to him!) insufficient evidence? I have tried to solve this difficulty by asking the beginner to present his case at our weekly staff conference and to be guided by the majority opinion. Thereby, I can also check my own assessment against that of others. This system works sometimes, but not always. Often we are unanimously opposed to an idea, and yet its proponent remains unconvinced. What then? In science, issues are not settled by majority votes, and we must agree that the single dissenter may be right.

When every effort has failed to convince by patient reasoning, the director of research is in trouble, because the only way left open to him is to pull rank and forbid publication. A scientist is too aware of his own fallibility to resort readily to such drastic means. Fortunately, it rarely comes to this point—but sometimes it does, and then I see no other remedy but to be firm and to act according to my conscience. Not only is the director of research responsible for protecting the scientific literature against the publication of worthless and misleading data, but he must think also of the dangers to the prestige of his institution and of his young colleague.

This problem is especially troublesome in the case of Ph.D. candidates who may spend several years unsuccessfully writing and rewriting their theses. The standard question, "Well, what do you want me to do?" can be answered only in general terms: "Express yourself more clearly, more concisely. Try to organize your material more logically," but the candidate evidently cannot do this, and I cannot rewrite the thesis for him. Here, the only remedy I know is to point out some specific but typical errors as examples and advise rewriting the work with special attention to similar points throughout the text.

How to take criticism.

"It is not every question that deserves an answer."   [Publilius Syrus]

The author of any popular but controversial subject will only waste time if he takes every inconsequential or unfounded critical comment to heart. Serious, well-founded critical remarks should always be answered—if need be, not only in writing but by performance of the appropriate experiments needed for a well-founded reply. But we must be on guard against giving too much attention to senseless attacks merely because they irritate us. In the long run, the truth will come out anyway, and unfounded criticism will be forgotten.

Not all of us have the wisdom and equanimity of Darwin [26], who said, "My views have often been grossly misrepresented, bitterly opposed and ridiculed, but this has been generally done, as I believe, in good faith." Indeed, not all attacks—especially the bitter and ridiculing kind leveled at Darwin—are offered in good faith, but for practical purposes it is good policy to assume that they are.

Self criticism.   An excessively self-critical attitude sterilizes by exaggerating the importance of obstacles. The bookworm who knows too much tends to become a pessimist who believes that everything has been done before, and, besides, it may be technically impossible to do it properly. A certain amount of optimism is indispensable for successful research. We must risk wasting some time now and then on a problem that may not lead us beyond what has been known before or that may be technically difficult of execution. We must also risk being attacked for a new concept as long as we are convinced that it is important and well supported by evidence. "When we risk no contradiction, it prompts the tongue to deal in fiction" [John Gay] or, what is more usual in science, in commonplace minutiae.

It is not easy to remain impassive in the face of narrow-minded, violent criticism and it is still more difficult to view it with sufficient objectivity to profit by whatever truth it contains, but this art must be learned.

Relations with Associates

Friendly and cooperative interdisciplinary contacts can be as stimulating as vicious criticism can be destructive. The gardens of

Academia near Athens, where Plato and his followers held their philosophic conferences, provided a perfect climate for such stimulation. In modern times, Oxford, Cambridge, and some of the small university towns in Germany are among the places that best retain this inspiring atmosphere. The old English colleges bring together medical students and young scholars in the humanities. Through the tutor system, a member of the staff personally looks after the manifold academic, philosophic, and even social problems of his junior colleague, as friend and adviser; this form of guidance is highly efficacious in creating a favorable milieu for both science and the humanities.

CHIEFS AND ASSISTANTS.   Beyond the student years, the most important scientific contacts are between the chief and his immediate assistants. It is here that harmony can be most stimulating and personality clashes most destructive. It is, naturally, advantageous to work with talented men, but here, scientific eminence is not the only consideration. The personalities of chief and assistant must be attuned to each other. The chief must not look upon his assistant merely as an employee, and the assistant should not consider his chief only as an administrator who provides him with the facilities for research.

There are senior scientists who no longer participate personally in experimental work because they spend all of their time in administration or teaching. These men cannot use scientific assistance, nor can they teach science by example. Conversely, the scientifically active chief needs assistance with his research, and his associates learn from working at his side. The passive chief offers more freedom, while the active leader's great interest in research may tempt him to overburden his assistants with routine work.

All of these points should be carefully considered before an assistant selects a chief, or a chief an assistant. If a young man already has an independent problem and no longer feels the need for learning from a senior colleague, he actually does not want to assist; he should select a passive chief who merely provides facilities. On the other hand, the man who still seeks guidance should choose a chief who will work with him in the lab, one who is known to be a good teacher and not merely an exploiter of his associates. Before accepting a position, the prospective assistant can easily check these points by informal conversation, especially with junior members of the staff. The chief has a more difficult problem because, in selecting an assistant, he must necessarily depend on a more formal personal interview with the candidate or on letters of recommendation, both of which are difficult to interpret. If at all possible, it is best for both parties to make a temporary arrangement at first—to see how the newcomer gets along, not only with the chief, but also with his other colleagues in the department.

ADMINISTRATIVE CONTACTS.

"As long as they give their lecture courses regularly, they deserve no reproach. I could cite many a distinguished and zealous professor who never produced anything original. This was his right. He was supposed to teach old discoveries, not to make new ones. . . ." "Independent, autonomous, scientific institutions must be created, whose only function will be the disinterested search for truth." [Charles Richet [59]]

"A great fault in the organization of the American university has been the use of productive scholars for administrative services."
[Walter Cannon [16]]

Next to relationships with other scientists, contacts with the administrative officers of the institution are of the highest importance. The scientist is particularly dependent upon the understanding of those immediately surrounding him—superiors, colleagues and subordinates. In this respect, difficulties usually arise as a result of opposition on scientific, administrative, and social grounds to the nonconformism which is an essential prerequisite of the ever skeptical and inquisitive scientific mind. The great innovator does not fit easily into the established order of things.

The scientist must be assured of wholehearted long-term support, and he must feel certain that he will not be overburdened with routine teaching and administrative duties.

For as long as I can remember, there has always been considerable debate about whether career scientists should give routine courses to beginners. This question is not easily answered. It is a full-time job to give a lecture course well, constantly keeping it up-to-date and interesting. I believe that this task should also be left in the hands of specialists. If a scientist teaches an elementary course merely out of a sense of obligation, his teaching will soon become stereotyped; it will then be no asset either to him or to his students. On the other hand, science cannot be taught well by those who know it only from books.

Both teaching and the creation of teachable knowledge are important. Some people have special predilections and talents for teaching, others for research; why not let each man do what he likes and does best? I believe that everybody who teaches in a medical school should do some original research himself, and be given the facilities for it. Only in this way can he maintain sufficient familiarity with the real issues of his subject to communicate a genuine enthusiasm for research to his students. However, no pressure should be put upon the teacher to produce many original papers; no stigma should be attached to his failure to do so.

In this respect, much more can be expected of the career scientist. In addition, he must assume the main burden of teaching graduate students, because their principal interest is to learn not the results of research but the way to do research. The scientist can best fulfill this teaching function by letting his students participate in his own work. The art of tracking down Nature's elusive mysteries is best learned by such a personal apprenticeship. The many intangibles necessary for good hunting or fishing are not easily acquired in a lecture room; they can be learned only by going out into Nature with an experienced hunter or fisherman. The same is true of research. The most important lessons—how to live the life of a scientist, the need for self-discipline, the enjoyment of discovery—can be taught only by example. Of course, the career investigator will have to complement this type of teaching with occasional, systematic advanced courses, but even these can be given well only on subjects with which he is familiar from personal experience.

SOCIAL CONTACTS.   Because of the uncommon nature of his interests, the social life of a dedicated basic scientist is usually quite limited (p. 145). Real "bosom friendships" are most common among children at play, sportsmen, pioneers in the wilderness, buddies in the army and others whose whole inner life revolves largely around group activities or dangers that throw them together in intimate comradeship. Their tasks may be strenuous and even perilous, but are easily understood and shared by others. In this respect, the basic scientist is a much more lonely figure. As he advances further and further in his special field, he becomes increasingly more isolated by the specialized nature of his concerns; therefore, he cannot establish meaningful friendships easily, although he may crave them in his austere loneliness.

Among scientists, friendships based on true affection and understanding develop most commonly when they work together as colleagues, or as teacher and pupil, in the same lab; sometimes, also, friendships develop when men share the same interests, although they work in different countries and rarely see each other. At any rate, in selecting a place of work, the social life of a community is rarely an important consideration for the scientist—unless his wife makes it one.

Teamwork

ORGANIZATION OF RESEARCH TEAMS. Nowadays we are largely dependent upon teamwork, especially in correlative research. Here, we meet essentially the same problems and can build upon those principles that govern interpersonal relations in any group. The basic prerequisites for success are:

1. *Esprit de corps,* built upon solidarity and mutual trust among the members.

2. The selection of people who want to join the group because they are interested in its work, and hence need not be coerced to adjust themselves to the team's requirements.

3. The creation of an atmosphere in which everybody contributes something and knows that he is judged by his colleagues and superiors on the basis of merit and merit alone.

4. The establishment of an organizational structure which permits the perfect coordination and supervision of all activities.

5. The demonstration of the feasibility of a task by example rather than argument.

These general organizational principles are even more pertinent to "Management and Supervision of Personnel," and we shall discuss them later (p. 179); here, I am thinking mainly of teamwork among scientists.

THE STRENGTH OF THE TEAM. It is often cited as an argument against teamwork that every great new concept originates in one brain. This is true, but tossing an idea around in group discussion helps to formulate it clearly in the brain of one participant or the other. Some of my best ideas came when I was trying to explain to my students and associates something that I myself only sensed but did not yet fully understand. That is why we try to encourage discussions at rounds and staff conferences. Such exchange of ideas is very fruitful but, as I explained elsewhere, they must always be objective and conducted in a friendly tone. Scientific debate must be free from excessive preoccupation with priority, tactless witticism, or any desire to save face when confronted with well-meant constructive arguments which are in contradiction with our own views.

Discussion with colleagues can be fruitful in several ways: it helps us to escape from established habits of thought and provides an excellent opportunity for detecting errors in our thinking. Even a person who is not a specialist may make valuable suggestions. When Koch was desperately trying to find some solid culture medium for bacteria, the wife of his colleague, Hesse, suggested agar which she used as a gelling agent in the preparation of foods (Bulloch [14]). Discussion also has the great advantage of stimulating others to participate and to carry further the kind of research we are interested in; enthusiasm has an infectious quality about it.

One of the best ways to stimulate helpful discussion and to bring unity to the work of a team is the presentation of periodic, verbal progress reports at staff conferences. These represent balance sheets, continuously kept up-to-date. They help to correct possible deficiencies in techniques or concepts before we have gone too far in the wrong direction.

SELECTION OF PERSONNEL.   It would be difficult to lay down any general rules that could guide us in the selection of personnel. In the final analysis, the choice of employees has to be adjusted to the particular requirements of every employer—and, indeed, of every job even under the same employer. However, after you have dealt for many years with many people of the most diverse nationalities, social backgrounds, and levels of education, certain general rules begin to emerge which are useful in the assessment of all kinds of people.

We cannot limit this discussion of personnel selection to the initial interview upon which appointments mainly depend; such selection is a continuing process, since the requirements of both employee and employer continually change. It is one of the most valuable assets of a good administrator to recognize immediately any changes in the personality of an employee or in the nature of the task assigned to him, so that suitable adjustments may be made as soon as they are required. For the sake of simplicity, I shall speak of "employer" and "employee," but what I have to say applies equally to nonscientific and scientific personnel on all levels wherever one person is responsible for directing the work of another.

Assessment of competence.   There are all kinds of point systems for assessing the qualifications of employees according to measurable criteria. The rationale behind these methods of judgment is seemingly very scientific, since the indices of competence can be expressed fairly well in quantitative terms. It is tempting to say that the value of a stenographer depends on her ability to type rapidly and accurately, so that the fairest way to judge her is on speed and freedom from errors. But what if she is in the cafeteria all the time or irritates everybody by her incompatible behavior? It is tempting to give credit for seniority because the technician who has held the same job for ten years should know more about it than a new employee. But the talented and interested beginner will soon be far superior to his senior colleague who has held the same detested job for ten years only because of his own or his employer's inertia. These limitations corrupt almost every quantitative, logically formulated point system. Letters of recommendation, certificates, diplomas, and various aptitude tests are also singularly fallible.

Despite all expert advice to the contrary, I still like to play the game of interpersonal relations by ear. I think I can learn much more than from any standardized test by looking at the eyes of a candidate, his facial expressions, his movements, the way he speaks about his ambitions or his previous chiefs, the way he reacts to his errors and successes. Often, the apparently most inconsequential actions are the most revealing. I think I can tell a lot just from the way a stenographer walks from one office to another along the corridor, or looks for a book on a shelf. There is the type whose every tired motion tells you that she merely wants to drag out this period during which she is not at her hated desk. There is the type whose every pert, undulating wiggle tells you that she thinks only of attracting attention. And finally there is the type who goes briskly after what she is looking for.

In essence, there are two types of people: the *personality-centered* and the *topic-centered*. Whatever the subject under discussion, the first thinks only of the impression he makes on you; the second concentrates on the topic.

You have only to walk up to a technician and say "Hello, how are things today?" (or, in our case "Comment ça va?") to make a diagnosis. The personality-centered girl will immediately show by her behavior that she interprets your question as an inquisition, if not an actual reproach. She may become very nervous and give you a long list of why (and, particularly, because of whose mistakes) she could not do what she should have done. Or she may proudly enumerate a long list of inconsequential little tasks, explaining to you how she managed to complete each of them successfully, despite seemingly insurmountable difficulties. Indeed, she may even take your question as an invitation to turn on the charm, showing by wit, wiggle, and giggle how likeable she is.

The topic-centered girl, on the other hand, will, without any affectation, just tell you how things are in words which show interest in the way her work progresses and perhaps preoccupation about some complications she foresees and on which she would like your advice.

These two types exist on all echelons, although their expressions differ. Even a fellow scientist may show that he is personality-centered by constantly trying to impress you with the excellence of his qualifications and the shortcomings of others. When an unexpected result is noted, he will immediately explain that it could not have been due to a mistake, but even if it were, it could certainly not have been his mistake. He may even resort to what we call the "inkfish technique" and mask the error by a cloud of irrelevant babble, which may include flattering comments on your sagacity in noticing the mistake.

The topic-centered colleague will try to analyze the possible source of error in a detached tone, trying to find out *what*, rather than *who*, is responsible. I am always deeply impressed whenever a person can do this objectively at times when feelings are high because the experiment was important—we were all interested in it—and yet, it may have been spoiled through unpardonable negligence. It is delightful to work with such people; by their obvious disregard of personalities, they radiate a particularly pleasing personal elegance.

There is another way of distinguishing between two kinds of people on all levels of scientific life. One asks, *"What do you want me to do?"* the other, *"What is to be accomplished?"* The first kind may be very effective in carrying out orders, but he always remains an underling. This kind comes a dime a dozen; if necessary, he is easily replaced. The other type does not need, and usually does not want, specific instructions on how to accomplish something. He is not an underling who merely seeks to please you; he is a creative person who, once having understood what is to be accomplished, wants to develop the means himself. These are born leaders, whether they are in charge of a whole research institute or of a group of cleaners. Even if asked to clean some cages, the underling will ask you where, with what, when, and by what time you want it done.

Actually, the two systems of classification overlap because the "What-do-you-want-me-to-do type" is personality-centered in his own way; he considers satisfying you to be his only responsibility, while the "what-is-to-be-accomplished type" is manifestly topic-centered.

All this may seem to be nothing but facile, amateurish chitchat about psychology, but I have yet to find a more reliable method in assessing people, a task with which all of us are constantly confronted. It is so easy to misjudge the gift because of the wrapping in which it comes. I have been fooled too often by candidates who come with M.D. diplomas and were among the best in their class, yet who prove to be quite useless in the lab; while other men who haven't finished high school eventually develop into extraordinarily successful leading administrators or even original research workers.

I have had, among others, a secretary who was able to administer the entire department, although her formal training was limited to secretarial school. We had a domestic servant whom I kept surprising in the act of reading my textbooks in the kitchen. I thereupon fired her at home but gave her a much better job as a technician in the department. Having had no formal schooling, it took her a decade to obtain the B.Sc. degree at night school. But she showed considerable originality and technical skill in research and, eventually, even published several interesting papers in medical journals.

I have had a man who quit his job as a lift boy to become an apprentice technician in this Institute; after having made several outstanding contributions to histology and histochemistry, he eventually became the chief of our histology division.

At the moment, one of my coworkers is a physician whom I have never met, but who wrote me a very impressive letter from the penitentiary where he serves a life sentence for murder. I have employed him to do translations of scientific texts, and he does this admirably, whatever his foibles may be in other respects.

All these people have taught me a great lesson, namely, that the secret of personnel selection is to find *people who want to do what you want them to do*. No matter what a man's formal qualifications, if he does his job only for the salary or even out of a sense of duty, he will rarely be as good, satisfied, and satisfying as another who works because the job interests him.

The inherent human values of leadership, originality, interest, and loyalty are much more important than formal training, because, unlike the latter, they are not easily acquired through experience.

Adjustment of people and tasks. If a man does not fit into a position, don't try to change him; change his position. Give him enough time and all the advice necessary to cope with one task; but if he cannot succeed, he will only come to hate his work—and no amount of talk will help. You can rarely change a man once he is set in his ways; you can rarely give him qualifications he lacks; but if he does not work out well and dislikes his occupation in one department, you need not necessarily discharge him. He may still be a great success in another division of the same institution. A man who is a complete failure as a technician because he dislikes working with animals may still be an excellent librarian or purchasing agent. The important thing is that he should be happy and successful at whatever he does. If, on the other hand, a man has had a chance to try his hand at various tasks and fits into no department, why be kind to him who has proven his incompetence, rather than to a new candidate who needs a job just as much and may be thoroughly competent? Usually, it is not even kindness but weakness and a sense of embarrassment that prevents you from dismissing an obvious misfit, who is a constant source of irritation and spoils the atmosphere for the others.

SELECTION OF A CHIEF.

Who makes a good chief? When I was a medical student, my great ambition in life was to work under the leadership of Professor Arthur Biedl. He was a great endocrinologist, but I had built up an even greater, idealized picture of him. When he finally accepted me as an unpaid, voluntary assistant in his department, I felt that now I had all that I could ask from Lady Fortune; the rest was up to me. Today I still feel that this is the most effective way of selecting a chief. You must respect and trust him. If he betrays your confidence, if he turns out to be the "big boss" type who merely wants to exploit you, leave him; but there is nothing to be gained from grumbling about his ways or trying to change them.

In selecting a job, think first of the chief; he will have a much more lasting effect upon you than the initial salary, rank, facilities, and all the other factors you may consider. The good chief will help you in many ways. The beginner tends to underestimate the technical difficulties and often plans to do in one or two months research which will occupy him for years. Since in school he has heard only of successful research, he gets the impression that investigative work is easy and can be performed rapidly. The senior research man is usually more aware of the difficulties and can be of great help in guiding the research of his pupils.

"The young scientist benefits more from working in collaboration with an experienced research worker than by only having supervision from him. Also in this way he is more likely to get a taste of success, which is a tremendous help. Moreover, the association of the freshness and originality of youth with the accumulated knowledge and experience of a mature scientist can be a mutually beneficial arrangement. Where close collaboration is involved, the personalities of the individuals are, of course, an important consideration. Most brilliant men are stimulating to others, but some are so full of ideas from their own fertile mind and are so keen to try them out that they have a cramping effect on a junior colleague who wants to try out his own ideas. Moreover, it is possible for a man to be a brilliant scientist and yet be quite undeveloped in the knowledge and practice of human personal relations." [W. I. B. Beveridge [11]]

As I said in "Where Should It Be Done" (p. 121), a young man who wants to learn something about science should select a chief who is still active in the lab and, hence, can teach by example. No matter how great and respected the name of a scientist has become because of his past accomplishments, he can teach you little if he has failed to resist the rot of adulation and has turned into a mere symbol of his earlier discoveries. Such an old war horse deserves gratitude and respect for what he has done, but he should be turned out to pasture on the peaceful green fields of representation. With his great experience and personal prestige, he can also do well as scientific adviser to university committees and governments. He can even be a great stimulus to youth as a lecturer, especially by discussing the historic, psychologic and philosophic aspects of research, but he can no longer teach the practice of it. It will look good on your curriculum to have worked with a man who has a great respected name, but it may give you no training.

In assessing your prospective chief from this point of view, keep in mind that age is not an all-important factor here. Some scientists virtually retire from the lab after a single great discovery when they are still young, others continue to do important original research and remain excellent teachers even after the age of formal retirement.

Be particularly on the watch against the temptation of working for *a chief who lets you do what you want*. The kindly laissez faire of the man who has accomplished all he expects to do in life is endearing but of little educational value.

Of course, there are opposite extremes. There are *tough chiefs* so exacting that they want to have their say even about the private lives of their assistants. The eminent German pathologist Ludwig Aschoff strictly disapproved of this. I was told by one of his former assistants that when this question came up, Aschoff indignantly exclaimed, "I want my assistants to work for me twenty-four hours a day, but what they do on their own time is strictly none of my business." Some young scientists may find even this compromise a little hard to accept, but the former Aschoff pupil related the story with an appreciative, warm smile which clearly revealed that he was grateful for his Spartan training. He certainly made excellent use of it later.

Of course, the good chief, no matter how exacting, likes his students and respects their interests. I am sure even Aschoff did not insist on being obeyed to the letter. It takes much more energy to lead with a strong hand than a soft one. It is much easier for an established scientist to get funds for two or three assistants to perform a job leisurely than to educate one to do it alone. Those who nevertheless insist on ironclad discipline and peak accomplishment rarely have any egotistic reasons to be ashamed of. Besides, these tough chiefs are usually the ones who turn out to be the softest at times when human understanding is needed. They are the most willing to help with advice, money, and even by exposing themselves to severe criticism, when a promising pupil gets himself into a mess in his private or academic life owing to some misfortune or to the scientist's impulsive nonconformity—which society is so reluctant to forgive. It is pleasant to see warm personal relationships develop between employer and employee, teacher and pupil, but they presuppose that both parties trustingly let their defenses down and open up; the tortoise and the porcupine are well protected but difficult to caress.

I have just noticed that, up to now, I have spoken only about the kind of chief you should select and not a word about what you should do to be accepted.

How to get accepted.   As I am speaking here into this dictating machine, I look at the old leather chair in front of me in which, throughout these decades, so many ambitious young people have sat while applying for research fellowships. Eighteen of them are now full Professors at various universities throughout the world; two of them are Deans of medical schools; others occupy leading positions in industry. Some worked here for a few years, and then I never heard of them again. But most of the applicants, by far, had to be refused. Rarely can we take more than three new Fellows a year, and there are many more applications; besides, the majority of the applicants are not cut out for a research career. Those who turned out to be successful in science were obviously well chosen, but how could I know that I did not turn down many who were even more highly qualified?

Every director of research has his own standards, and what impresses me in a candidate may not impress others. Still, here again, the best I can do is to show by one example what goes on in the mind of an interviewer who has to make his decision mainly on the basis of a single conversation.

The candidate walks in; we exchange a few meaningless words of greeting, and, as I ask him to sit down in this chair, he has already given me an enormous amount of information merely by the way his expression responds to my welcoming smile. There are blank faces, behind which there is nothing—or something that needs to be hidden. There are satisfied, prosperous faces, behind whose pink plumpness there is too much contentment with things as they are. There are sensitive, somewhat restless, hungry faces with some lively wrinkles around even the youngest eyes; the skin is usually thinner and less shiny than that of the others. I like these faces but I have learned that even they may be deceiving. They undoubtedly have personality, but they may belong to the neurotic (the tortured, persecuted) type who represents the greatest danger to harmony in a lab; they may belong to an ineffectual dreamer. But this may also be the face of "John," the pupil I always wanted to have.

Still, you must not judge too hastily. Some of my best students were thick-skinned, a few even corpulent; but the eyes—the eyes rarely fail me. Scientists always have sensitive lively eyes, although not all such eyes belong to scientists.

The candidate is usually nervous, sitting on the edge of his chair, so I make some chatty remarks and offer him a cigarette to put him at ease. As he reaches for it I notice his hand. There are beefy hands, thick-set athletic hands, fine sensitive hands; there are all kinds of hands. But the kind I like best is narrow and long; its skin is thin, its motions sure, and it does not tremble even during excitement, as I hold out my match to light the cigarette. This hand will be an asset in surgery or any other fine micromanipulation. Besides, I don't know why, but it reveals the soul. Still again, there are many exceptions.

I first ask a few general questions about past training, age, family status, his trip, if he comes from afar, or anything else that is easy to answer, because the most important thing is to get him relaxed; otherwise, the interview cannot be revealing. At this point he usually produces some letters of introduction, certificates or a diploma; all of these do not interest me much, but I read them slowly to give him time to look around and get used to his surroundings. Still, I do note the kind of school he comes from and, if he has done research work before, what kind of chief he worked with; this shows, at least, whether the candidate has received proper formal training. I believe it is much more important to know where and with whom he has worked than what rank he held in his class. Education in the atmosphere of a first-rate school is undoubtedly an asset in creating a proper cultural orientation while high scholastic standing may merely indicate a conformist, bookish attitude that will only be a handicap in original research.

At this point, I quietly ask the question that usually gives me the most significant information: "Why do you want to do research?" Although it is rather obvious that I should want to know this, the candidate manifestly does not expect the question. In fact, often he has never analyzed his motives clearly. Now he must think—and give an articulate reply—about a very complex and fundamental problem of motivation. This is not easy and I do not expect a perfect point-by-point analysis of all his reasons for entering research; but I find the reply very revealing. The same is true of my next question: "Why do you want to do research here, at this particular Institute?"

There are thousands of ways of answering these questions and I am not sure I could explain why I react this or that way to one or the other type of reply. It would take a whole volume to describe every possibility and, in any event, I could not write such a book —it would give all my tricks away.

I also place great emphasis upon the eagerness of the candidate to get the Fellowship. If a man is offered a position immediately and prefers to wait a month or two—in order to clear up some private matters or to get a rest after what he has been doing before—I begin to wonder. The real scientist cannot wait to start.

If at all possible, I ask the candidate to join us on a trial basis for a few months to see how he likes our way of work and to give us a chance to know him better. This is often not feasible because, if we make no definite promise, he has to look for other possibilities. However, if the candidate agrees to such a "test tube experiment," it is an excellent way to establish how we get along with each other.

In interviewing candidates for technical, administrative, or secretarial positions, I am also guided much more by criteria of personal characteristics than by certificates or aptitude tests indicative of formal training; although, of course, a typist must know how to type and an accountant how to count.

Well, you will have to forgive me if I say no more about this subject, but since I am still far from retiring I must think of my future interviews. Hence, much to my regret, I cannot tell you all about the most interesting feature of these conversations: my vicious "interview traps."

TWOSOMES IN RESEARCH. In addition to group work performed by large teams under the direction of one senior investigator, fruitful cooperation may develop between two senior scientists of approximately equal competence. It is often said that there can be only one captain on a ship, and, in general, this holds for research projects as well. In twosomes, the danger is that one partner may become domineering and the other submissive and sterile. This danger is greatest in *teacher-student* teams. When one of the associates is much younger and perhaps the former graduate student of the other, it is especially important to take care that the junior colleague nevertheless retains final executive responsibility for his share of the work. Otherwise, the younger or weaker partner will fall into the habit of relying on the stronger and always asking what to do. Muscles become atrophic when not used, and so does creative ability. If the more modest or weaker partner is reluctant to assume authority, he must be forced to make decisions—even if his apprenticeship is costly because of errors resulting from comparative inexperience.

Cooperation between *two directors of independent departments* is particularly difficult. Such twosomes work best when only the major object of research is common, but the approach fundamentally different. For example, a chemist and a surgeon may work out a fruitful cooperation concerning the metabolic effects of a complicated operation. Here, it is unlikely that one partner could interfere with the other's freedom of action or originality of thought. The surgeon may work out the techniques for a complicated operation, such as the removal of the pituitary or of the sympathetic nervous system, while his partner, the biochemist, examines the blood and excretions of patients requiring these interruptions. Here, the two associates are totally independent of each other; the work of the surgeon is finished when that of the biochemist begins. There is no possibility of conflict, only of mutual help in a task that neither partner could have performed by himself. Similar cooperations may develop fruitfully between a chemist who synthesizes a drug and a pharmacologist who tests it on animals, or between this pharmacologist and a clinician who carries the work to its final application in the treatment of disease.

A special form of the twosome is the *husband-and-wife team*. Here, complete independence is impossible (at least on social grounds) but this is not necessarily an unwelcome source of irritation. Indeed, in husband-and-wife twosomes, a certain submissiveness on the part of one member of the team may be quite acceptable or even desired by one or both partners.

Some husband-and-wife teams have produced the most remarkable brain children in the history of science. I am thinking particularly of the Pierre Curies, the Carl Coris, and the Howard Floreys. The Curies were both physicists, the Coris both biochemists who shared the same techniques and facilities, working in close association during the major parts of their lives. Howard Florey was mainly responsible for the discovery of penicillin, while his wife, Ethel, tested the drug on patients, as a separate but related research project.

Much more often the wife does not directly participate in the research, but helps her husband as a technician, secretary, or by just being an understanding, good wife, which is even more important. Unfortunately, sometimes the reverse is true. Mrs. Robert Koch was constantly nagging her husband to give up the dissection of smelly animals and became famous only in a left-handed sort of way for her part in the discovery of the tubercle bacillus. But even Xanthippe, the ill-tempered wife of Socrates, became a historic figure for the inhibitory role she played in the development of Greek philosophy.

ASSIGNMENT OF SCIENTIFIC CREDIT. I have learned by experience that you cannot donate scientific credit. You can show your appreciation for the work of a useful and industrious junior colleague by recognizing it generously in front of his peers, by advancing him rapidly in academic rank, or by raising his income; but if his contribution—no matter how important—is limited to administration, supervision, or teaching, you cannot compensate him by putting his name on scientific papers unless he has directly participated in the research work described. I have succumbed to the temptation of acting against this principle many times, but it has never worked. I thought that it would be just to acknowledge, by scientific credit, any type of contribution that plays a decisive role in the success of a research team, but I have learned that you cannot compromise with the strict application of the merit principle. And scientific merit is essentially different from all other kinds.

The young man likes to see his name in print and usually cannot resist when offered co-authorship on a paper to which he has contributed only quite indirectly. But, after a while he feels that he did not deserve the honor and becomes dissatisfied with the whole organization for not being given the chance to contribute in a more scientific way. On the other hand, it is very important that the names of all those who do really share in the scientific investigation should appear as authors on the team's publications.

This problem is extremely delicate, because, when a group works together on a subject, it is virtually impossible to decide exactly how much each member has contributed. And besides, constant preoccupation with credit is embarrassing and disruptive. However, my Notes on the psychology of research would be incomplete if this undoubtedly important topic were not faced frankly and discussed fully. I, therefore, brought it up at a staff conference so that it might be dealt with openly. Various possibilities were suggested, and three rules were eventually adopted by unanimous vote:

1. Any member of a team should be given the chance to pursue certain personal observations independently of the group, if he wishes, and to publish them under his own name. Thereby, we eliminate any feeling of compulsion to cooperate with the team. (Participation in group work is encouraged merely by natural selection—that is, by the enrollment of scientists who happen to share the group's interests anyway.) This rule does not apply to Ph.D. candidates during the first eighteen months, when they are strictly under the guidance of the director of their thesis.

2. The man who suggests an investigation, or who has made the original key observation, automatically becomes the senior author of the paper which describes this work. He also decides who among his associates should be named as co-authors and in what order.

3. Except in rare instances, no more than three members of the team should be named as authors; in practice, if a paper is signed by too many people, only the name of the senior investigator is recognized. When larger groups work together on an extensive project, several papers are usually published; it is up to the senior investigator to see that all contributors are equally recognized in the long run, although no more than three are mentioned on any one publication.

This system is still very artificial, but in all our discussions among ourselves and with visiting scientists we were unable to develop anything better. In the past, we have tried many other ways of handling this problem, but our present system is undoubtedly the most satisfactory for all concerned.

Even if we hate to admit it, the problems concerned with credit and responsibility for scientific work do play a decisive part in determining the happiness and efficiency of a research team. It is wrong to dismiss these questions easily with a show of indifference, because few people are indifferent to them; in this respect, I believe every team should have a clearly established policy. We are well satisfied with ours and have had little difficulty since we decided to follow it rigorously, but there are always some people who present special problems. For example, it seems to be an inherent characteristic of human nature that, if three people carry out and publish a research project conjointly, each member of the group is tempted to consider his own as being the crucial contribution. No harm is done as long as the feeling is kept private, but it must not lead to obnoxiously conceited behavior.

Many young scientists experience serious difficulties of adjustment during the period of transition between work under guidance as a graduate student and participation in team work as a full-fledged scientist. It is not easy for some of them to strike a proper balance between the conflicting feelings of finally having arrived and of still not being prepared to accept full scientific responsibility.

This dichotomy is well illustrated by the case of a senior Ph.D. candidate who worked with me many years ago at McGill on some problem related to sex hormones. It was his first research project, and he was very possessive about it. Whenever I wanted to suggest something, he took the attitude that, after all, he was no longer a baby and knew how to proceed. When the time came to apply for Fellowships he was quite insistent in his demand to be recommended for the best senior scholarship available. Having completed two years of postgraduate training, he considered himself a fully trained, eligible, independent investigator.

Our joint work was eventually to be communicated at a local meeting of a scientific society and, since I knew that he wanted it that way, I asked him to present our paper, acting as the first-mentioned author. He took this as only natural and on the platform spoke of every experiment in the first person: "I have done this," "I conclude that." But in the ensuing discussion, when our conclusion was violently assailed, he did not remember how I had arrived at it. He became panicky because he thought that we might be wrong.

There was a long, embarrassing pause, during which the boy looked desperately at me. But, of course, I didn't have the floor so I could not help. Finally, with a sheepish grin, he said, "Well, I don't think this is a justified conclusion either, but I did this work as a graduate student and I was told that this is the conclusion I must draw." Fortunately, during the ensuing discussion period, I had a chance to explain the justification of our argument to the satisfaction of every-one—but I shudder to think of the impression my young associate would have left with the audience had he spoken in my absence.

The moral of this story is that a junior member of a team can neither be held fully responsible nor claim full credit for the group's work. It is difficult to cope with a man who feels justified in demand-ing all the privileges of a senior, responsible investigator as long as things go well, but as soon as there is a question of possible mistake, pathetically exclaims, "Don't blame me, I am only a child, acting under Daddy's orders." The members of a team must clearly understand that if they agree to publish their results together, each author shares equally in the credit and the responsibility; no one can agree to co-authorship on a paper if he does not fully understand and agree with the text.

RESEARCH IN INDUSTRY. If teamwork has its great advantages in pure basic research, it is even more efficient in the systematic development and application of scientific achievements. Industry could hardly exist without it, and at least a few words should be said here about teamwork in the drug industry, which I know best.

The greatest advantage offered by industry is *better pay*. To many researchers this is no negligible factor, especially during the early years when young men in academic careers must live on Fellowships or ill-paid, junior, university posts. Yet, with the constant growth of government interest in basic research, this situation rapidly changes; some of the best industrial scientists are now beginning to apply for pure research positions at universities.

Another feature of industrial teamwork is that the director of a research group can, and indeed, in the financial interests of his company must, exercise much more power than his academic colleague in coercing his associates along a certain line of study. Many a complex task, such as the preparation of steroids or antibiotics, would have been impossible without this *enforced execution of carefully prepared master plans*. However, the individual members of a commercial team have less freedom for the expression of their own creative originality than most of their colleagues in academic life.

A great disadvantage of industrial teamwork is that, in many companies—though certainly not in all—management imposes too many monotonous, *routine tasks* (such as toxicity tests, assays of activity) and insists on the observance of deadlines by which certain assignments must be completed. In many industrial labs there is too little opportunity for leisurely, independent scientific work and for contact with the academically minded colleagues in different fields that one meets daily on a university campus or in a faculty club. There may be no obvious relationship between the pharmacologist's work and that of professors in other scientific disciplines or in the humanities, but it certainly is a stimulus to an intellectually minded person to be surrounded by such men.

Probably the worst aspect of teamwork in industry is the practice, in at least a few establishments, of *forbidding publication of dis-*

coveries unfavorable to the company's financial interests. For example, information may be suppressed if it could help a competitor. Permission may be refused to publish observations concerning the toxicity of a drug sold by the company, even if the findings are of considerable theoretic importance. As long as management is convinced that the drug is not really dangerous, withholding such information may seem justified because it can draw attention to the possibility of claiming damages on unjust or even fraudulent grounds. Suppose that a drug produces kidney stones or cataracts in animals. A patient who took this product might hold the company liable for damages if later he accidentally happens to develop kidney stones or cataracts. It may be impossible to verify a causal relationship between the treatment and the malady, but the courts have shown a great tendency to find for the plaintiff whenever there is a question of physical injury. The great abuse of liability suits in this connection makes such preoccupations understandable, but the scientist resents seeing scientific data censored on any grounds.

Finally, difficulties may arise if *a new drug is discovered which, though superior to all others made for the same purpose, is financially unprofitable.* For example, a compound may be prepared which is less toxic, more effective, and cheaper than all other drugs available for the treatment of hypertension. However, the company may have already invested enormous sums in the development and promotion of another antihypertensive drug which sells well. In such instances, it is often financially disadvantageous for a company to enter into competition with itself. Here, the decision may be reached to use what industry calls the "deep-freeze technique" and just store the information until market conditions will make its use profitable. It is not for me to sit in judgment over the ethical problems involved here. I suppose, legally, the information belongs to the company that paid for it. But for a scientist, and particularly for a physician, it is difficult to accept that patients should be deprived of valuable and inexpensive drugs merely on the basis of financial considerations.

Interdepartmental Scientific Cooperation

A project carried out conjointly in two or more departments usually involves cooperation between independent senior investigators, a problem with which we have dealt already. This type of cooperation works only in the most exceptional cases. As we have seen, here the prerequisites for success are that the two groups must be *administratively independent, but scientifically interdependent.* In other words, each group must be entirely autonomous regarding finances, physical facilities, and scientific direction, but interdependent for success. Only when these conditions obtain will both groups feel perfectly free to proceed in their own way, assured of fullhearted mutual interest and assistance.

For example, in our work on calciphylaxis, we have performed the animal experiments but have cooperated with other departments as regards the crystallographic identification of the calcium deposits. We knew nothing about crystallography and they were equally ignorant of our animal-experimental techniques. All we had to do was to perform the animal experiments conducive to calciphylaxis and then send specimens of calcified tissues to our physicist colleagues. However, since the object of both groups was to establish the crystallographic properties of calciphylactically induced calcium deposits, we were highly interested in each other's work and totally interdependent for success. This type of cooperation can be extremely fruitful, since it may lead to the solution of problems which neither of the two cooperating teams could have solved alone.

On the other hand, I have never yet seen a lastingly successful interdepartmental cooperation organized on any other lines. In the course of conversation between colleagues, a pharmacologist may mention the need for certain biochemical determinations and, under the spell of the moment, the biochemist may lightheartedly offer to do this work. Motivated by momentary enthusiasm or mere courtesy, a pathologist may agree to examine a few tissue specimens for his biochemical colleague. But in the long run interest fades; reports are increasingly more delayed, all kinds of other duties get priority, and finally the cooperation dies of apathy. Indeed, many times this type of conjoint effort is an unwanted Christmas present to both parties, because both feel the other wanted to have it, although actually there was little interest for it on either side.

National and International Scientific Cooperation

The first systematic efforts to stimulate cooperation in science and the humanities on a broad national or international scale were made through the foundation of various academies. The word "academy" is derived from the olive groves of Academe where Plato retired for meditation and discussion with his friends and pupils. An academy "may be defined as a society or corporate body having for its object a cultivation and promotion of literature, of science and of art, either severally or in combination, undertaken for the pure love of these pursuits, with no interested motive" [*Encyclopaedia Britannica* 34]. The first academy in this sense was the Museum of Alexandria, founded at the beginning of the third century B.C. by Ptolemy I. At this center of learning—which may be regarded with equal justification as the first university—all sciences known at the time were pursued by the most eminent scholars of Greece and the East, who traveled great distances to profit from mutual stimulation. This group eventually founded the nucleus of the famous Alexandrian Library.

In the course of time, most civilized countries established academies, among which the following are especially noteworthy:

Academia Secretorum Naturae (Italy, 1560)
The Royal Academy (England, 1616, later The Royal Society, 1662)
Academia Naturae Curiosi (Germany, 1652, later the Academia Caesarea Leopoldina)
Académie des Sciences and Académie Française (France, 1666)
Real Academia Española (Spain, 1713)
Imperatorskaya Akademiya nauk (Russia, 1725, later the Academy of Sciences of the U.S.S.R.)
Kongelige Danske Videnskarbernes Selskab (Denmark, 1742)
Académie Royale des Sciences, des Lettres et des Beaux-Arts de Belgique (Belgium, 1772)
Academia das Ciências de Lisbôa (Portugal, 1779)
Akademie der Wissenschaften (Austria, 1847)

Although all of these were national societies, most offered membership to outstanding foreign scholars, recognizing that the development of science and the humanities should not be hampered by nationalistic considerations. Because of the success of these associations, numerous other national and international societies and schools with similar objectives were formed.

Today, every civilized country has a national Academy of Sciences or its equivalent, as well as a host of specialized scientific societies. These offer ample opportunity for the exchange of scientific information and for the establishment of personal contacts between scientists and humanists who work in widely separated areas. Most countries also have a national research council or some other governmental agency responsible for the financing of research. In addition, we now have numerous international organizations (WHO, UNESCO), all of which have contributed to the present upswing in research. Our own group has been greatly assisted by several among these organizations, and particularly through the substantial grants, in support of our work on stress and calciphylaxis, generously offered by the United States Public Health Service, in complete disregard of the border that separates (or, perhaps more correctly, unites) our two countries.

International scientific cooperation can be very efficacious, but its most heart-warming aspect is the eloquent demonstration that, despite the strong feelings that develop between nations, races and religions, there are still basic human needs—such as the thirst for truth and compassion for the sick—that are common to all of us. It is one of the noblest, ethical accomplishments of a scientific institution to show how all the barriers between men can crumble into insignificant nothingness, in the common search for the mastery of Nature's secrets.

It is gratifying that in our little Institute, right at this moment, representatives of twenty-four nations work together harmoniously. During the war, at McGill, I had a Jewish boy and the son of an interned German-Canadian Nazi working with me in perfect harmony. But perhaps the sweetest little incident illustrative of this spirit happened only a couple of years ago, in my present Institute. A Roman Catholic nun from the U.S.A., a Hindu from India, and a Communist from Czechoslovakia, worked in the same laboratory on calciphylaxis and eventually even published their results conjointly. Just before the sister had to return to her convent, my wife asked her over to the house for a Sunday farewell dinner and we discussed life in our cosmopolitan lab. "Well, you know, Mrs. Selye," she said, "at first it was really quite startling to work under these conditions and I felt the need to discuss certain doubts with my father confessor. But after a few weeks I began to realize that . . . well, it's hard to say such a thing . . . but one of these people is a pagan, the other an atheist . . . yes, an actual atheist! And there, by God's will and the force of circumstances, I was working side by side with them. But, you know, it is astonishing that otherwise they are intelligent and really nice people—both of them."

Management and Supervision of Personnel

ESPRIT DE CORPS. The most valuable social asset of any scientific organization is *esprit de corps,* a feeling among its members of attachment to each other and to the purposes of the institution. This sentiment is often highly developed in units of the armed forces, athletic crews, and clubs, but it can be awakened even in commercial establishments, so there should be no difficulty in creating it in a scientific institution. To achieve this, the personnel must understand and approve the purposes of the organization and be inspired by a *feeling of belonging,* of participating in its accomplishments.

To establish *esprit de corps,* the administration must see to it that the members of the staff on all echelons get to know and like both each other and the work they are doing. It is difficult to lay down hard and fast rules about the way to do this, but here are a few of the practices which we found useful in this connection.

Any new employee, let us say a female technician, is first received by the personnel manager, Mrs. Kaden, a very friendly and understanding lady, who explains to the new girl what her duties and rights are (working hours, holidays, marginal benefits, etc.). She also gives a brief outline of what the Institute is trying to accomplish, just where the new employee's work fits into this general scheme, and in what direction she might develop her talents in the future as she gains experience. Then, the newcomer is introduced to her immediate superior and colleagues, one of whom takes her on a tour of the Institute so that she may get oriented as soon as possible.

At four o'clock every afternoon we have a tea break at which all members of the staff have a chance to get together. In addition, recently we have established the custom of arranging informal, small dinner parties at the Students' Union, where the chiefs of the various services act as hosts. They can ask three or four of their coworkers to spend the evening together in a more social setting, discussing anything that is on their minds, be it related to the work of the Institute or not.

For the creation of healthy interpersonal relations it is also important to strike the right tone in contacts between various ranks. *Excessive chumminess* between chiefs and subordinates undermines discipline. The assistant who plays favorites or, on a day when he feels good, is overly intimate with a technician, cannot expect her next day to carry out a monotonous or otherwise unpleasant assignment without argument.

Undue manifestations of respect for authority are equally unwarranted. If a man is no authority he does not deserve to be treated as one; and if he is, he resents flattery because it implies that he is considered to be naïvely vain. When an assistant stops and asks me the question, "May I ask you something, sir?", he already has done so and thereby has interrupted my thoughts anyway. Besides, how could I say, "No"? If the question is really urgent and needs my immediate decision, he might as well go ahead and ask without preamble, and if the matter can wait, why not bring it up at one of the many daily occasions (lab rounds, autopsy conference) foreseen for consultations.

The innumerable variants for the formal expression of respect are all embarrassing. There is no point in expatiating upon the monumental nature of the chief's scientific accomplishments in his presence. Nothing is gained by three people getting in his way in a frantic rush to open the door for him. Conversely, there is no harm in criticizing the chief for what you think he should not do; if you are right and he reasonable, the criticism will be welcomed and he will try to correct his ways. But even if you are wrong, it is healthy to ventilate your grudges and to verify their justification by the reactions of others.

When I was a child, my governess, Madame Totier, and later in school my philosophy teacher Dr. Bognár, had the greatest influence upon my mental development; I loved them both dearly, but I admit to having sometimes referred to them as grumpy old fools in conversations with schoolmates. Had they heard me, I am sure they would not have minded, because they also liked and understood me. Owing to the political upheavals in Europe, both of them spent their old age in abject poverty and it warmed my heart that it was to me that they turned for assistance in their need and never doubted that they would get it, although we hadn't seen each other for decades.

Natural rather than formal expressions of respect are needed for harmony and understanding in an Institute. I hate to ask a person to do a disagreeable and monotonous job for me; but if he senses my need and does it unasked, I am deeply grateful. It creates a pleasant feeling of camaraderie if a man stays unasked until late at night to help me accomplish a task which he knows I want to see finished. It is particularly gratifying to find out accidentally that he helped me with something without even having told me of it. These are true manifestations of goodwill and respect which make us like each other. The cliché, "We are all just one big happy family," has been abused in business life, but it can be given reality, especially in a medical research institution, in which the disturbing element of personal profit is minimal.

Finally, a word about the *recognition of merit*. We are too prone to speak only of errors which should be corrected and to disregard successes which require no interference on our part. I have said a great deal about the scientist's need for recognition, but this craving is quite general among people whatever their occupation. Those who are responsible for the work of a group should never forget to show their gratitude and appreciation for any task well accomplished. We need not worry too much about the possibility that applause may make our associates swell-headed. It sometimes does, but the danger of this is much less than that of creating apathy by being too indifferent to accomplishments.

It is also good to remember that people are not machines; they need a little *personal warmth*. A kind word to the night watchman or the cleaning woman, a compliment to the stenographer (not when you feel it is her turn, but when she really looks pretty) can go a long way in creating *esprit de corps*.

DON'T LET GO OF THE JOB. *Do it now.* The administrative motto of our Institute is "Do it now." Everything that man's mind can encompass will be discovered eventually. The problem of each scientist is how much he can accomplish in his own life span. I seem to have especially much trouble in getting this slogan accepted, or perhaps I am just especially sensitive to waste of time. But this is how I see the matter:

Supposing, at an autopsy conference, we decide to do an experiment for which we need some materials that are not immediately available in the lab. For example, we may require three books from the library to look up some technical details about a procedure, and two chemicals available only from a company at the other end of town. Here, the normal procedure would be to ask an assistant to take notes of all these requirements and to bring up the matter again when we have all we need to start.

Now, assuming that he forgets nothing and expedites things in a "normal" manner, the assistant will go to Mr. Brunet, our Institute's purchasing agent, explain what chemicals we want and ask him to order them "as soon as possible." Mr. Brunet makes out a requisition and sends it by the next departmental mail to our administrator, who has to countersign it after having checked that the item was charged to the proper fund. Then the requisition for an order goes by the next interdepartmental mail to the University's purchasing agent, who checks that the fund to which we charged these items has enough money left and that the purchase is in conformity with what the donors of the grant permit us to buy. When all this is done, in due course an order is sent to the company, and—usually after two weeks or so—the mail brings us either the drugs or a letter indicating that they are not available.

Of course, things go that smoothly only if there is no hitch. Usually there is. The order is mislaid in one or the other office; the name of the chemical is misspelled and instead of adrenaline they send us adrenalone; or they misaddress the shipment, and it is shelved in another department.

Now, what I like to do is to call Mr. Brunet on the intercom, right from the autopsy room, immediately after having decided what we need. Mr. Brunet phones the company, explains clearly what we need and finds out whether or not they have it. If so, he sends down a messenger boy in a taxi (paying for the material and the transportation from petty cash), and we have the drugs in the lab within a couple of hours. We still have to go through all the paper work because we must account for the way we spend our funds; but this is done in the form of "confirmation orders," while the experiment is already well under way.

I shall spare you the details of all the formalities necessary to get the wanted books, if they are not available at the Institute and must be obtained from another library. But according to my preferred system, the messenger boy picks them up on the way back from the pharmaceutical company and we get them simultaneously with the drugs. The amount of time and energy saved by this system is certainly worth the price of being criticized a bit for using the "confirmation order" procedure too often. Of course, things cannot be arranged quite so easily if materials must come from out-of-town, but, even then, a long distance call and a few extra dollars for shipment by air freight are little to pay for the enormous advantages offered by the "Do-it-now" system.

Follow up. If an order cannot be carried out immediately, at least make sure that it is not forgotten. If the needed drug must be synthesized especially for us by the company and we are told that this would take three weeks, the ever-efficient Mr. Brunet makes an entry on his calendar and calls up a little before the expected delivery date to make sure they did not forget about it. If you consider all the activities that go on simultaneously in a large research department, it is astonishing how much can be accomplished by the principles of "Do it now" and (if this is quite impossible) "Follow up." It takes some time for people to get used to this way of doing things, but eventually it becomes a good habit just as easily as the most complicated, ponderous, bureaucratic procedure can become a bad habit.

GENERAL ORGANIZATION. A detailed account of how our Institute is organized would not be of sufficient general interest to warrant the space it would take to describe it. Besides, the activities of some departments, in which original procedures are used, will be discussed later in "How to Work" (p. 199), and the rest is largely routine. But a brief sketch of the whole organization may be justified since all these Notes refer to work done within the framework of this structure.

In order to organize the management of the Institute efficiently, we have formed an *administrative committee* consisting of the chief administrator (Mr. Mercier), my two senior assistants (Drs. Jean and Prioreschi), the chief of our documentation service (Mr. Ember), and myself. We meet only when major problems arise and decisions are taken by majority vote. Minor problems can be settled by any member of this Committee on his own responsibility, or, if he feels the need for it, after discussion with one or two others who are familiar with the question. However, we do not bring up at full committee meetings problems that touch only one or two of us, because the other members would merely waste their time listening to deliberations that do not concern them.

The major administrative units of the Institute are: *pharmacology* (animal experimentation including experimental surgery), *the pharmacy* (filling of prescriptions), *histology, biochemistry, the library* (codification of the literature, photo-reproduction of scientific documents, obtention of unavailable volumes from other libraries), *protocol* (filing and retrieval of protocols describing our own experiments), *illustration* (photography, preparation of drawings, diagrams, museum specimens), *extramural relations* (grants, reception of visitors and relations with the press), *purchasing, personnel and maintenance, secretariat* (general correspondence, editing of papers and books, proofreading) and *general administration* (coordination of all administrative activities). Each of these divisions is headed by a departmental chief responsible to the administrator who coordinates the entire management of the Institute and is, in turn, responsible to the administrative committee of which he is a member.

LATHOTROPISM AND THE SPOT TEST. "Lathotropism" (from the Greek *lathos,* error, and *trepein,* to turn toward) is a word designating a particular instinct which guides its possessor straight to an error, even though it may be the only flaw in an otherwise perfectly accomplished, complex task. The term has been coined by my assistants as part of a shrewd campaign to blame me for their errors. They say that I am blessed (or cursed) with an extraordinary degree of uncanny lathotropism because, allegedly, the Institute runs virtually without errors, and yet, wherever I go, I immediately turn to the one mistake that happened to slip into whatever I am looking at. Lathotropism is in action, for example, if you just quickly leaf through a ten-page manuscript and pick out the only three typing errors in it, or if you look at a rack of a hundred rat cages and instinctively check the one water bottle that happens to be empty.

A *spot test* is a control limited to a few key or sample points, or to a relatively small percentage of random spots. The best way to supervise and keep in touch with a complex organization is the spot test guided by lathotropism. The spot test part is a logically conceived and consciously planned system of verification and, hence, can be explained. Lathotropism, however, is an instinct presumably based on the unconscious evaluation of past experience and, hence, its mechanism cannot be dissected. Let us, therefore, limit our disquisition to the spot test.

In the final analysis, the director of research is responsible for everything—research, teaching, and administration—in his department. He may and should delegate responsibility for individual tasks to departmental chiefs responsible to him, but, if they fail, the director is justly blamed for having shown poor judgment in the selection of his associates. People (university authorities, granting agencies, readers of the Institute's publications) are interested only in the quality and reliability of the work done, not in arguments intended to shift the blame for failure. In any event, the real scientist wants his unit to function perfectly because he is interested in its work, irrespective of whether he will be blamed for errors or not. Since no man can personally perform, or even supervise, every activity of a large Institute, he has to resort to special techniques.

Here again, let me discuss the subject as far as possible from my own experience. It is mainly the fear of errors that makes me base my work principally on techniques I can personally supervise. I follow the clinical behavior of our experimental animals daily. In addition, I check all autopsies and read all histologic slides myself. Though this is time consuming, I find it rewarding because it keeps me in direct touch with my experiments and gives me a chance to detect possible errors. At the same time, this close participation in the most important aspects of our work provides an excellent opportunity for man-to-man teaching.

Writing papers and books is another activity that helps us to analyze and evaluate our results, without incurring the danger of our work being corrupted by the errors of others; if the results are poor, at least we have only ourselves to blame.

Supervision is more difficult when it comes to experimental techniques. Whenever a fundamentally new procedure—for example, a new surgical operation—is to be used, I like to develop the technique myself. But once I am satisfied with it I must rely upon associates to carry it out on a large scale. The successful performance of most surgical interventions can be verified objectively at autopsy, but this is not so with many other techniques. Here, the spot test must take over. The best I can do is to wander about the Institute and check various procedures more or less at random, but giving particular attention to those manipulations that are likely to be performed incorrectly. Such spot tests can verify how solutions are prepared in the pharmacy; how injections are given in the pharmacology division; whether or not a student does actually understand the principles of that which he may be doing only mechanically. It is impossible to verify that each of the approximately thousand weekly new entries in the library are correctly typed, but, as a sample, some can be carefully checked. Of course, in all this, lathotropism is a great help.

I do not know why I noticed that a gallon jar of alcohol on the shelf in a stenographer's office was full one day and empty the next. But when I asked her next day what she needed alcohol for, her answer that she used it to clean her typewriter was not really satisfactory since the keys were still dirty.

I do not know why, a few years ago, I suddenly distrusted the standard errors on a table prepared by an assistant. But when I asked him to verify them, it became quite obvious that he did not know how to calculate standard errors.

I do not know why a friend of mine happened to tell me that he saw some beautiful portraits of Einstein and Schweitzer at the home of one of my most intellectually minded technicians. But these particular portraits had disappeared a few weeks before from our picture gallery.

Some of the sins—revealed by spot tests, lathotropism or both —are minor peccadilloes, unworthy of attention. Others can seriously affect the interpretation of our research. It is unnecessary to say more about the subject, but in closing, I would like to call attention to one of the most fruitful fields for spot tests: the control of apathy.

The job carried on by inertia. Many a task, once established as a routine, escapes attention, then, as a result of a lack of supervision, it is continued even after it is no longer needed.

I remember that, in 1945, when I left McGill University to found this Institute, I made arrangements with my friend Professor J. S. L. Browne (then head of the department of medicine at McGill) to furnish him with carbon copies of all the subject, author, and abstract cards we prepared for our library. In exchange, he agreed to share expenses. This cooperation worked very well for a time; but it was discontinued in 1948, and I told the girl in charge to stop making carbon copies.

I gave the matter no thought, until in 1953, I happened to notice two enormous wooden boxes hidden underneath a table in the library. "What is in these?" I inquired. "The carbon copies of all the cards made during the past five years," I was told, "we were always wondering what they were going to be used for." It turned out that the girl originally in charge of this job left to be married just a few days after I had told her to stop making carbon copies. In the excitement over the forthcoming events in her private life, she had—quite understandably—forgotten to leave instructions about Professor Browne's filing system. I must admit that, in this instance, my lathotropism exhibited a regrettably delayed reactivity.

I trust that such monumental examples of the job carried on by inertia are unlikely to occur in this Institute now that we have perfected our techniques for supervision and management. But the fact is, they did occur. This was one of our main reasons for placing so much emphasis on spot tests, and I believe it is well to re-examine all routinely performed tasks from time to time to see whether some should not be discontinued, or at least modified, to fit current requirements.

Don't argue, demonstrate. In making spot tests, sooner or later you are bound to meet the problem of an employee who insists that the job cannot be performed the way you think it should. Here, the solution is not to argue about the feasibility of a task but to prove it by a demonstration. If a technician tells me that a certain surgical operation cannot be done, I just do it. No amount of arguing would have the same convincing power and, in addition, the demonstration may bring out the reason why the technician failed to accomplish the task in the way I suggested. The more a scientist works in the lab himself, the more opportunities he has to learn and demonstrate techniques personally.

Even the feasibility of work we cannot perform ourselves is more eloquently demonstrated by example than by words, but, in this case, we must get an expert to do the demonstrating. For instance, I cannot type; hence, if a typist insists that it would be impossible to type more abstract cards with less errors during a working day than she does, I am hard pressed to persuade her. However, if I know from experience that she is wrong, the simplest way to prove my point is to get a good typist (and I mean a really good one!) to prove it eloquently for me. This system has rarely failed me.

DEALING WITH NEUROTICS AND PSYCHOTICS. Few people realize and fewer still readily believe that one out of every ten North

Americans has to be committed to a mental institution because of mental illness at least once in his lifetime. Many more receive treatment for minor derangements that do not necessitate actual hospitalization. Thousands more need treatment and never get it because of prejudice or lack of understanding—but principally because to the mentally unbalanced there is nothing odd in his own condition.

Some relationship between genius and insanity has long been suspected(p. 66), and it is certainly true that the incidence of mental abnormalities is even greater in the unusual walks of life. The solid, well-balanced citizen seeks a well-established, safe career and becomes a farmer, merchant, postman, doctor or engineer. He is not in the least attracted by such uncommon and uncertain occupations as those of poet, musician, scientist or writer, in which success depends mainly upon originality—an unpredictable, largely uncontrollable deviation from the norm.

All of us, deep in our hearts, believe in the myth of the "mad genius." We want our scientists to be an eccentric, absent-minded bunch; then, when they do something brilliant, the great mass of the people feels less separated from them.

However, it is not as well recognized that even the auxiliary positions in science attract unusual personalities: people unable or reluctant to take up routine jobs. In a sense these people are social misfits, but it must be remembered that their odd tastes are often highly valuable. The bourgeois type who likes photography sees much more future in the career of a commercial photographer who takes pictures of people than in that of a microphotographer whose subjects are cells. The average girl who likes nursing will seek a hospital post, not one in the lab where her patients are likely to be rats. The typical librarian is very unlikely to be interested in codifying scientific literature.

Many of those who find a place in a scientific research institution have tried and failed in all kinds of other jobs. Some are displaced persons, the refugees of political or religious persecution; others could never hold a job because of morbid timidity, personal incompatibility, instability or a deep aversion toward routine. The only characteristic common to all these people lies in their difference in background or personality from the average type in the community. Whatever the cause, they do create social problems, and we must learn how to profit from the valuable mental quirks and how to control the weaknesses. The solution is certainly not to eliminate unusual people on principle, although it is difficult to live with them unless you, yourself, possess rare gifts of adaptability and understanding of human nature.

Besides those with minor abnormalities, any large research institution unfailingly attracts a fair quota whose neurosis, or even psychosis, is so severe as to be unmanageable. Then, the problem is to diagnose the situation early and to eliminate the disturbing element with a minimum of fuss before it poisons the atmosphere.

In my own experience, the most common features of mental derangement in scientific institutions are ideas of persecution, of being misunderstood and hated by everyone. These feelings may lead to singular acts of vengeance against the imagined foe. I had one technician who came to detest her immediate superior so much that she decided to drive him into insanity. She started conservatively with anonymous phone calls, explaining in an altered voice that she had inside information about his imminent dismissal. When this didn't work, she dialed drugstores and restaurants, placing orders for urgent delivery to her victim's home throughout the night, to keep him from sleeping. Finally, she resorted to more drastic measures. While the hated superior was out of town, the technician dispatched an undertaker with a coffin to his house where the children were asked whether their father's body had arrived.

Such macabre excesses are exceptional. But it happens quite often that a neurotic laboratory assistant punishes her supervisor by purposely spoiling an experiment, or that a stenographer takes it out on her boss by willfully mislaying important documents.

In coping with these aggressive types, the greatest difficulty is to convince their colleagues that they are dealing with sick people. Irrational acts of hostility generally lead to lengthy futile arguments about the utter senselessness of the offensive behavior and to emotional responses in which hate is met by hate. You do not hate a man for being blind, nor do you try to talk him out of it; however, you cannot employ him as a chauffeur. Yet it is difficult to explain that, in this respect, a mental disease is no different from a physical one.

What we must try to do is to detect the derangement early so as to forestall further trouble. "But where is the borderline between the normal and the abnormal?" you may ask. "There are all kinds of transitional types. Everybody gets angry when unjustly or stupidly provoked and many a serious misunderstanding is rectified by a heart-to-heart talk. Should we eliminate feeling and reasoning from our dealings with people?" Certainly not, but it is difficult to give generally applicable directives. The simple rule of thumb I follow is to answer emotionally with warmth or intellectually with argument, in accordance with a person's responsiveness. There are no sharp borderlines between the types, and the transitions between extremes are gradual; but, once you know a person well, you realize to what extent he is responsible for his actions and responsive to your own. Learn to adjust your reaction accordingly and you will rarely go wrong.

PLAYING HOOKY. I didn't mean to start anything. I was just on my way from the Thursday staff conference to the lab, minding my own business. These new observations on neurotropic calciphylaxis that we had just been discussing seemed to open up fascinating new possibilities for the study of the nervous system and I was feeling good, full of *joie de vivre*. So, as I was passing Miss Johnson's office, I thought I might as well say hello to the old girl. She had been a perfect dear, slaving away at that manuscript of the Mast Cell book, staying overtime to keep one step ahead of me. Finally we had to assign two typists to help her, and I wondered how they were getting along.

"Hello, Miss Johnson, and how are you today?" I said from the door, with that radiant smile of confidence that seems to adorn my countenance only when experiments are going well.

"Hello, Doctor Selye," she replied, but I felt her usually friendly blue eyes fixed upon me in an unseeing stare of horror. She leaned forward, placing both hands palms down on the desk in a futile effort to cover everything, papers, typewriter and all with her pudgy arms and ample bosom.

All I wanted to do was to stop at the door for a moment and be sociable, but her singular gesture disturbed me. What was cooking? As I walked in, she quickly closed the drawer of her desk, but not quickly enough to prevent my seeing in it a cup of coffee (with the usual rim of lipstick) spilling over a half-chewed apple and Harrap's *Standard French and English Dictionary* (Part II, English–French).

I always knew that Miss Johnson had a very healthy appetite and nibbled at one thing or another all day long, but she is an excellent and hard-working secretary, so who cares? Yet now she was obviously trying to hide her work; writing personal things on office time was not like her at all.

I did not want to ask any embarrassing questions, but this was so unexpected, it intrigued me. I stepped just a little closer and sat down on a chair in front of her desk. She reached nervously for the pages and turned them upside down; then she began to play non-chalantly with the typewriter cover, folding it one way or another first on her lap, then on the desk top until it ended up over the page that was in the typewriter. However, suddenly she thought better of this transparent game and in a second round of equally absent-minded, playful gestures, turned the pages right side up again and removed the cover from the machine. Then, in the midst of a veritable salvo of inconsequential chitchat, she got up and maneuvered herself between me and the incriminating evidence, leaning against the edge of the desk with the broadest part of her generous anatomy, which now acted as a living screen to whatever was behind her.

It was too late. I had already noticed Shakespeare's name on a page and a copy of *Julius Caesar* underneath it; I was sure I had not quoted the Bard in my dictation for the Mast Cell book.

Oh, no, I thought, not Miss Johnson! Miss Johnson, the very image of the conscientious secretary, the understanding friend, on whose absolute reliability I knew I could always depend. She was the one whom I chose to supervise others! Yet, the evidence was conclusive. My dear Miss Johnson was working on some essay for her evening classes in English literature while I was so desperately waiting for my Mast Cell copy! I remembered two lines in that book she was trying to hide: "A friend should bear his friend's infirmities, But Brutus makes mine greater than they are."

Well now, I must not humiliate the poor girl. Besides, the whole scene embarrassed me as much as it did Miss Johnson. I had to find some nice indifferent subject quickly to make her think I hadn't noticed anything.

"I was just going to ask," I heard myself say, "are you satisfied with those two new typists you got to help you with the Mast Cell work? Do you think the three of you will manage without any over-time?" (Oh God! This was the wrong question at this moment. Well, it's too late now.)

"Oh yes, sir," she replied nervously, breaking out in an avalanche of information. "Of course, they don't know the medical terms yet, but they will learn fast. I'm sure they are very anxious to succeed in their new job. Anyway, we only took them on temporarily on a trial. In the beginning, you know, one has to watch them. We mustn't let them pick up bad habits, but they do relieve me of a load of routine . . ."

"Well, I'm glad you like them so far. That's really all I came to find out. I must be running because they are waiting for me in the lab."

There was no point in letting her know I had caught her playing hooky. Perhaps she suspected it anyway. Once in a while it will happen to anyone. Miss Johnson is not so young any more. She leads a lonely existence and one of her great ambitions in life is to get a B.A. in English literature. Probably she was late with some homework needed for tonight. What of it? In any event, I never again caught Miss Johnson in the act of being unfaithful to my Mast Cells. Still, I would never have thought ...

Now, this story is not very well told. I rewrote it twice, but it is still trite. I thought I would just throw it in the wastepaper basket, but then decided against it. This incident really did happen, though I had to change it considerably so as not to embarrass the real Miss Johnson. There is actually no one by that name on my staff; but, unfortunately, there are so many who act like her that it was easy to draw a composite picture from similar real-life incidents. Whenever these events happen, they succeed in upsetting me; so if these Notes are to be honest and complete, the story should not be censored. The reason I am unable to tell it well is that it embarrasses me. Whenever I voluntarily or involuntarily catch someone playing hooky at work, I am upset—probably "offended" would be a better way to put it. I know this is silly; I should not worry about such trivial things, but it is true that I do nevertheless, so the story should be admitted.

As best I can analyze my feelings, I am offended because:

1. If I work hard on my part of a job, it humiliates me to see others take it lightly.

2. I am ashamed of paying any attention to such petty details. I feel indiscreet watching what people do, even when they are supposed to work for me. It seems inelegant and avaricious to force people to produce their money's worth. And yet, it isn't the loss of money but the impudence—perhaps also the fear of such an attitude spreading in the department—that irritates me.

3. I am ashamed to let the reader of these Notes know that such things do happen in my Institute.

4. I feel duped by people who express so much respect for my work by empty words and then sabotage it by lack of interest.

5. Why is it always I who has to notice these things? What do we have a personnel manager for?

I know I should be above these things, but the fact is, I am not.

I am ashamed to admit it—but would be still more ashamed if I were not to admit it.

Oh well, it doesn't matter. This sort of thing doesn't happen so often, and besides, I have my consolations. Today I noticed that, through calciphylaxis, it is possible to induce calcium deposition selectively in the vagus nerves. A great thrill! What mysterious chemical processes could be responsible for the fact that the body can send calcium selectively into these two nerves? Innumerable ideas come to mind; countless new experiments are suggested by this finding. By comparison, Miss Johnson's essay on Shakespeare is of no great consequence, why should I bother about it? ... The annoying fact is that I still do—a little.

Render unto Caesar

Being an incorrigible individualist, the scientist finds it especially difficult to take orders and bow to authority. If he wants to express his originality, he cannot accept willful interference with his research; he cannot work under a director who forces him to investigate problems that he considers unimportant or to use techniques that he distrusts. However, all of us must be pliable enough to adapt ourselves to the social structure which furnishes us with our facilities. It depends upon the philosophy of each individual scientist to what extent he feels justified in making compromises with the political and philosophic principles of the nation, the university, or the donors who provide him with the facilities indispensable for his research. But sooner or later he will have to make some compromises to protect his work.

DEALING WITH THE STATE. If a chemist violently disagrees with the political principles of his country, he will accomplish little by making aggressive speeches against the government. Usually, the chemist proves to be quite ineffectual as a politician, but he will be barred from continuing with his chemistry in which he could have excelled. Too many scientists have spoiled their careers and become unproductive, unhappy misfits because of an uncompromising attitude toward administrative authority or a refusal to accept help from donors with whose philosophy they disagree.

I know that I shall be seriously criticized for my attitude. Even the act of admitting it leaves me wide open to attack for being spineless and unprincipled, I can already hear the usual objection of conformist mediocrity: "What if everybody would take this attitude?" But not everybody does. Nobody should compromise in every respect, as a matter of principle. Bad politics should be attacked by good politicians, by experts who carefully study and fully understand all the issues, by men who make politics their career. But the chemist does not ask the statesman to express an opinion on the way a chemical reaction should be performed; he does not invoke the argument that there would be no chemistry if everyone refused to worry about it.

The problem is admittedly somewhat different in political and philosophic issues. Every citizen feels more competent to assess these than scientific problems. But is he really much more prepared to direct them? Everyone is competent, and need not hesitate to express his own feelings about an opera, a painting or a sculpture, but few could give useful directions to the artist on how to do better. Of course, by their reactions to works of art, the masses can influence the artistic tendencies of a nation. But they will accomplish this in the long run, even without becoming vociferous, pseudo-professional art critics. Similarly, every citizen has a right to say what he thinks and to vote accordingly, but this does not mean that it is his civic duty to neglect his work and become a political agitator, in an unbending struggle against every principle of which he disapproves. There are so few great scientists and artists; they would not serve mankind well by sacrificing their rare gifts merely to become martyrs of lost causes.

Many years ago I had an unforgettable conversation with a scientist in a country run by a ruthless dictator. My colleague asked me whether I thought he should attack the government openly in the newspapers. He felt this was his duty because, being highly respected as one of his country's most distinguished scholars, he knew his opinions would be taken seriously both at home and abroad. He was afraid that it would not be honest for him to keep silent, although he knew that dissension would be the end of his career and only "a drop in the ocean" of the masses opposed to the dictator.

It is not easy for me to admit this, but I advised him to compromise. I told him that, in my opinion, it would be better both for him and for his country if he continued with his important scientific work and retained his academic chair. By remaining in contact with the student masses he could show in many ways what he believed in, and what he condemned. In his influential post, as full professor at a large university, he could help many of the oppressed and quietly disown the oppressors' views without risking the virtual certainty of being silenced.

He did not listen to me and he was silenced. He published a violent manifesto; but the government was not overthrown as a result of it. The dictator was much more shrewd; he did not risk a frontal counterattack against the great, much admired scientist. Instead, the professor was just quietly retired on some pretext quite unrelated to politics. But the scientific work of the great man came to an abrupt end, and he could no longer influence his many students through more subtle ways.

In these important questions everyone has to listen to his own conscience. I have no proof that mine guides me on a true course, but I act according to what it tells me to do. I know that I have little to gain and much to lose by describing these views here, because many will disagree with me. But this is what I think, and by owning up to it I can at least prove that it is not lack of courage that dictates my philosophy. Never having had to work under a tyrant's government, I did not need to devise these principles to justify my own past conduct.

But while I recommend far-reaching compromises, I do not believe that scientists should shirk the duty of discussing science's responsibilities toward society. Here, they, more than anyone else, are competent to judge. Here, they are not just a small group among the countless dilettantes who talk about how to run the country. In this respect, they are the specialists who should have the courage to say what they think, even if they know that their beliefs will shock the masses.

DEALING WITH SPONSORS. The scientist must cope with essentially the same ethical problems in dealing with many of the less transcendent questions of his daily life. His efficiency as an investigator depends upon the cooperation he receives from university authorities, granting agencies and sometimes even from private men of wealth and influence. I have followed the same middle course here as in my attitude toward national and international politics.

Disregarding short study trips, I have worked in three countries (Czechoslovakia, U.S.A., Canada) and four universities (Prague, Johns Hopkins, McGill and Montréal), but I never felt called upon to make a detailed study of the political and philosophic motives that activated the governments and universities whose assistance I accepted. Even now, I have no qualms of conscience about receiving financial aid for our Institute from private donors without investigating how they made their money. I have no reason to believe that they have used unethical means, but even if they had, I do not see why a dollar earned by any means should be disqualified forever from use for a respectable purpose.

The scientist meets much more difficult ethical issues in his daily dealings with his sponsors. Here, it may become very hard for him to remain aloof from worldly motives. Even the worst-paid basic-researcher must have the moral fiber to refuse funds ear-marked for scientifically unimportant problems whose only purpose is to increase the incomes of donor and recipient. Even at the times of my greatest financial need, I have consistently refused to accept consultant fees from pharmaceutical companies who wanted me to do routine tests for them. Such research would have distracted my attention from more important though less remunerative tasks, and besides, being personally in the pay of any one company would undermine the confidence of others that might subsidize more significant investigations by grants given to our Institute.

Even in his dealings with the most reputable sponsors, a scientist may run into serious difficulties. The laboratory man who becomes impatient about inefficient bureaucratic techniques should keep in mind how difficult it is to organize the just and efficient distribution of large sums of money. The donors themselves cannot be asked to acquire the technical competence required to judge every kind of project on its merit; they must rely upon scientific consultants— and to choose these is no easy matter.

DEALING WITH SCIENTIFIC CONSULTANTS OF SPONSORS. I must admit to having become very irritated at times about the techniques used in appraising applications for research grants. I will never forget one particular occasion when we applied for a large grant in support of our research on stress, from one of the agencies I respect most highly for its competence and understanding. But, on this particular occasion, I was submitted to the most humiliating experience of my career; the date has come to be known in the Institute as "the Day of the Court-martial."

A so-called site visit was organized. About half a dozen representatives of the agency and their scientific consultants came to inspect our Institute, and we were looking forward to this opportunity of discussing our problems and plans with understanding friends who offered help. We did not think of the fact that the consultants were themselves busy research men and clinicians who greatly resented having to interrupt their own work to make this trip to Montreal. They accepted only out of a sense of moral duty because "What if everybody refused." They manifestly wanted to be correct, but they just could not overcome their feeling of resentment for having to perform such tasks.

I was first interrogated by a group of coldly polite but un-smiling men, in a tone which gave me the impression of being suspected of some serious crime. Then, in my absence, the dean was asked whether I would not be likely to commit this or that misdeed. He told me later that he said, "No," but he wondered just what made them ask these questions.

Then, one after the other, my graduate students were called before the committee for interrogation in closed session. I do not know exactly what questions were asked and how, but when the boys came out, they looked pale and seriously shaken. They reported that, in order to put them at ease, they were assured that nothing they would say would be repeated to me, but, "just between us," is it not true that I asked them to do the most menial routine tasks in disregard of their interests as students? The postgraduates assured the committee that I didn't—in fact, that I did not even have any motive to do this, since we had enough technicians to do whatever routine work I might need. Then the students were asked whether they did not resent my emphasis upon simple methods. Would they not prefer to have more technical courses which would initiate them in the procedures of complex physico-chemical techniques, crystal-lography, the electron microscope, and the like? The reply was, "No." Such technical instruction, if desired, was available in other depart-ments of the University; from me, they wanted to learn the art of observation and interpretation of biologic phenomena. They insisted that my constant association with them in the lab was much more useful than formal courses. But they felt that their answers were distrusted, and they were embarrassed by the leading questions about their chief in his absence.

Finally, the committee came to see me. Their faces were stern and noncommittal. In carefully measured terms they emphasized only that they would have to deliberate further at their hotel before reaching a conclusion. I wondered why this had to be said, since I naturally had not asked for any immediate assurances.

The anticlimax to this story is that we did receive a substantial grant, but the experience, nevertheless, was a shattering one for all of us. Is there a moral to this story? I really do not know. At the time I felt very humiliated and the experience left a scar which was not healed even by the subsequent award of the grant. But what could they have done? I am not sure that I could have done better had I been on such a committee. The responsibility for distributing substantial sums is a serious one. Bad judgment may lead to scandalous results. I can think of no better way to find out something about the director of research than to ask his associates and his dean about him. In order to obtain frank opinions, it is essential to do this in the applicant's absence. And yet, there seems to be something wrong with this system. Would it not be preferable to judge a scientist only on the basis of his past accomplishments? I think so, but it would be difficult to prove my point without comparative tests.

In any event, there would be no point in rebelling against existing systems. The best we can do is to "Render unto Caesar the things that are Caesar's," objectively voicing our doubts about his ways, without irritation and petulance, but also without fear. That is what I have tried to do here, although I know that the spirit of my remarks may be misunderstood, and that this could hurt my chances in future demands for assistance. But, in this respect, I feel that it is up to us, the scientists, to say clearly what we think. Here, we are the specialists, and the issue cannot be decided by a majority vote of the masses, nor by executive decisions of law makers and donors.

7. How to Work

A Fable

Once upon a time, there was a college girl who really wanted to cook; not just scrambled eggs and lamb chops and soup out of cans, but dishes that take originality and imagination—*cuisine à la Savarin*.

Yet, however hard she tried, she just couldn't cook.

"Crying won't do me any good," she sobbed. "I must apply reason. I must cook by the book." So, she studied all the great cookery books. But still she couldn't cook.

Did she get discouraged? No! She only loved cooking all the more. "I'm an intelligent college girl," she said to herself, "I can think this out." So she went and bought all the best precision-balances, thermometers and stop-clocks—this made her very happy and sure of herself. "After all," she thought, "everything in cooking is subject to the laws of logic, chemistry and physics, and when it comes to these, I am much better equipped than Savarin ever was."

But now, with all this precision, it took her so long to think and measure that she never did get to the actual cooking.

Well, finally, the poor girl became so frustrated that she gave up cooking and got married instead. And then when she looked at her first-born child, she wondered how she had ever managed to make such a complex and wonderful creature—without ever having used any books or scientific instruments at all.

The moral of this story is not to throw away your books and instruments, but to realize their limitations. They do help now and then to clear things up a little, but creative ability is far too complex to be broken down into its elements and directed at will. It would take an eternity to work under the constant guidance of a step-by-step intellectual and instrument control. Man's life span is too short for this. Perhaps that is why perfect creative ability and infallibility are dependent on immortality.

GENERALITIES

The following pages will deal with those aspects of a scientist's work most closely related to research: laboratory techniques and procedures for the coordination of knowledge. The object is certainly not to prepare a complete procedure manual, but merely to offer some quite informal, rather personal comments on scientific methodology, on the basis of experience with techniques developed by my associates and myself. I shall have nothing to say about complex laboratory machinery or involved procedures for the mathematical expression and epistemologic interpretation of data—not because I doubt their merit, but because I have no experience with them. Besides, I am quite convinced that even nowadays many fundamental discoveries can be made by the simple observation of natural phenomena which is less subject to instrument error and faulty interpretation.

Of course, whenever possible, the changes we want to observe are induced experimentally, but even this is not always necessary. Experimental research as we know it today is a newcomer to science. It was virtually unknown until the Renaissance, and yet man succeeded in penetrating deeply into many secrets of Nature by profiting from the innumerable experiments she constantly performs without any encouragement on our part. This is how we have learned the first rudiments of astronomy; this was the basis of descriptive biology, and it is this kind of unintentional, chance experiment the physician uses whenever he first observes a spontaneous disease, a sign of aging or an accidental cure. In discovery, unconscious intuition precedes consciously guided logic (p. 266); in scientific research, the observation of spontaneous phenomena usually comes before the designed experiment. We have already dealt with observation (p. 77); now let us turn to the practical aspects of experimentation.

THE NATURAL SIZE OF A DEPARTMENT. Research is a highly personal activity; hence, a lab should reflect the personality of its chief and few general rules can be laid down concerning its organization. In any event, the ideal is not to get as many coworkers, machines, and labs as possible but to obtain the type of personnel and facilities really needed. The requirements may be very few in the case of a histochemist who, because he prefers to do all the technical work himself rather than direct others, might want no more than one lab and a cleaner. Conversely, a correlator who, in addition, likes to teach may be able and willing to direct a huge institution.

Owing to a misplaced sense of acquisitiveness and the erroneous belief that success is proportional to facilities, many scientists spend most of their time trying to increase their department's budget, personnel and floor space. This results inevitably in their becoming mere administrators. Others can never give their best because, out of shyness or a lack of worldiness, they do not even try to fight for badly needed facilities.

There is a "natural size" for any department, determined by the inclinations and capacities of its director. Under perfect conditions, an investigator should have as big a lab as he can and wants to direct—but to direct as a scientist, not as an administrator. A department should be split into independent units as soon as it develops to a point where the leaders of these units are, in fact, scientifically independent and the position of the over-all director becomes nominal. Thereafter, it may still be useful to retain a general administrator who looks after the material interests of the group, but there is no longer any need, or even justification, for the subordination of the members' scientific work to one chief.

THE BLUEPRINT FOR WORK. Those faced with the task of creating a new university or research institute, habitually tend to underrate the importance of the human element in their future organization; it is tempting to think primarily of budgets, real estate and equipment. Naturally, the physical facilities are indispensable, but they can serve no purpose unless fully adjusted to the needs of those who will use them. The most decisive and valuable, though quite intangible, asset of any institution is its *idea* as conceived in the minds of those who run it. This plan, if good, acts as a magnet for the material assets needed to make it function. An inspiring group of eminent scientists quite easily attracts competent assistants, promising students and grants even to the most modest building. On the other hand, many an ill-conceived palace of learning makes a good showpiece for tourists, but its intellectual vacuity remains a permanent monument to the incompetence of its founders.

The paramount importance of the plan, the blueprint, as compared with the materials necessary for its execution, can be illustrated by many examples. Man himself, mind and body, is built from the code inscribed in two minute germ cells which attract all the materials required.

Most of our century-old library went up in flames last year, yet only a small portion of it was really lost. Its basis, the system, survived in the brains of its staff, and proof of its usefulness in the minds of its former users. After the fire, my main preoccupation was to save these assets before we lost the plan, the concept. Much to my delight, innumerable donations of money, books, journals, and reprints came in soon enough so that we were able to retain the people who were competent to reconstruct the collection. No amount of tangible assistance could have accomplished this reconstruction without those in whose memories all the necessary procedures were safely carried through the tragedy.

The same principle was exemplified on a national level by the recent history of Germany. During the war, the material assets of the nation were virtually annihilated, but the plans and traditions of science, art, industry, and commerce survived through the conflagration. That is why, in the short span of twenty years, Germany has rebuilt a civilization which many an underdeveloped nation could not equal in the course of centuries. In the same manner, a modern state has risen out of the wastelands of Israel through the plans of a civilization, transplanted to its undeveloped soil in the minds of its recent immigrants.

The blueprint—indeed, the idea of the blueprint—is what really counts. In itself, it can do nothing; but all values, material or spiritual, depend upon it. That is why, in science, as in any other activity, we must pay special attention to methodology, the planning and organization of our work.

SPECIALIZATION. In discussing methodology, our first concern is the desirable degree of specialization. Here again, as in discussing "Simplicity vs. Complexity" in general (p. 94), we are up against the perennial problem of balancing the breadth against the depth of our work; the more we specialize in one respect, the smaller the field we can cover. As Alan C. Burton said in his presidential address to the American Physiological Society in 1957: "Over the physiological chemist, and the biophysicist, must stand the integrative physiologist who looks at the whole and the connections between its various parts, and who can utilize the knowledge of mechanisms gained by the biophysicist and biochemist to complete his own study of biological organization. . . ." We need correlators who have at least a superficial knowledge of many subjects so that they can scan the horizons, detect connections, and sketch the broad outlines, the general maps of wide areas; but we also need specialists who, even at the cost of losing perspective, have learned the techniques with which to dig deep at individual points.

The balance between breadth and depth of knowledge must be adjusted to individual talents and predilections; every intermediate has its justification, we must beware only of the extremes. *Over-specialization* leads to a point of no return: extreme preoccupation with techniques breeds only more techniques, philosophy of science more philosophy, statistics more statistics. This "running to seed" usually justifies itself with the last argument of failure: the hope that the next generation will be able to accomplish something with the techniques of work or thought that we have developed. Excused by the precept of sacrificing ourselves for our successors, we pass the buck to the next generation, forgetting that methods of thought or action can be fruitfully developed only if constantly checked by their applicability and perfected by adjustment to use. The pure theorist, like the pure gadgeteer, rarely contributes much of value.

In selecting our particular field and techniques, we must keep in mind that broad outlines are best seen from a distance; close inspection reveals only details which may be trivial aspects of the whole picture. The microscope can see things the naked eye cannot, but the reverse is equally true. You certainly would not find out what a dog looks like by assiduously examining its every separate part under the electron microscope. If it were a matter of one or the other, I would rather know what one can learn about a dog by just playing with it during moments of leisure. Still, tastes differ and our techniques should be adapted accordingly.

You can copy details accurately by painstaking, slow work, but you can draw an elegant curve more easily with one quick flourish. Classic art, like photography, insists on detail; while modern art tries to symbolize by abstraction from detail, thereby emphasizing the essentials. Both these schools have a place in science. The fashion of the day undoubtedly gives preference to investigation in depth, with instruments and calculation of ever-increasing precision. This approach is very efficacious, but it is not the only one; we may lose sight of the principal issues in our frantic chase after detail. Who wants to explore the intricate physicochemical composition of a chair? We just want to sit in it comfortably. Its gross structure is what counts. The problem is often the same in science.

Nowadays, extreme one-sidedness in complex technology interferes too often with the learning of the simplest techniques needed to scan the surface. An eminent biochemist came to see us the other day. He was an expert in the complex enzymatic reactions involved in the production of adrenal corticoids, but complained that no one in his laboratory knew how to adrenalectomize a rat. In the course of conversation, it turned out also that he had no idea of how to give an intravenous injection!

Next day we were visited by a distinguished morphologist, one of the greatest authorities on the histology of the parathyroids, who wished he had someone who could perform blood-calcium determinations. Of course, all these experts could easily learn the required simple methods which are usually performed by junior technicians, but the fact is that they don't. As they get older, they develop a block against even trying to learn anything about the most primitive manipulations outside their own accustomed methodology.

There is a crying need for *general practitioners of medical research* who have acquired at least the rudiments of many varied techniques (histology, biochemistry, surgery, instrument making, documentation, statistics) and have thereby overcome the fear of the unfamiliar. Even if their knowledge in any one field remains superficial, they will not be stopped by the need for a simple histologic or biochemical examination, a primitive surgical intervention, or the necessity of manufacturing some rudimentary tool.

The situation is very much the same when a scientist, who knows only his native tongue, is faced with the task of reading an important foreign publication. He will merely shrug his shoulders and laugh (I don't know why he will laugh instead of cry, but he will laugh), and since a good translation of highly technical material is difficult to come by, he will just do without it. By contrast, a scientist with even the most superficial reading knowledge of foreign languages loses this fear, and, although he may have to use a dictionary, he will translate an indispensable publication and not be blocked by such a minor hurdle. Indeed, a man who has learned to get along in two or three languages, will more readily learn yet another, chiefly because he is no longer bewildered by the very idea of speaking a foreign tongue.

Underspecialization is just as bad as its opposite. I certainly would not recommend dilettante dabbling with an excessive number of varied skills, merely because of a habitual underestimation of the difficulties and the time involved in thorough work. The temptation must be overcome to do "quickies" (projects which can be solved rapidly) without any over-all plan, just because they are "quickies."

LABORATORY TECHNIQUES

General Considerations

Technology is the application of scientific knowledge to practical purposes, that is, applied science; but it is also the operational approach to the acquisition of additional basic scientific knowledge.

Choice of experimental animals. One of the first considerations in experimental medicine is the selection of the animal species on which the work is to be done. The small laboratory rodents (mouse, rat, guinea pig) are most commonly used, especially for large-scale experimentation, because they are comparatively inexpensive, easy to maintain and commercially available in large numbers from various inbred or even genetically pure strains.

Certain species have special advantages for certain types of experiments: the rabbit is especially suited for studies on arteriosclerosis because of its high degree of susceptibility to this disease. As a result of their great blood volume, horses lend themselves well to mass production of immune serums. The rat is singularly resistant to infection. This is a disadvantage in bacteriologic work, but an advantage in experimental surgery where it obviates the necessity for absolute sterility. The guinea pig is extremely susceptible to scurvy while the rat, which makes its own vitamin C, does not develop this disease even on vitamin-free diets. Most experiments on central nervous activities are best performed on monkeys and apes because of their highly developed brain.

Some species possess advantageous anatomic peculiarities: My teacher, Biedl, succeeded in showing the indispensability of the adrenal cortex for life by using certain types of fishes in which this is an organ completely separate from the medulla. In these—unlike other species—the cortex can be removed selectively without damaging the medulla.

These few examples suffice to show that the choice of species depends upon the kind of experiment we want to perform. No species is the best for all purposes, but there are a few general rules. Whenever you discover a biologic phenomenon in one species, check it in several others to see whether the observation is generalizable; besides, another species may lend itself even better to further work along the same lines. Usually, it will also pay to verify whether or not sex, age, pregnancy, lactation, or hibernation affect the outcome.

Unnatural conditions of experimentation. When Roux first wanted to show that diphtheria bacilli can produce a poison, he injected moderate amounts of germ-free, diphtheria culture broths into rabbits and guinea pigs, but none of the animals showed any sign of damage. Finally, in desperation, he injected 35 cubic centimeters (cc.) of the broth subcutaneously into a small guinea pig. This time he did obtain symptoms of diphtheria and the animal died, but the experiment was considered perfectly foolish because 35 cc. of the broth corresponds to about 10 per cent of the body weight of a guinea pig. Yet, it was this highly "unnatural" first experiment that permitted the concentration of the diphtheria poison to a point where, as DeKruif [27] puts it, "One ounce of that purified stuff was enough to kill 600,000 guinea pigs—or 75,000 large dogs!"

It happens very often that the initial experiment, which shows the way, appears too artificial to have any real significance. As far as possible, experimentation should be performed under conditions close to those that occur in normal life, or at least in disease; but this is not always necessary, or even possible, especially in the initial stages of an investigation, when we are still probing for optimum work conditions. Unfortunately, unnatural conditions of experimentation lend themselves especially well to the display of sarcastic wit, and many a promising investigation has been nipped in the bud by ridiculing calculations of the kind made about Roux's experiment. Even the most mutilating operations are not nearly as unnatural as work on isolated organs or cells in which not only one or the other part is removed, but the whole animal except for the part under study. Yet, such "in vitro" work has furnished much fundamental information.

Personally, I am a fervent proponent of experimentation under the most natural circumstances; indeed, if possible, I like to study entire physiologic phenomena (inflammation, adaptation syndrome, calciphylaxis) or models of disease, rather than their individual components (changes in single structural or chemical elements). But no investigation should be disqualified merely on the grounds that it was performed under "unnatural conditions." Besides, what are unnatural conditions? Total pancreatectomy is a very "unnatural" way of producing diabetes; yet it came sufficiently close to the spontaneously occurring disease to permit the discovery of insulin. What does it matter that we had to give mineralocorticoids in enormous doses to show that they can cause cardiovascular and renal lesions? Before we had learned about the "conditioning factors" that increase the disease-producing effects of these hormones, there was no other way to reveal such actions; indeed, we could not even have devised the experimental arrangements that led to the discovery of the conditioning factors themselves.

Apparatus. Little need be added to what has already been said in another connection about tools (p. 96). The gadgeteer, who comes to use the lab instead of having an amateur workshop in his basement, may be a good instrument maker, but he hardly contributes much to science unless his tools are really needed. A certain amount of manual dexterity is a great asset. A surgeon should be able to modify an instrument to suit his needs; a chemist should learn to work with glass; but this kind of activity can easily become an aim in itself, a mere pastime, an excuse for intellectual torpidity. I often find it useful to make simple gadgets for lab work myself—but before embarking on any extensive project of instrument construction, it is well to ask two questions: (1) Isn't the desired gadget (or one just as good) in mass production already, although perhaps for an entirely different purpose? (2) Wouldn't it be simpler to have a professional instrument maker do the job from a sketch?

For example, some years ago I became interested in studying the laws of growth by forcing tissues to grow into subcutaneously implanted molds, or "tissue scaffoldings." It turned out that if straight, Y-shaped or X-shaped, open pyrex tubes are implanted subcutaneously in the rat, the adjacent connective tissue grows into them forming, respectively, straight, Y-shaped or X-shaped, perfectly vascularized living cords of connective tissue. By merely changing the shapes of these tissue scaffoldings, it was even possible to induce the formation of fat, bone, bone marrow, cartilage or cancer cells. At first, I made a few basic patterns of such tissue scaffoldings out of glass or plastic myself. But later, when I wanted to try more complicated shapes and needed considerable numbers of such objects for large-scale experimentation, this was no longer convenient. It became easier to have them made to order by professional glass blowers, or to use commercially available objects that had the desired shape, although they were not sold with my special problem in view (e.g., coils, segments of ping-pong balls, thimbles). In this study, my requirements were rather modest, but, with the flourishing gadgetry of today, it is well worth looking through some catalogues to see whether any of the available devices could not be adapted to our purpose before embarking on a time-consuming project of instrument construction.

Surgical Techniques

Experimental surgery comes very close to gadgeteering except that, here, it is living tissues that have to be molded or cut to order. The manual dexterity, the sense of tissue texture and shape needed for the two types of work, are very similar. Whenever applicable, I like to use surgical techniques because they can sever or make connections and remove or transplant functioning organs in a very clean-cut way. Thereby, they offer an excellent chance for devising really crucial experiments. Many surgical problems are mainly mechanical, in that we must find ways to get at an organ in order to destroy or modify it with the minimum of injury to adjacent tissues. Often, however, the solutions are to be found in entirely new formulations of the questions themselves, and success depends much more upon freshness of aspect than upon mechanical skill. Let us illustrate:

The "granuloma pouch." In our studies on the effect of stress and stress hormones upon inflammation, we badly needed some quantitative and reliable technique for the analysis of the inflammatory process itself. Usually, inflammation is produced for such studies in animals by rubbing some irritating material on the skin, instilling it into the eyes, or injecting it subcutaneously. But under these conditions, the causative irritant (microbes, chemicals) becomes intimately intermixed with the fluid (exudate) and cellular (granuloma) parts of the inflammatory tissue itself; furthermore, the outlines of the whole focus (abscess or boil) are irregular and unpredictable, so that a quantitative analysis of the constituents is virtually impossible. What we really needed was an experimental model of inflammation, readily reproducible in animals and possessing the following features:

1. The model must not permit the causative irritant to escape; otherwise it would be impossible to establish the quantitative relationships between irritant and response.

2. It must have a predictable, regular shape and size, so that it may be accurately measured.

3. The two major components of inflammation, the cellular barricade and the inflammatory fluid, must not be intermixed (as are the solid and fluid parts of a wet sponge), so that they may be separately measured.

4. The wall must form a sac of even thickness, so that its functional value as a barrier may be measured (for example, by injecting microbes or corrosive chemicals into the cavity and determining how much the pouch wall can stand before it perforates).

This was quite an order, and I spent many years unsuccessfully trying to devise such a test. I always felt that some kind of mold could do it: for instance, a glass bead or a small ball of metal which would force connective tissue to take on a regular, spherical shape. But it would have to be a very bland and elastic foreign body and, indeed, one which would eventually disappear, so as to leave a cavity for fluid accumulation. All the molds I tried were hard, and caused the surrounding skin to perforate wherever the rat pressed against it; besides, there still remained the problem of removing the mold after the barricade had formed. The idea of such a test was intriguing, but it seemed quite impractical until a lucky accident finally showed the way.

In patients suffering from consumption, it is often useful to inject air (or some other gas) into the chest cavity, so as to collapse a diseased lung and give it a rest to promote healing. Since, on the other hand, any kind of stress is particularly bad for tuberculous patients, I was interested in finding out exactly how stressful the air injection itself would be. To determine this, I injected air into the chest cavity in rats, with the intention of later measuring their adrenal response as a stress indicator. While I was doing this, a group of visiting Brazilian physicians were shown into my lab. As I turned to greet them, my needle slipped out of the rat's chest cavity and all the air went under the skin; there, it formed a perfectly regular, roughly egg-shaped, connective-tissue sac. Why not use air as a mold with which to force connective tissue to form a sac of predictable size and shape? Air is very elastic, and being gradually absorbed, it need not be removed to permit fluid accumulation in the pouch. I deliberately made such air-sacs and injected some irritant (usually croton oil) into the cavity, so as to transform the connective-tissue lining into an inflammatory barricade.

This proved to be a very practical procedure: the lining formed a granuloma pouch and the cavity filled up with inflammatory fluid. After the rat was sacrificed, this fluid could be measured accurately by aspirating it into a graduated syringe, and the connective-tissue barricade could be dissected and weighed separately. In fact, if the rats were shaved, the progress of inflammation could be followed every day by transilluminating the sac with an electric flashlight and measuring the height of the fluid-column. Even function tests for the delimiting value of the barricade could be performed quite easily on this test object by injecting microbes or corrosive chemicals into the cavity of the sac and determining the concentration which can be tolerated without causing perforation.

This "granuloma-pouch test" proved very helpful in the analysis of the effect of stress and stress hormones upon inflammation. It is also used extensively in studies on the biochemistry of inflammatory fluid and the growth of microbes or transplantable cancers in "a living test tube" of connective tissue. It is likewise commonly employed by the pharmaceutical industry for the testing of pro- and anti-inflammatory drugs.

This is what the pouch looks like on a rat

walking about in daylight

or held up straight for transillumination in the dark

The "endocrine kidney." Another surgical problem, which arose in the course of our stress studies, concerned the relationship between the urine-secreting and the blood-pressure-regulating endocrine actions of the kidney. Through the classic investigations of Goldblatt, it was known that, in dogs, compression of the main renal artery can produce hypertension and certain morbid changes in the cardiovascular system, quite similar to those that we had produced (also in combination with hypertension) by an excess of mineralocorticoid hormones. The rise in blood pressure, induced by compression of the renal artery, was ascribed to the increased production of some hormonal substance by the kidney. However, the operation also caused a variable, though never complete, disturbance in urine formation; hence, it was impossible to determine whether the hypertension was due to interference with the endocrine or the urine-producing functions of the kidney.

What we wanted was a technique which would abolish only one of these two main renal functions. But how could this be accomplished? If you tie the duct, urine secretion ceases, but the whole kidney is eventually destroyed by the pressure of the accumulating fluid. If you tie the artery completely, the kidney also dies, and if you tie it partially, as Goldblatt did, both kidney functions are altered.

One possibility that occurred to us was to tie off the renal artery partially to a point where the pressure in the kidney would no longer be sufficient for urine secretion (which largely depends on blood pressure), but would still be adequate for hormone secretion (which would presumably be increased when pressure was diminished). However, to complicate things, we had to accomplish all of this in rats (suitable for large-scale experimentation) in which the smallness of the renal artery makes such delicate operations particularly difficult.

While wondering about these points during dissection of a rat we noted that, in this species, the two renal arteries arise from the aorta at some distance from each other. Between the two, there is a sufficiently long piece of aorta on which to perform a well-gauged degree of constriction. A clamp placed here would diminish the pressure in the left kidney (whose artery arises at a relatively low level), while the right kidney would continue to secrete urine and prevent death from uremia.

We had to find some way to constrict the aorta consistently to the same degree. In the rat, even this main vessel is rather narrow for such fine manipulations, but the difficulty was circumvented with the aid of a simple piece of wire (the stile of a hypodermic injection needle). One end of it was curved back so that it could easily be held between two fingers; then it was placed on the anterior surface of the aorta, parallel to its main axis, between the two renal arteries. After this, a nylon thread, which neither shrinks nor swells, was passed around aorta and wire, embracing both. This loop, tied firmly, stopped the circulation. Now, we only had to remove the wire to establish a bore corresponding accurately to the caliber of our stile. This solved the problem of obtaining an exactly reproducible degree of constriction but, of course, this was not necessarily the desired degree. How could we decrease the pressure in the left kidney just enough to stop urine secretion without damaging the organ? At first, we thought we would have to adjust the aorta ligature in each rat while measuring the pressure in the renal vessels, but this would have been technically quite impossible.

Fortunately, a simple trick helped us to circumvent the need for measuring the pressure, still being sure of obtaining exactly the desired degree of constriction. We argued that, for a rat of any given size, there must exist a caliber of wire to the size of which the aorta should be constricted to produce the desired effect. So, the only task remaining was to find a wire thickness suitable for any one rat.

This is how we solved our problem: By that time, I had done a good deal of work with the piece of wire used in the initial experiments and had become rather attached to it; so, instead of laboriously trying to find a caliber of wire to suit a given rat, I reversed the problem and did the opposite. Taking rats of various ages, I determined the size of animal which happened to fit my wire.

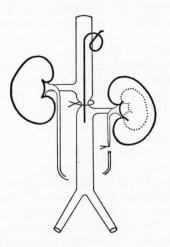

Schematic illustration of "endocrine kidney operation." A loop of thread embraces aorta and curved wire between origins of two renal arteries. Duct of lower kidney is cut. Dotted line shows size to which the organ will shrink as a consequence of endocrine transformation.

It was obvious a priori that, if I took rats of different weights [ranging between, say, 40 and 200 grams (gm.)] and constricted their aortas in all cases to the caliber of my particular wire, there would have to be one size of rat in which the resulting degree of constriction would be just right. The success of the operation should then be readily detectable if we also sectioned and tied off the duct of the left kidney, the one in the low pressure territory. If the pressure fell exactly to the right level, there should be no accumulation of urine in the tied-off stump of the duct, and yet the kidney should not become necrotic. If the pressure did not fall sufficiently, there should be urine accumulation and if it fell too much, there should be renal necrosis.

All these predictions were confirmed by actual observation, and it turned out that rats of about 100–120 gm. body weight just fitted my favorite wire. In larger animals, the constriction was too intense and there were more or less extensive white patches of necrosis in the kidney, while in smaller rats urine continued to be secreted into the tied-off duct stump. The blood pressure rose markedly only in animals with the perfect degree of constriction. In these, the left kidney shrank and was completely transformed into an organ with the histologic structure of a typical, active endocrine gland.

This "endocrine kidney" procedure has been very useful to us in all kinds of investigations on the functional and histologic aspects of renal endocrine activity.

The "suckling reflex." We ran into a rather similar problem in an entirely unrelated field when we became interested in the mechanism of milk secretion. It had long been known that lactation stops if the milk is not removed from the mammary gland. The mother's breast dries up if she loses her baby. So does the udder of a cow if milking is discontinued. Over the years many theories were put forward to explain this phenomenon but none could be supported by objective evidence.

Some physiologists thought that the pressure of the accumulating milk causes atrophy of the breast, just as tying off the pancreatic duct induces "pressure atrophy" of all but the endocrine islets of the pancreas. It will be remembered that Banting used this technique in connection with his work on insulin (p. 48).

Other investigators believed that it is the nervous stimulus of suckling that maintains milk secretion. Of course, when the young are separated from a lactating animal, both the removal of milk and the nervous stimulus of suckling are abolished. Tying off the duct would not help in clarifying this problem, because the young would die of starvation. Theoretically, denervation of the gland would be the perfect test, but technically this is impossible. The nerves approach the breast through so many pathways that complete denervation would involve extensive trauma and destruction of the whole organ. Instead of trying to improve denervation techniques, a hopeless task, we proceeded as follows:

In one group of lactating rats, we tied off all the milk ducts, while another group acted as foster mothers. During the day, each litter was allowed to be with its own mother. Since the experimental rats gave no milk, we changed the litters during the night so that the young of the foster mothers were placed with the rats that could give no milk and vice versa. Thus, both litters were sufficiently nourished since they had access to milk during twelve hours a day and the stimulus of nursing was constantly maintained in both groups. Indeed, in the experimental animals, the stimulus was excessive, because the baby rats became very hungry and suckled all the more voraciously when they were offered nipples that gave no milk. The trouble was that this intensive suckling caused necrosis of the nipples, already traumatized by the operation.

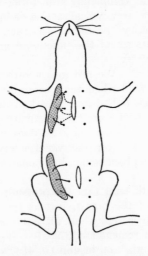

Schematic illustration of the two mid-line incisions through which the ducts (solid lines) of the mammary glands (stippled) can be approached. For simplicity's sake, the glands and ducts are drawn only on one side and the subcutaneous channels of approach (interrupted arrows) are indicated only for one set of three ducts.

To overcome this second complication, and to simplify the rather complex surgical procedure of tying off a dozen ducts (the rat has twelve nipples), we had to modify our technique. Two mid-line incisions were made between sets of six nipples each. Then, we approached the ducts through long subcutaneous channels, so that the incisions lay far from the nipples which now remained quite undamaged and resistant to the vigorous suckling.

This simple trick solved our problem perfectly and the results were quite clear: the stimulus of suckling was in itself sufficient to maintain lactation even if the milk was not removed. As long as the mothers were supplied with vigorous young, milk secretion continued to a point where the glands burst under pressure and the entire subcutaneous region of the belly became infiltrated with enormous amounts of milk. Obviously, here is no "pressure atrophy." The nervous stimulus of suckling suffices to maintain lactation despite pressure.

With this technique, it later became possible to identify the pathways of the "suckling reflex" and to show that the stimulus of nursing not only maintains lactation but also keeps the pituitary and ovary in the functional state necessary for milk secretion. This condition, during which the sexual cycle is suppressed, is now known as the "pseudo-pregnancy of lactation."

The lesson. Perhaps the most striking feature of all three surgical procedures used here as examples is that they circumvented—rather than overcame—certain insurmountable technical difficulties. The lesson learned from these experiences often stood me in good stead later in trying to develop experimental surgical techniques. Whenever I came to the conclusion that a desired operation could not be performed, I did not even try to perfect the techniques. Instead, I tried to approach the problem from an entirely different angle. For example, when I have found it impossible to cut out the medulla of a rat adrenal without damaging the cortex, I did not attempt to improve my dissection instruments or my approach, but adapted the housewife's vacuum-cleaner method. It turned out that the mushy adrenal-medullary tissue can easily be removed by suction through a glass tube connected with a vacuum pump, a technique which also helped me in developing our procedure for hypophysectomy in the rat.

Techniques of Observation

Simple observation is the noblest of all biologic techniques—upon which most of the others depend. Of course, just keeping our eyes open is rarely enough. We have to learn how to look, what to look for, and how to bring the desired target within our visual field. We must acquire the capacity to contemplate a natural phenomenon with complete objectivity and concentrated attention, without being influenced by prejudice or distracted by irrelevancies. And yet, a certain amount of prejudice—or call it the unconscious guiding of attention by experience—is also essential to cut through the fog of irrelevant detail.

As explained elsewhere, the great advantage of observation is that, unlike chemical or physical determinations of individual characteristics, it shows us innumerable features of an object as well as the relationships between them. It presents an entire, natural image rather than a limited number of distinct points. The simpler the method of observation and the less we rely upon magnification or dissection, the broader and the more naturally preserved will be the field we can survey.

The most straightforward approach is to explore natural phenomena unadulterated by preparation and undistorted by instruments. The first and, hence, most fundamental observations were made by looking at stars, plants, animals, or minerals, and merely noting their visible features and behavior. In time, this simple relationship between the observer and the observed has been changed through introduction of techniques which enable us to bring individual features into sharp focus. There came instrumental observation by telescope, microscope, or dissection. And there came experimentation with the artificial creation of conditions which question Nature on the way she would respond to any change. In biology, simple observation—the way of the naturalist, the oldest technique—has been most thoroughly exploited ever since man appeared on this globe. Hence, we are increasingly more dependent on instrumental observation and experimentation for further discovery. Yet I cannot agree with the current view that, by now, all the possibilities of simple instruments and simple experiments have been exhausted. On the contrary. My own experience in the lab leads me to believe that we have barely scratched the surface of what can be discovered with the simplest tools and the simplest experiments—providing that the tools are well handled and the experiments properly designed.

Today many life scientists have learned to use such complicated machinery as the electron microscope, the electrophoresis apparatus or the ultracentrifuge. But few know how to apply to their most common experimental animals those time-honored techniques of clinical observation that every practicing physician uses in examining his patients. Why is it that so many of our young experimental physicians lack even the most rudimentary knowledge of the simple tricks for the proper *physical examination* of small rodents. Let us list a few examples:

I wonder how many biologists know that, with a little experience, it is quite easy to determine by palpation the size and shape of the spleen, kidney and adrenal in a small rat.

The animal will not say "Ah" when we want to examine its oral mucosa. But it will open its mouth and stretch out its tongue for inspection if pressure is applied in the proper way to the angle of the jaw.

Skin lesions are almost invariably overlooked because of the fur, but few laboratories resort routinely to electric clippers.

Laboratory rats are gentle but they bite when in pain or frightened. In this case, they do not like to be picked up "carefully" by fingers delicately encircling their trunk, but they do not mind being lifted up by their strong tail for inspection.

After certain operations, rats may inflict unnecessary pain upon themselves by chewing their wounds, and no bandaging can prevent this. But clipping the incisor tips protects them perfectly—and this intervention represents a very minor injury to rodents whose teeth, unlike those of man, soon regenerate.

An exaggerated tendency for extensor cramps can be detected by the "flick test": a sharp flick with the index finger in the lumbar region is followed by a prolonged extension of the hind limbs.

A slight disturbance in equilibrium (owing to internal ear damage) may not be obvious. But if the rat is held by the tail, it exhibits this defect by a violent circling motion; if placed in water, it is unable to swim as any normal rat will.

In young rats and mice, it is possible to visualize the stomach merely by feeding them milk, whose whiteness shines through the thin abdominal wall. Against this white background even the liver and spleen become easily visible.

Within limits, even auscultation and percussion are possible in most laboratory animals, including the small rodents, and their retina can be inspected by the ophthalmoscope, just as that of man.

A whole book could be written about the techniques for the simple physical examination of laboratory animals. It would be very useful, but no such text has ever been compiled. I wonder why not? It would help many more investigators than yet another treatise on some complex technique employed by only a few specialists.

The same could be said about simple *morphologic techniques.*

An ordinary stereoscopic binocular loupe, worn on your nose like spectacles, permits you to perform autopsies (or operations) on the smallest laboratory mammal with almost the same visibility as on a dog or a man. Without this loupe, in our experiments on calciphylaxis we could never have detected the deposition of white calcium salts in the carotid body (a pin-point sized organ) or along the course of the almost invisible abdominal ramifications of the vagus nerves.

The rat adrenal is a very small, soft, mushy organ and I have never seen anyone inspect its medulla at autopsy. Yet, this can easily be done by splitting the gland in two with a sharp razor blade. Then, even minor structural modifications of the interior (e.g., slight calcium deposits) can readily be seen with the loupe or even with the naked eye.

Some structures are very difficult to expose by artificial means, but they may be naturally "prepared" for inspection in some parts of the body if we just think of looking for the right place. Certain histologic studies on mast cells can best be done on thin spreads of connective tissue in which the blood vessels (surrounded by mast cells) are not cut, as they would be on histologic sections. Mast cells immediately disintegrate when we touch them. To eliminate this complication, a great variety of ingenius embroidery-hoop and plate-like structures have been constructed, over which connective tissue can be spread. In the process, however, many mast cells still disintegrate and the handling of these gadgets is rather tedious. We were unable to overcome these difficulties to our satisfaction until it occurred to us that on the flat skull cap of the rat, the periosteum (the connective-tissue membrane closely investing the bone surface) is spread out already by Nature. This thin membrane can be fixed as a flat sheet for histologic study without ever touching it.

All these are exceedingly simple techniques which a ten-year-old child can learn with ease. Yet so few of them are in current use. It is well to think of such elementary tricks before resorting to complex methodology just because it is commonly employed in the study of a given problem.

Pharmacologic Techniques

Pharmacology deals with the action of drugs upon the body. Here we shall use the term "drug" in its widest sense and discuss conjointly the biologic effects of all chemical compounds (including physiologic, toxicologic, and dietetic actions). In any case, pharmacology does not have any techniques of its own; it merely adapts those of other disciplines to its particular problems. For example, bioassay—the most commonly employed pharmacologic technique —is designed to determine the relative effective strength of a substance (vitamin, hormone, artificial drug) by comparing its potency with that of a standard preparation. But the ingredients of a bioassay procedure merely represent a combination of chemical, surgical, morphologic, physiologic, or dietetic techniques. In assaying the tissue concentration of a hormone, for instance, we may first have to extract the substance by chemical means; then inject it into animals surgically deprived of the gland that normally makes such a hormone; and finally establish the presence in the animal of histologic changes characteristic of this particular hormone.

Certain drug actions have to be studied on *isolated tissues* in the test tube if at all possible. But here, again, it is best not to deviate much from natural conditions. It stands to reason that an excised piece of tissue—a muscle, for example—will not react the same way in a test tube as it does in its natural habitat where it is constantly influenced by nervous and blood-borne impulses coming from other parts of the body. It is also well to keep in mind that the efficacy of therapeutic drugs can best be assessed on test objects which most closely imitate the diseases they are supposed to cure. It is convenient to test an antibiotic simply by adding it to a culture of bacteria and, because of its simplicity, this test lends itself well to a general first screening. But the final proof of practical worth will depend upon the antibiotic's ability to fight infection in the experimental animal or, even better, in man.

Curiously, such elementary considerations are often overlooked by the specialists. For example, certain male hormones have been used to *increase the body weight and develop the musculature* of patients convalescing from severe diseases. It turned out that, among all the muscles of small laboratory rodents, the masseters (concerned with mastication) and the levator ani (which raises the anus) are the most sensitive to this muscle-mass increasing effect of the male hormones. Hence, the most popular tests for the selection of clinically usable endocrine preparations were based on their power to develop the musculature related to chewing and defecation! Actually, the very fact that these muscles are so exquisitely sensitive to stimulation by male hormones shows that they are not representative of the skeletal musculature as a whole—and few patients are especially eager to develop athletic prowess in these particular muscle groups.

We have, therefore, designed a bioassay based on the ability of male hormones to increase body weight and to develop the entire skeletal musculature evenly in animals which had lost a great deal of weight as the result of exposure to severe stress. It is true that, in this test, the response of the muscles is not as pronounced as in the earlier ones, but the assay does appear to rest on a more realistic foundation.

Similarly, some twenty-five years ago when we discovered that, in response to stress, the adrenals produce life-maintaining corticoids, a great many bioassays and chemical tests were recommended for the determination of these hormones in the blood and urine of patients under stress. However, it seemed to us that the object was not so much to determine with great accuracy the presence of substances which have some singular biologic effects or produce certain chemical reactions, perhaps quite unrelated to resistance, but rather to *detect anti-stress activity*.

Consequently, we developed the "cold test," in which rats were deprived of their adrenals (to remove the source of all endogenous corticoids) and then exposed to the stress of a refrigerated environment. As we expected, the animals became very sensitive to cold. But their resistance could be restored by extracts of the blood and urine in proportion to the life-maintaining corticoids that these fluids contained. Today, we know just which corticoids are responsible for this function; we possess complex but highly accurate chemical techniques for their identification. Hence, the cold test has become obsolete. Yet, it was this simple assay method which first revealed the increased excretion of life-maintaining corticoids in the urine of animals and patients under stress, and the test played an important role as a reference standard in the subsequent development of the other corticoid estimation procedures.

As far as I am concerned, I have rarely found it advisable to deviate from my preferred path of simplicity in working out pharmacologic techniques. The more complex, the more involved and indirect our methods become, the smaller the field they embrace and the greater the chance of error. In looking over results obtained with highly complicated artificial methods, I cannot help feeling that too many of them are soon rejected because of errors in procedure or interpretation. Why, even our simplest techniques present many hurdles which are not overcome by the specialists who employ them only as first steps in a long and complex method. Let me illustrate the reason for my somewhat unique timidity in this respect by an observation we made in the lab only a few weeks ago.

As stated elsewhere, it is our custom to have every experiment performed in duplicate, by different people, on separate floors of the

Institute. This rule was followed in a recent experiment in which toxic doses of *parathyroid extract* were to be injected into rats to produce soft-tissue calcification. On the seventh floor, a given dose of the extract accomplished this perfectly. In fact, most of the rats died from excessive organ calcification. But the technician on the eighth floor obtained completely negative results. We repeated the experiment three times with exactly the same results; calcification on the seventh floor, none on the eighth floor. The wildest theories were advanced to explain this "regional difference," but none proved to be correct. I pointed out to my assistants that some technical error must have been committed and that the experiment should be repeated in the presence of both the seventh and the eighth floor technicians, so that they might intercompare techniques. This was considered useless (and offensive) because the work had been done by highly competent people on both floors and it involved only ordinary hypodermic injections which even the most inexperienced technician can perform perfectly.

I did not want to insist and allowed myself to be talked into a compromise: the physicians in charge of the seventh and eighth floors respectively would be present, while the technicians of each floor would give the injections. No difference in technique was detected and the results were still the same.

Now, I insisted on repeating the experiment in the presence of both technicians, and the reason for the discrepancy immediately became obvious. The eighth-floor technician used the most careful technique for hypodermic injection: she infiltrated a large subcutaneous area with the hormone extract and then massaged the region to distribute the preparation even better, so that not a drop would be lost by reflux through the injection point. However, this procedure apparently led to such a rapid absorption of the hormone from the large infiltrated surface that most of it was too rapidly eliminated or destroyed to exert a persistent effect upon calcium metabolism. By contrast, on the seventh floor the technician took no particular precautions. She injected the whole dose on one spot where it formed a vesicle which was very slowly absorbed and, hence, caused a much more persistent effect.

It is well known that delayed absorption increases the activity of many hormones; indeed, special absorption-delaying materials are often added for this reason. Now, whenever we inject parathyroid hormone, we insist on always making a circumscribed hypodermic vesicle and our results are consistent on both floors of the Institute —no matter who performs the work.

No great shrewdness is necessary to avoid these simple errors. But the fact is that parathyroid hormone was discovered forty years ago. It was used for the most complicated biochemical and biophysical studies; yet no one had called attention to the enormous difference in the results obtained by varying ways of giving a hypodermic injection. After obtaining totally dissimilar results again and again for such simple reasons, you become a little hesitant to venture too far from techniques which you can personally supervise and control at each point.

Finally, a warning against the current *unnecessary use of gadgets* for simple procedures requiring only a little manual skill. It is significant that, during the last few years, I have come across six scientific publications describing different—and, in some instances, quite complicated—pieces of machinery for the simple procedure of feeding a rat by stomach tube. Actually, you just have to dunk the tube into oil to make it slippery, hold the animal with its head straight, without frightening it, and push. If performed this way, the manipulation takes only a few seconds—or about the time necessary to get any one of the recommended gadgets out of the drawer.

Natural Phenomena and Models of Disease.

I shall use the term *"natural phenomena"* to designate a set of changes that usually occur conjointly in Nature and tends to impress us as a unique reaction form. To this group belong, for example, pregnancy, hibernation, various types of inflammation, anaphylaxis, anaphylactoid reactions, the stress syndrome, and calciphylaxis. By contrast, contraction of a muscle, enlargement of a single cell, or a change in the blood level of one chemical substance represents a more elementary component of vital responses.

Of course, we need techniques both for the study of entire natural phenomena and for the determination of individual target changes: the former give us the picture as a whole; the latter help us to identify its constituent elements. The two methods are equally useful, there is no more reason to brand as shallow those interested in natural phenomena than to criticize investigators of detail for their seemingly limited and narrow-minded pursuits.

We need investigations both in breadth and in depth. No one could study immune reactions on a molecular level unless someone else had first discovered immunity. Yet it is only through investigation in depth that we can come really close to a complete understanding of this natural phenomenon. In practice, most investigators engage in surface and in depth research, but the latter is much more common. It can be planned, while the discovery of entirely new phenomena depends upon intuition.

One of the most useful techniques for basic research in medicine is the *experimental model of a disease.* This is also a complex natural phenomenon in the sense in which we use this term, but, in addition, it simulates a spontaneous malady. Therefore, these models are ideal test objects for potentially curative drugs and for the analysis of disease-producing mechanisms.

In general, experimental medicine develops from the purely static description of structures (gross and microscopic anatomy, chemical composition, physical characteristics), to the study of more complex natural phenomena (inflammation, degeneration, tissue growth or atrophy) and experimental diseases. It stands to reason that, whenever possible, we should study disease on complete disease models. We must not be discouraged by the fact that no model is identical with the original. Whenever our disease models simulate the essential characteristics of spontaneous maladies, they usually provide helpful information, as long as we do not assume that whatever is true of the model must also necessarily hold for the corresponding disease of man. Whenever a new experimental disease model is produced, some critics are sure to point out, knowingly, that in many respects the model differs from the original. This is necessarily so or else it would be the original and not a model. Even the same causative agent does not produce the same lesions in man as in animals. Deficiency of vitamin C, lack of insulin, or infection with tuberculosis bacilli does not produce the same disease manifestations in man, rat and guinea pig. Yet the information derived from all these disease models contributed information valuable for the comprehension and cure of the corresponding diseases of man.

As I look back upon the experimental models of disease that my associates and I have developed, I must admit that critics have questioned every one for not being a perfect model—without realizing that there are no perfect models. A transplantable tumor is not the same as a human cancer. An arthritis, cardiac infarct, blood-vessel lesion, renal or skin disease, produced in animals by any means, can never be expected to be the perfect replica of the corresponding spontaneous human maladies. Yet, such models are the very basis of experimental medicine.

There is a gradual transition between what we have called "natural phenomena" and "disease models." The latter are usually complex combinations of the former. The worst that can be said about a disease model is that it merely represents a natural phenomenon and is not a perfect replica of a disease. But in this type of work the object is to come as close as possible to spontaneous maladies. Even natural phenomena (e.g., anaphylaxis, inflammation) come closer than isolated changes in individual morphologic or chemical elements of the body.

THE DESIGN OF EXPERIMENTS

To start with, we should recall that only development can be guided by a preconceived design. True discovery is an unconsciously directed intuitive process. "If one can tell ahead of time what one's research is going to be, the research problem cannot be very deep and may be said to be almost nonexistent" [A. Schild [61]].

A competently performed task of scientific development evokes such responses as, "Wasn't this well done?" But when faced with true discovery, we are not likely to respond in this way; we merely exclaim, "How in the world did he ever think of that?" Discovery of a novel phenomenon is more valuable than development, because fewer people can find something utterly new than can exploit and develop a new finding by additional exploration in depth.

Whenever a new discovery is made, the crowds are ready with suggestions that this or that technique should now be used, but no one could have advised Fleming to discover penicillin or Columbus to look for America.

Still the techniques of experimental design are extremely important because few discoveries are immediately useful as such. Indeed, most of them are soon forgotten unless their ingredient elements are meticulously analyzed according to a well-conceived plan.

Experimental design consists of *strategy* (the general policies we wish to follow) and *tactics* (the execution of a definitely formulated research plan). Strategy is mainly concerned with the choice of what we consider a subject worthy of our attention; this has been exhaustively discussed from many viewpoints throughout these Notes. Hence, we shall give our full attention here to tactics, the performance of a planable research project.

The subjects to be discussed in the following pages as well as the "Techniques for the Coordination of Knowledge" to be dealt with immediately afterward, are of special concern only to scientists and to prospective scientists. Nevertheless, I intend to present them at some length, because they are eminently suitable for the illustration of the scientific approach to various questions. Besides, they represent an excellent exercise for the analytical mind, and, with some modifications, can be applied to many complex problems in everyday life.

"Divide and Rule"

"Divide ut regnes," the political maxim of Machiavelli, is eminently applicable to the tactics of research although, here, we usually refer to it by the slogan: "Vary one thing at a time." No matter what the subject of research, there must be only one variable, one difference between a control and an experimental group. Even in the most complex experimental project, every group must be matched by its binary, from which it differs in one respect only, just as in every simple equation there can be only one unknown. To accomplish this, we must carefully analyze all observations and define their basic constituents. Unorganized, undivided masses of information only confuse. All our materials—observations and interpretations alike—must first be subdivided into the smallest units that can be individually handled.

Still, in the initial stages it may sometimes be advisable to test the whole before the parts. For example, before reproducing a disease with a pure culture of bacteria, it may be well to attempt transmission with diseased tissue. Before you perform bioassays with individual hormonal fractions prepared from a gland, it may be wise to test the whole crude glandular mass to see whether it has any activity that deserves more detailed exploration. But if the complete raw material is found to be active, eventually the constituents will have to be separated for identification.

The Analogy Principle

The design of experiments is largely inspired by the perception of analogies between the newly observed thing and past experience. Planning usually progresses in four steps:

1. We observe a fact or formulate an idea: for example, we first observe an anaphylactoid reaction with sudden swelling of the lips following treatment with egg white in the rat.

2. We ask: "What do I know that is like this?" We try to think of any other reaction in animal or man that may have something in common with the anaphylactoid reaction, so as to anchor the latter in past experience. It occurs to us that the anaphylactoid reaction resembles certain sudden swellings of the face (Quincke's edema, urticaria) that occur in man; on the other hand, the reaction also has something in common with anaphylaxis. This juxtaposition of the new with comparable past experiences brings out both sim-

ilarities and differences. We notice that the facial swellings of man, unlike the anaphylactoid swelling in the rat, are not caused by egg white injections, and that anaphylaxis (again unlike the anaphylactoid reaction) requires previous sensitization to the eliciting agent.

3. We realize that what we have learned about similar things may hold here. It may be rewarding to explore whether or not agents known to produce or prevent anaphylaxis have a similar effect upon the anaphylactoid reaction.

4. We suspect that what we can learn here may hold for similar things. It may be possible to use the anaphylactoid reaction as an experimental model of disease. In view of the resemblance between this phenomenon and certain maladies of man, whatever we may learn about the production or prevention of the model disease has a certain chance of being applicable to clinical counterparts with analogous characteristics.

The Test Tube Experiment

We have already mentioned the great advantages inherent in trying every experiment first on a test-tube scale. This applies not only literally, as practiced in chemistry, but also figuratively, in that it rarely pays to start immediately with large-scale experimentation on many animals or patients before we have first explored the practical applicability of our procedure by prospecting on small samples. Disregard of this rule because of unwarranted enthusiasm and confidence, has caused so much loss of time, money, and indeed, sometimes life, that it is well worthwhile to stress this important point.

One variant of this principle is applied in what Beveridge[11] calls the "sighting" experiment: Here, dilutions of the solutions to be tested are widely spaced (e.g. hundredfold) and few animals (e.g. two) are used for each dilution. After this rough test, dilutions less widely spaced (e.g. fivefold) are chosen just around the probable end point, and larger groups of animals are used. Thus an accurate result can be obtained with a minimum of animals.

Indeed even before its performance on a test-tube scale, every experiment should first be carefully performed in the mind to probe its potential value. Before embarking on an experiment, always ask yourself two questions:

1. On the basis of past experience, is this plan really likely to be feasible?

2. Even assuming that the experiment works exactly according to plan, will it provide a conclusive answer to my question?

The Work-flow Chart

Inspired by the perception of analogies, experimental research tends to progress along fairly standardized lines that can be outlined in the form of a work-flow chart. The starting point is usually the observation of a fact or idea. This is then analyzed by breaking it down into the smallest recognizable constituents. Often we find that laws which hold for the whole, hold for its parts also (deduction). Finally, we proceed to synthesis, the construction of generalizations. We find that what we have learned about individual details holds for entire classes (induction). Thus we arrive at general laws that help to predict unsuspected relationships.

The whole process can be roughly subdivided into stages. As a rule, the first steps are purely descriptive static observations, in which experimental design plays no important role except, sometimes, indirectly, by providing techniques that bring the object into our field of vision.

A simple example from the history of endocrinology, the discovery of ACTH (the adrenocorticotrophic hormone), will help to illustrate this:

1. The target exists. Discovery of the adrenal (here, a recipient of the stimulus).

2. The agent exists. Discovery of the pituitary substance (here, a source of the stimulus).

3. The target is analyzed. The adrenal consists of a cortex and a medulla.

4. The agent acts upon the target. Injection of a crude pituitary extract causes adrenal enlargement.

5. The agent is analyzed through its action upon the target. The ACTH fraction of the pituitary extract contains all the adrenal-stimulating potency of the crude extract.

6. The agent-target relationship is further clarified. Only one structural detail of

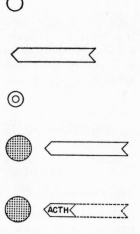

the target is influenced by one component of the agent. The entire adrenal-enlarging effect of ACTH is due to its effect upon the cortex, while the medulla remains uninfluenced.

7. Analogous agents are discovered. By experiments corresponding to steps 1–6, other pituitary hormones are identified, for example, the thyrotrophic hormone (TTH), responsible for the growth of the thyroid and the gonadotrophic hormones (GTH) which stimulate the ovary and testis.

8. Generalizations about the target. For example: Certain histologic details of the adrenal are common to all endocrine glands. The adrenal cortex, like thyroid and the ovary, is regulated through a common center, the pituitary.

9. Generalizations about the agent. For example: All pituitary hormones belong to the chemical group of the polypeptides. The hormones of the pituitary, like those of other endocrines, act in very small quantities upon distant organs.

Of course, this particular sequence, in which static observation is followed by analysis and then by synthesis and generalization, is not always rigidly adhered to. Often, chance leads us to an advanced step, and we must then work backward from there. The chart only attempts to depict the most usual plan for experimental design.

TECHNIQUES FOR THE COORDINATION OF KNOWLEDGE

INDEXING OF SCIENTIFIC DATA

The Problem

One of the most important and urgent tasks of contemporary medicine is to create an index of its contents. If the number of medical publications continues to increase at its present rate, it will soon become impossible for anyone to keep up with current progress, even in a limited field. Yet, the full exploitation of discoveries and the logical design of new experiments must depend upon knowledge of all available facts. The time has come to face this situation as a major scientific problem, characteristic of our century; otherwise, "... science may become bogged down in its own product, inhibited like a colony of bacteria by its own exudations" [Vannevar Bush].

I was first confronted with this problem as a medical student, when I realized the impossibility of taking adequate lecture notes about what had just been said while listening to what was being said. The only way I could cope with this difficulty was by substituting simple, self-explanatory symbols for long technical words or for complex descriptions of procedures. During the subsequent thirty years, this set of symbols has developed into a system of shorthand for medical subjects. It has helped me considerably in taking notes during scientific congresses and in annotating the literature on stress, calciphylaxis, and endocrinology (the principal research subjects in our Institute) for subsequent filing by office personnel, not medically trained. It was this timesaving device that made it possible for us to prepare a detailed subject index for the 500,000 reprints and books that constitute our research library. I am using medicine as an example, but the basic problem is essentially the same in all fields of science. The solutions that we have worked out for handling medical literature would, I believe, be applicable, with suitable modifications, in other disciplines as well.

Virtually every physician and investigator has some sort of personal index in which he can file away interesting publications for future reference. In most cases, these systems consist of abstracts typed on cards, reprints (roughly arranged according to major subjects), and a cross index of the authors. The author index of such files is almost always satisfactory, but the subject divisions are generally quite vague, so that the owner must rely largely on his memory to find any one paper. These personal indexes are not usually based on any set of written rules, and the systems of classification tend to change from time to time, with shifts in the owners' interests. Very few private files that I have seen were considered adequate even by the most inexacting owners.

In order to prepare for a rich harvest of really significant discoveries, we must constantly consolidate our gains by cataloguing them effectively. A great deal of creative thinking by many original minds will be required for the development of a truly satisfactory system, one fully adapted to the needs of all branches of medicine. The bibliographer who systematizes knowledge so that it may serve as a basis for the design of experiments; the physiologist who devises animal experiments to prove that a given body constituent exerts certain desirable actions; the chemist who synthetizes the constituent, and the clinical investigator who finds out how to use it for treatment—all are doing research, equally original and useful to medicine, though their methods are quite dissimilar.

Superficial indexing of the medical literature by main subjects or titles is grossly inadequate. Yet a more detailed cataloguing is impossible without a simple international code. The first problem is not what kind of mechanical device (ordinary file cards, punch cards, electronic brains) we want to use for the retrieval of information, but what basic system of codification, what "language" is best suited to our purpose?

The Decimal System

The most commonly used system, the decimal classification for use by general libraries, was devised by Melvil Dewey. It comprises main classes and subclasses designated by a number composed of three digits with further subdivisions shown by numbers after a decimal point. For example, $500 =$ natural science, $550 =$ geology, $553 =$ economic geology, $553.2 =$ carbon series.

Since there are only ten digits available for the classification of all subjects, it becomes necessary to compose rather long numbers, to add punctuation signs, and to assign different meanings to the same digit, depending upon its position. This makes it impossible to remember the signs, and, of course, the slightest error in coding or decoding totally deprives them of significance.

It has often been emphasized that the decimal system has the advantages of avoiding synonyms and the communication difficulties due to differences in world languages. Huet [43] points out that the number 616.314 represents odontology in America, England, Italy, or Russia, and that even such a specialized tool as a hypodermic syringe has received a decimal designation, namely: 616.314 089.5]032: 611.779 × 7.

But I find it difficult to follow Huet when he says:

"This system is of such simplicity that its formulations are at the same time more concise and clearer than ordinary language, which makes it very mnemonic."

In any event, an accidental transposition of only the first two digits in the number for hypodermic syringe would alter its meaning sufficiently to transfer it into the philosophy section.

One cannot help but agree with the remark of Rider [30] "that the more complex it [the Dewey decimal system] is made, the more its original, easily grasped simplicity becomes lost." On the other hand, in the original system (Huet [43]) which tends to avoid extreme specification by the construction of long numbers, we have only 616.4 to designate the adrenals (easily confused by many Europeans—who write 1 with a hook—with 646.4, which designates the homemaking of lingerie), and the same number (616.4) also means thymus and thyroid. This does not leave much scope for a detailed classification of the entire literature on endocrinology.

On the other hand, all systems of classification based upon code numbers, letters, and punctuation can be adjusted to designate even certain relationships between objects. Some artificial languages of this type have been developed to a point where virtually anything that can be said can also be catalogued. A most impressive example is the procedure described by J. H. Woodger [90] in the *International Encyclopedia of Unified Science.*

ADVANTAGES. Procedures that code information in terms of numbers, letters, and other arbitrarily selected signs (e.g., punctuation) offer the following advantages:

1. *A left-to-right order of precedence.* By this we mean that, in any designation, the main group is listed on the left and consecutive subdivisions are gradually added on the right (according to a rigidly determined order of precedence), as in the earlier example: 500 = natural science, 550 = geology, 553 = economic geology, 553.2 = carbon series. This is an important advantage, compared with the rather haphazard and variable manner in which objects and relationships are described in living language. It lends itself particularly well to the systematic arrangement of information in a card index.

2. *Freedom from confusing synonyms.* Whether we use numbers, letters, or any other kind of standard sign to denote a subject, we will avoid the confusion that normally arises out of the several possible ways of designating the same subject in a living language. In English, it would be equally correct to say corticoids, corticosteroids, adrenocortical hormones, or hormones of the suprarenal cortex when we speak of substances related to cortisol and cortisone. When it comes to complex chemical names or diseases designated by various names and eponyms, the number of possible alternative terms is often even greater. Such synonymous designations do not lend themselves to classification, since they permit the registration of the same topic under any of its many names. When consulting an index, we do not always think of all possible synonyms for a subject; even if

we did, it would involve a great loss of time. All systems based on standard signs avoid this difficulty.

3. *International understandability.* Actually, this is a mere extension of what we have said about freedom from synonyms. A system based on arbitrarily chosen signs transcends language barriers, because it assigns only one meaning to any one sign, even beyond the limits of our native tongue. An arbitrary number- or letter-designation for corticoids eliminates not only all English synonyms, but also all the alternative designations in foreign languages.

DISADVANTAGES. 1. *Arbitrary signs have no mnemonic value.* It is extremely difficult to remember mere combinations of numbers, letters, or signs that have no relationship to the subjects—or to the names of the subjects—to which they refer. One would think that it should be just as easy to associate in our memory a newly encountered subject with its number-letter code as it is to remember it by any other designation. But in practice this is not so. If six people are introduced to us at a party, we can usually manage to remember their names (at least for the duration of the party), but few people would remember their telephone numbers with equal ease. This may find its explanation in "Gestalt psychology." Names can be pronounced as one unit and, hence, are remembered as a single form, while arbitrary number-letter signs have to be spelled out and each part must be remembered separately. This is probably why foreign names that are simple but difficult for us to pronounce are also more difficult to remember.

2. *Extreme complexity of signs for relatively simple subjects.* The "left-to-right order of precedence" makes it obligatory to construct each number-letter type of sign by putting together, from left to right, all the signs of the larger groups of which the subject to be coded forms a part. For instance, in the example we selected from the decimal classification, we had to start with the number for natural science, then add geology, then economic geology, then the carbon series, before we could arrive at a sign for any one compound within this series. Although this is rational, it is extremely inconvenient. The simplest and most common objects must, of necessity, have the longest names, since they represent the finest subdivisions of larger categories. This leads to such fantastic signs as 616.314 089.5]032:611.779 $\times$ 7 for an ordinary hypodermic syringe.

The Symbolic Shorthand System (SSS)

Would it be possible to construct a system that retains all the advantages of a systematic number-letter type of classification and yet remains simple to write and remember? The Symbolic Shorthand System (SSS) presented here appears to fulfill these requirements.

MNEMONIC SYMBOLS. Instead of the usual code designation composed of numbers, letters and other signs which in themselves have no meaning, the SSS uses mnemonic symbols and signs reminiscent of the subjects they denote. For example: Adr = Adrenal, Tr = Thyroid, ↑ = increase, Tr↑ = hyperthyroidism.

All possible subjects and relationships between subjects are first arranged in one dimension, according to a rigidly fixed order of precedence, so they may be typed out on one line of a card (the subject card). For example: the effect of thyroxin (TX) upon the adrenals of the rat would be written: Adr ← TX/Rat.

The statements are then arranged by filing the subject cards one after the other according to the fixed order of precedence.

Since all symbols have only one fixed meaning, the possibility of synonymous designations is eliminated. In coining such symbols we have been guided by the following principles:

1. *Elimination of language barriers.* These symbols transcend language barriers because they are abbreviations derived from internationally understandable Greco-Latin roots and technical terms (Cr = cardiac, R = renal, ACh = acetylcholine).

2. *The most common symbols must be the shortest.*

3. *Use of self-explanatory signs to promote brevity and clarity,* e.g., ↑ = increase; A ← B = action of B on A; B < A = B content in A; A:B = relation of A to B.

ORDER OF PRECEDENCE. The first step in any type of indexing is to establish an order of precedence, the sequence in which topics are to be mentioned. This must depend upon the field of personal interest. For example, an endocrinologist might arbitrarily arrange medical subjects in the following sequence: (1) endocrines, (2) nonendocrine organs, (3) connective-tissue reactions, (4) infections and serologic reactions, (5) tumors, (6) metabolism, and (7) various topics not specifically mentioned above. This is only a rough outline; but it becomes obvious that, if every possible subject has a well-defined "precedence rating," it can be found—even within the most voluminous file—just as easily as any one among the 450,000 entries in

Webster's *New International Dictionary* [88] is located by any reader familiar with the "order of precedence" in the English alphabet. Indeed, just as words not yet coined have a place (and only one place) foreseen for them in the dictionary, so discoveries to be made in the future will fit quite naturally into a well-conceived system for indexing scientific literature, in consonance with its order of precedence.

STATIC OBSERVATIONS.   All possible medical subjects can be subdivided into static and dynamic observations. The former are purely descriptive (e.g., the normal microscopic or chemical composition of an organ), while the latter are concerned with the response of a target to an agent (e.g., the response of cancer to X-rays). The systematic registration of static observations presupposes an order of precedence only while the manifold interactions, often complex, between targets and agents necessitate a more refined lexicographic procedure. Our system employs only self-explanatory symbols and simple abbreviations. These can be rapidly copied into a notebook during a lecture, or on the corner of a printed article we happen to read, and they are much easier to remember than the customary numerical library codes. In our Institute, journals, reprints, books, and abstract cards, thus annotated by my associates or myself, are then handed to office personnel. These employees (though not medically trained) have no difficulty in decoding our shorthand information sufficiently to type it out on small, handy, $1\frac{1}{4}$ by 5-inch index cards, which are then filed (according to order of precedence) in convenient flat drawers. This procedure provides an expandable subject index to the entire bibliographic system.

After a publication has been selected for indexing, it receives an accession number and is filed according to the first author. Here, I should merely like to give a few examples of the type of codification which the medically qualified person must make, himself. It will be seen that, with an adequate symbolic shorthand system, it takes only a minimum of time and effort to jot down the symbols that enable a typist to index the material so that it can always be easily located.

For example, an article published by Smith in 1956 has received the accession number 27001. It contains purely static information concerning the histologic structure of the chromaffin cells in the adrenals of normal human subjects. Only a scientifically qualified person can judge that this is the topic of the paper; hence, he must codify the article by noting on its corner (in handwriting) the re-mark:

Adr / Hi / Chromaffin / Man

This is then clearly typed out on an index card by the bibliographic assistant, as follows:

Adr/Hi/Chromaffin/Man
Smith 27001/56

It is easy to keep in mind such abbreviations as "Adr" and "Hi," because they are reminiscent of adrenals and histology, while the two numerals after the accession number are a convenient indication of the year in which the paper appeared. The reprint itself can then be placed on a shelf in the simple numerical order of its accession num-ber and is henceforth readily located, either through the alphabetic author file (under Smith) or through the subject file (histology of chromaffin cells).

DYNAMIC OBSERVATIONS. To exemplify the annotation of a simple dynamic observation, let us consider an article by Smith and Klein published in 1958 and given the accession number 33001. It deals with microscopic changes obtained in the adrenals of guinea pigs (Gp) by treatment with adrenocorticotrophic hormone (ACTH). Here, we have a *single simple target influenced by a single simple agent*. In our system the target is always mentioned first; hence, the scientist will codify:

Adr ← ACTH/Gp

The typist will write:

Adr ← ACTH/Gp
Smith and Klein 33001/58

Now, take a paper published by Johnson in 1956, that describes the effect of ACTH upon the basal metabolic rate (BMR), the erythrocyte sedimentation rate (ESR), and the temperature (Temp) in normal human beings. Here, we have *several single targets in-*

fluenced by a single simple agent, and the most time-saving way to codify this would be:

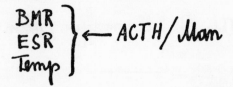

The typist will then have to prepare three subject cards, so that each observation may be individually registered in the particular place foreseen for it, according to the order of precedence in the file drawers. These cards will read:

BMR ← ACTH/Man
        Johnson 31074/56
ESR ← ACTH/Man
        Johnson 31074/56
Temp ← ACTH/Man
        Johnson 31074/56

An example of a *single simple target being influenced by several simple agents* is a paper describing the effect upon the hamster's adrenals of treatment with ACTH, somatotrophic hormone (STH), thyrotrophic hormone (TTH), a gonadotrophic hormone (GTH) mixture [containing both follicle-stimulating hormone (FSH) and luteinizing hormone (LH)], and luteotrophic hormone (LTH). All this is described in the same article, but we are not dealing with a compound treatment; the effect of each hormone was examined on separate groups of hamsters. It would appear that a very extensive description of the paper (at least as much as I have just said about it) would have to be written out by the scientist to permit filing of all this information by a typist. Actually, all the scientist should write is:

Adr ← {
ACTH
STH
TTH
GTH (FSH + LH)
LTH
} / Hamster

To show that actually we are dealing with five separate experiments, the typist will break down the information into five cards, this way:

Adr ← ACTH /Hamster
    Scott 23123/48
Adr ← STH /Hamster
    Scott 23123/48
Adr ← TTH /Hamster
    Scott 23123/48
Adr ← GTH (FSH + LH) /Hamster
    Scott 23123/48
Adr ← LTH /Hamster
    Scott 23123/48

As shown by the example of the gonadotrophic hormone mixture, explanatory remarks can be inserted in parentheses after the symbol of the agent, without changing the precedence order. Of course, the same is true whenever explanations concerning special features of the target are necessary. It is inadvisable to burden our memory by establishing abbreviations for comparatively uncommon topics. For instance, in our file, such common laboratory animals as the rabbit (Rb) or guinea pig (Gp) are represented by abbreviations, but the less commonly used hamster is not.

Frequently, the same paper may deal with several targets as affected by several agents. For instance, in the same communication there may be evidence concerning the effect of heat and of lack of oxygen on both the adrenals and the thyroid of a guinea pig. Here, we have *several single targets affected by several single agents*. Again, the handwritten codification may be quite simple:

$$\left.\begin{array}{c}\text{Adr}\\\text{Tr}\end{array}\right\} \leftarrow \left\{\begin{array}{c}\text{Temp} \uparrow\\O_2 \downarrow\end{array}\right. \Big/ \text{Gp}$$

However, to file the evidence properly—according to the precedence order of each entry—it will require four separate typed cards, like this:

Adr ← Temp↑ /Gp
    Miller 27944/50
Adr ← O_2 ↓/Gp
    Miller 27944/50

$$Tr \leftarrow Temp\uparrow /Gp$$
Miller 27944/50
$$Tr \leftarrow O_2\downarrow /Gp$$
Miller 27944/50

The symbols for thyroid (Tr), for a rise in the surrounding temperature (Temp$\uparrow$), or for hypoxia (O$_2\downarrow$), are all rather self-explanatory.

We may now turn to the case of a *single compound target influenced by a single simple agent*. This is exemplified by a paper that describes the changes in the glucose (Glu) content in ($<$) the blood (B) that occur after treatment with adrenaline (A) in the rabbit (Rb). It may be simply codified:

$$Glu < B \leftarrow A / Rb$$

Data can be typed on a file card in the same manner (except that author, accession number, and year of the publication will also be listed in the usual manner).

Frequently, *both the target and the agent are complex*, for example, when the blood sugar is examined in adrenalectomized (Adr-x) rabbits, as affected by simultaneous treatment with adrenaline and cortisone (CON). This can be codified:

$$Glu < B \leftarrow Adr\text{-}x + A + CON / Rb$$

It should be mentioned, in closing, that this system was primarily devised for the classification of observations; it is not meant to indicate the *direction of the changes* observed. However, if it is desired to register such additional information, this can easily be done with arrows placed just before the target. Thus $\uparrow$Glu $<$ B would indicate hyperglycemia, $\downarrow$Glu $<$ B hypoglycemia and $\uparrow\downarrow$Glu $<$ B an initial rise followed by a drop in the blood sugar level.

Of course, everybody who uses our system modifies it somewhat to fit his personal interests. But the experience of many years has shown that the basic principles of this symbolic shorthand are readily adjusted to the problems and economic means of the medical student, the practicing physician, the specialized research worker, or the well-endowed, large institutional library. In the course of time, the system has undergone only minor modifications, but additions to it are constantly being made. Perhaps better systems can be devised. In any event, it seems to us that *the time has come to develop a special script for medical topics—a set of shorthand symbols which corresponds to the structure formulae and equations of chemistry, the symbols of algebra, and the notes of music.*

SYSTEMATIZATION OF SCIENTIFIC DATA

The Problem

We have seen in the preceding section that even the mere indexing of scientific data is a complex task which requires highly specialized techniques. But the most difficult step in the coordination of knowledge is the systematization of scientific data which, when first observed, appear to offer no basis for classification and, indeed, may give the impression of being quite unrelated to each other. We shall discuss elsewhere (p. 269) the immense importance of classification as the first step in giving structure to a new field of knowledge. Here, we shall limit ourselves to the purely technical aspects of this problem.

What do you do, for instance, if you observe ten new facts which seem to be more or less evidently related to each other? Unbelievable as this may seem, often it is not even quite clear just what the "facts" are that make up our observation, or, to put it more precisely, what terms could describe the finding properly. I seem to have run up against this problem all my life, and it will be easiest to explain it by a few examples of systematization which gave me a particularly hard time.

The Stress Concept

Let us take the ingredients of the stress concept first. Among many others, the following observations were made at different times by different investigators:

1. In rats, removal of the pituitary causes involution of the adrenal cortex.

2. People who have suffered severe skin burns often develop gastric and duodenal ulcers.

3. In children, the thymus (a lymphatic organ, then of unknown function, in the chest) shrivels up during diphtheria infection.

4. Animals and people whose pituitary or adrenal glands are destroyed, become extraordinarily sensitive to cold but, curiously, also to heat.

5. Now, I find that, in rats, intoxication with impure tissue extracts enlarges the adrenal cortex and simultaneously causes thymus atrophy and gastric ulcers.

All these observations can easily be described in simple words—I have just done so. But such a description is not useful. It shows no connection between the various facts nor does it indicate where further research might be illuminating. These and many other apparently unrelated facts became understandable and useful in promoting further research only after they were systematized through a coordinating concept.

We now systematize this information by saying that: 1. Infections, cold, heat and many other agents that create a need for adaptation, act as nonspecific stressors. 2. By causing stress, all these agents induce the pituitary to secrete ACTH which in turn stimulates the adrenal cortex to produce cortisonelike compounds. 3. These corticoids increase nonspecific resistance against various agents, but at the same time they also cause involution of the thymus and predispose to the formation of gastric ulcers.

Of course, it is not false to say that infection with diphtheria causes involution of the thymus, but the incompleteness of this statement is misleading. It is not "very true" in our sense (p. 102). Neither would it be false to say that pressing the button brings the elevator to your floor, but you could not learn much about the underlying mechanism until you had succeeded in systematizing the ingredients of your observation in the altogether different terms of electricity, gravity and so forth. As Bridgman [13] would say, you need a properly worded, complete "operational definition" of the machine.

The Pharmacology of the Steroid Hormones

It had long been known that compounds with essentially the same basic chemical structure, the "steroid nucleus," can have actions which imitate those of the adrenal cortex, the male or the female sex glands. Indeed, we found that some of these steroids stimulate the kidney, and others can even cause anesthesia. At first sight, it seemed that a steroid may possess all of these actions, singly or in any combination. There appeared to be no relationship between these effects and the comparatively minor changes in the steroid nucleus that brought them about.

Yet, systematic studies did bring some order into this apparent chaos. We know now that certain chemical structures are compatible, others incompatible, with a given pharmacologic effect. We have also learned something about the rules that govern the interactions between one and the other pharmacologic effect of the same hormone molecule. The irregularities which thus came to light are known as "pharmaco-chemical" and "pharmaco-pharmacologic" correlations. They deal respectively with the influence of chemical structure upon a pharmacologic activity and of one pharmacologic activity of a compound upon another.

Calciphylaxis

In order to illustrate fully the techniques involved in the systematization of scientific data, I should like to relate, step by step, the evolution of at least one concept. I shall use calciphylaxis as my example, because it demonstrates particularly well the many difficulties encountered when we have to find a natural basis for the classification of numerous definitely established but incompletely understood facts. The choice of this particular example seems appropriate, also, because I have followed the evolution of the calciphylaxis concept at firsthand over a period of some thirty-five years and have seen that, despite ardent interest in the subject, no definite progress could be made by merely accumulating new facts. Then, two or three years ago, the pieces of this jigsaw puzzle suddenly all fell into their natural positions through the systematization of the ingredients of calcification into distinct classes.

Our analysis of the historic development of calciphylaxis will also help us to explain the essence of this phenomenon to which reference is made, in many connections, throughout this book. Finally, now that we have become familiar with our SSS (p. 233), we shall use this symbolic shorthand in our discussion, merely to demonstrate its concise simplicity when applied to complex subjects.

PRELIMINARIES. The importance of soft-tissue calcification has long been known to physicians. Normally, most of the calcium of the human body is in the skeleton associated with phosphate. Under abnormal conditions, however, the bones may become "demineralized," their calcium being transposed into soft tissues which then become hard and inflexible. Here, as almost everywhere in the body, calcium is accompanied by phosphorus, but for the sake of simplicity we shall henceforth speak merely of "calcification" in referring to calcific deposits.

Demineralization of the skeleton normally occurs in old age. It accounts for the brittleness of senile bones that is associated with abnormal calcification in soft tissues such as the arteries (senile arteriosclerosis), the tendons and connective-tissue capsules around joints (calcified shoulder), as well as in the lens of the eye (senile cataract), and the cartilages of the ribs and larynx.

A similar transposition of calcium from the skeleton to the soft tissues occurs in people who suffer from excessive bone destruction by cancer, as well as in some rare diseases known as the "calcinoses," in which the source of the abnormal calcium deposits and the cause of their precipitation are unknown.

The principal endocrine regulators of calcium metabolism are the parathyroids and the chief nutritional factor concerned with calcification is the antirickets or vitamin-D group of compounds, of which dihydrotachysterol (DHT) is a member.

It has also been long known that, even in the absence of any general predisposing elements (bone destruction, or intoxication with parathyroid hormone or with vitamin D), there are some local factors that can induce calcium deposition even in the soft tissues of otherwise healthy individuals. For example, a so-called dystrophic calcification may occur in scars or in severely damaged "dystrophic" tissues.

The facts just mentioned represent a brief inventory of the principal observations concerning the calcification of soft tissues in disease and aging that served as a background for the development of the calciphylaxis concept. This construct began to take form very slowly. It brought innumerable new facts to light but these appeared to be quite unrelated, both to each other and to what was already known.

THE HISTORY OF CALCIPHYLAXIS. Now, let us survey the highlights in the history of calciphylaxis, to see how the knowledge concerning this complex subject has gradually been systematized to a point where, now, selective calcification of various organs can be produced or prevented—at will and predictably—almost anywhere in the body.

The purpose of this survey is to show how a new concept gradually takes on a definite form and structure. At first, all we knew was that certain agents cause tissue calcification, while others do not. Then, it became evident that some drugs, which do not cause calcification by themselves, did so when they were administered in conjunction with other compounds which likewise proved to be inactive in themselves. Even the sequence in which these agents were administered appeared to be of decisive importance. But it was impossible to understand the mechanism of calciphylaxis or to predict the result of a particular treatment until we succeeded in specifying and classifying its ingredient parts. Through the history of this research project, I shall try to show how we arrived at operational definitions of such concepts as direct calcifier, sensitizer (indirect calcifier), direct challenger, indirect challenger, critical period, adjuvant, overchallenge, calciphylaxis, and anacalciphylaxis —all of which are indispensable for planned research in this field.

THE FOURTEEN STEPS. In the evolution of the calciphylaxis construct, we can distinguish fourteen major steps which we shall now consider individually. In each case we shall indicate the basic experimental arrangement (in both English and SSS terms), the observations made and the concepts derived from our findings, thus illustrating the operational basis of each conceptual unit. This form of presentation will also provide us with ample opportunity to comment on the laboratory techniques that had to be developed and the psychologic difficulties in the evaluation of data that had to be overcome to make the work meaningful.

Step 1. (1927–1928) SSS: $\mathbf{Ti(Ca)} \leftarrow \mathbf{Vit\text{-}D}$ *
Intoxication with a crude vitamin-D preparation produces calcification in various tissues.

In 1927, while still a medical student, and just having reached the mature age of twenty, I embarked upon my research career by purchasing, from the janitor of our pathology department, a few elderly rats, which I poisoned with a very impure vitamin-D preparation that had just been placed on the market. Although the vitamin was administered with the food, it caused no local calcification on the lining of the intestinal tract with which it came in direct contact. Instead, it induced massive calcium deposition in various distant organs, particularly the heart, blood vessels, kidneys and lungs.

---

* Most of the SSS signs are self-explanatory. Suffice it to say that the symbols for chemical elements (not for compounds) and for diseases are boldface italics and

Ti	= various tissues
Ct	= cutaneous or skin
Ct-scl	= cutaneous sclerosis or scleroderma
:	= related to
-x	= extirpation of the organ to which this sign is affixed
[]	= square brackets encompass a target and the agent which acts upon it locally
()	= parentheses enclosing remarks which specify the nature of the preceding symbol
Chron	= chronology or chronicity of interventions

A few of my rats happened to be pregnant or lactating and their young responded to the vitamin D (which they received through the milk or placenta) with an altogether different syndrome. In them, the usual soft-tissue calcification was negligible, but multiple spontaneous bone fractures occurred as a consequence of bone absorption. Simultaneously their skin—especially the scalp—lost its elasticity and adhered to subjacent tissues so that the animals became "hidebound." Here again, the effect of vitamin D was indirect: no evidence of damage was seen in the mammary gland or placenta through which the toxic substance had to pass in order to reach the tissues of the offspring. Evidently, vitamin D exerts some indirect toxic and calcifying actions, not by an immediate effect upon the tissues with which it first comes in contact, but only in distant organs—such as the heart, vessels, kidneys, and lungs—that are naturally predisposed. This calcification is nonspecific or nonselective in the sense that it cannot be directed at will to any one particular region of the body.

All these facts were duly (though somewhat haltingly) reported to the "Verein Deutscher Ärzte in Prag," on October 26, 1928, in what happened to be my first lecture.

Since the offspring of the vitamin-D treated mothers also suffered from malnutrition and dehydration, little importance was attached at that time to the skin lesions in comparison with the much more striking skeletal changes.

CONCEPT: Vitamin D is an "indirect calcifier" which produces nonspecific calcinosis in naturally predisposed organs, but not at the site of its application.

Step 2. (1929) SSS: $Ti(Ca) \leftarrow Ptr\uparrow : R$

Generalized tissue calcification can occur in man as a consequence of parathyroid enlargement and the latter is apparently related to spontaneous renal disease.

Soon after finishing my work on the vitamin-D intoxicated rats, the cadaver of a patient was sent to the pathology department where I worked as a demonstrator. By sheer coincidence I was assigned to perform the autopsy and found multiple calcium deposits very similar to those induced experimentally with vitamin D. The patient also had a serious kidney disease, an extensive inflammation of the large intestine, and an enormous enlargement of the parathyroid glands.

At that time, it was already known that the parathyroids are chiefly responsible for calcium metabolism. Hence, I assumed that here an excess of parathyroid hormone must have acted as the vitamin D did in my experimental rats, inducing calcification in certain predisposed organs. The parathyroid enlargement itself was thought to be a possible adaptive hormonal reaction—an attempt to rectify the derangement caused by damage to the organs normally concerned with the absorption and excretion of calcium. This supposition could not be proven at that time, and we had to consider alternative interpretations also. However, our case appeared to shed new light upon nonspecific calcinosis as a consequence of renal disease. Here, calcium deposition was apparently mediated through the parathyroids as a result of a "pathogenic adaptive reaction," a type of derangement we would now call a "disease of adaptation." In other words, tissue calcification could be an undesirable but unavoidable side effect of a necessary adjustment of parathyroid-hormone production to the increased requirements occasioned by the disturbance in calcium metabolism that is, in turn, induced by renal and intestinal disease.

It may be mentioned incidentally, that later I was able to confirm this interpretation experimentally by showing that in rats, removal of the kidneys causes loss of bone calcium under normal conditions but not if the parathyroids are also removed. Evidently, renal failure acts on the bones only through the stimulation of the parathyroids.

CONCEPT: Spontaneous renal and intestinal disease can stimulate the parathyroids to produce an excess of their hormone which in turn suffices to cause nonspecific calcification in man.

Step 3. (1932) SSS: **Ct(Ca) ← Ptr-E**
Cutaneous calcification can be produced by the injection of large amounts of parathyroid extract.

In view of what has just been said, I was naturally interested to see whether I could duplicate the vitamin-D intoxication syndrome using a parathyroid extract which had just been prepared for clinical use at that time. Unfortunately, in Prague I had no funds for research. I managed to save enough from my allowance to buy the rats, and vitamin D was given to me free of charge by its makers. But parathyroid hormone was beyond my means, and in 1928 its manufacturers were unwilling to give it away for the dilettante experimental efforts of a medical student. However, a few years later as a postgraduate student at Johns Hopkins University, I managed to obtain a small sample of parathyroid extract to continue this work. The amount at my disposal would not have been sufficient for the repetition of my experiments on adult animals; hence, I used newborn baby rats.

Parathyroid hormone cannot be administered by mouth so I had to inject it. To my great surprise, I found that the animals developed symmetrical hard skin lesions with cutaneous calcification in the region of the nape of the neck. In their microscopic appearance, these skin lesions resembled the calcifying scleroderma of man, a malady long associated with local calcium deposition in the affected regions.

Scleroderma belongs to the so-called collagen diseases which affect the connective tissue in general and represent a most important group of maladies. Hence, I became very interested in the possible participation of the parathyroids in collagen disease, but I could not imagine why the skin lesions of my rats were limited to symmetrical spots in the neck region. As we shall see, it was not until 1961 that this mystery was solved, thereby furnishing the key to the entire calciphylaxis construct.

CONCEPT: Parathyroid extract produces cutaneous calcification in animals. There may be some relationship between the disease known as calcifying scleroderma and the parathyroid glands.

Step 4. (*1932–1963*) *SSS:* **Ct-scl** ← **Ptr-x**
> *The influence of parathyroid removal upon cutaneous sclerosis (scleroderma) in man.*

Our observations on the production of sclerodermalike lesions with parathyroid extract in animals induced numerous surgeons to remove the parathyroids in an effort to cure scleroderma in man. The results were variable, but, allegedly, sometimes marked improvement did occur, as witnessed by the numerous publications of surgeons who employed this operation for the treatment of clinical scleroderma.

CONCEPT: In man, scleroderma may improve upon removal of the parathyroids.

Step 5. (*1957*) *SSS:* **Ct(Ca)** ← **DHT**
> *Cutaneous calcification can be produced by feeding excessive amounts of the vitamin-D derivative, dihydrotachysterol (DHT).*

It was not until twenty-five years after the production of cutaneous calcinosis by parathyroid extract that we succeeded in reproducing similar sclerodermalike lesions in rats by treatment with a vitamin-D derivative, namely DHT. It will be remembered that we had used small rats for the induction of these lesions with parathyroid extract because of the expense involved in purchasing amounts large enough for adult animals. Later, when various vitamin-D derivatives became available at comparatively low cost, we tried to reproduce cutaneous calcinosis in adult animals, but did not succeed even by the administration of fatal amounts of DHT and other vitamin-D derivatives. Since these latter preparations were inexpensive, there seemed to be no point in using small rats which are more difficult to handle and it did not occur to us that perhaps only baby rats were sensitive to this effect.

However, eventually, we found that even parathyroid extract produces no cutaneous calcinosis in adult rats, and the possible importance of the age factor at last became apparent. It was only then that we decided to feed DHT to newborn rats, and these did, in fact, respond with cutaneous calcinosis, again especially around the head and neck region. Yet the lesions produced either by parathyroid extract or by DHT could not serve as practical models of disease because they were invariably accompanied by high mortality and developed only inconstantly in newborn rats on the scalp and neck—not wherever we wanted to produce them.

CONCEPTS: DHT, which in many respects resembles parathyroid hormone, can also produce cutaneous calcification. There may be some relationship between calcifying scleroderma and the vitamin-D group of compounds.

Step 6. (1957) SSS: $[Ti(Ca) \leftarrow Ta \text{ (hemostat)}] \leftarrow DHT$
Calcification can be induced in various tissues if these are traumatized (with a hemostatic forceps) following feeding of dihydrotachysterol.

The next experiment was rather instructive. It was inspired by a completely irrational hunch which proved to be correct and could have led us to the concept of calciphylaxis, but did not because I failed to evaluate it properly. The hunch was that DHT may sensitize the organism in such a manner that it would then respond to injury with local calcification. To prove this, we fed rats large amounts of DHT and then caused local trauma to arteries or skeletal muscles by pinching them with a hemostatic forceps, such as is used for crushing blood vessels. We also built up pressure on the kidney (due to retention of urine) by tying off its duct. In all these locations, tissue calcification occurred at the site of injury in DHT-pretreated, but not in unpretreated control, rats.

These findings were briefly described, but I attached no particular importance to them because the traumatic injuries were very severe.

Besides, the rats were so heavily overdosed with DHT that they even developed spontaneous calcifications at naturally predisposed sites—although, here, the mineral deposits were never as pronounced or as constant as in the damaged areas.

CONCEPT: Following overdosage with DHT, local trauma can cause calcification in injured tissue.

Step 7. (1961) SSS: [Ct(Ca) ← Ta (epilation)] ← DHT + Chron(C.P.)

> *Cutaneous calcinosis is produced, even under the influence of such a mild trauma as removal of the hair, but only in animals overdosed with dihydrotachysterol, and only during a certain time interval. This necessary chronologic sequence between dihydrotachysterol administration and the epilation represents a "critical period" (C.P.) which must elapse before cutaneous calcification can be induced.*

This work represented a turning point in our studies, since it first called our attention clearly to what we now know as *local calciphylaxis.*

The story behind this experiment is as follows: A group of young adult rats received DHT in connection with some unrelated work on the production of cardiac lesions by sudden intoxication with DHT, phosphates and stress. However, the control animals treated with DHT alone also became very sick, and one of my coworkers called my attention to the fact that they were beginning to lose their fur as severely damaged rats often do. Upon close inspection I noticed, however, that the loss of hair was limited to the head and neck area where the underlying skin had become somewhat hard and scaly. The picture immediately reminded me of the cutaneous calcinosis previously obtained in newborn rats. Although we had not succeeded in producing such changes in older animals, the possibility had to be considered that they would develop in young adults such as those of the present series.

In order to see the skin better, I removed some of the fur over the scalp. To my surprise, next day the epilated region became solidly calcified. The experiment was then repeated, and, to determine exactly when skin calcification begins, we plucked the fur from the scalp of some rats on several successive days after DHT administration. It turned out that spontaneous calcification was again barely apparent, but the rats epilated on the second day after DHT treatment—and these only!—all developed intense cutaneous calcification at the site of plucking.

Removing a few hairs certainly cannot be considered a severe trauma, hence, the calcification was hardly "dystrophic." Furthermore, the response occurred only during a sharply limited "critical period," some 24 hours after sensitization with DHT.

These observations also solved the mystery of why only the surroundings of the nape of the neck calcified in the early experiments (Step 3) in which baby rats were treated with parathyroid hormone and later (Step 5) with DHT. In handling these little animals, we always picked them up by the nape of the neck and never realized that the local calcification was induced by incidental trauma to their sensitive skin.

CONCEPT: Following sensitization with DHT, a stimulus as mild as epilation can cause local cutaneous calcification, but only during a "critical period." Since this response occurs at a skin site that shows no obvious sign of damage, it cannot be called "dystrophic." A response in which local calcification occurs at the site of mild injury during a critical period after sensitization with DHT is named *local calciphylaxis*.

Step 8. (1961) SSS: $[Ct(Ca) \leftarrow Ta(\text{hemostat, FeCl}_3)] \leftarrow DHT$
Cutaneous calcinosis is produced by local trauma with a hemostat or local treatment with ferric chloride after pretreatment with DHT.

What would happen if, instead of the mild trauma of epilation, we were to crush the skin severely, for example, with a hemostat? Would calcification of the skin be proportional to the intensity of the damage in this case? How would chemical irritants affect the skin of the DHT-sensitized animal? Once we had learned that, during the critical period, epilation causes local skin calcification, all these additional questions could easily be asked in the form of experiments, and the answers were unambiguous. Crushing of the skin produced no calcification at the site of severe injury, but a lip-like halo of calcium deposition surrounded the crushed area. Here, calcification is definitely not proportional to the degree of injury, hence, it cannot be regarded as "dystrophic." However, apparently some substance is liberated from the severely damaged skin and diffuses into the surroundings, thereby inducing a calcified flare around the area of severe damage.

Other experiments proved that minute amounts of ferric chloride (and incidentally many other metallic salts and a few nonmetallic compounds) produce a calcified wheal wherever they are injected into the skin of a DHT-pretreated animal. Thus, chemical substances can also act as challengers, eliciting local calciphylaxis. Here again, the efficacy of the challenger did not depend upon its tissue-damaging effect, because most of the highly potent challengers caused no detectable tissue damage, while strong irritants (croton oil, formalin) were ineffective. Indeed, even large tissue-damaging amounts of ferric chloride (a salt highly potent when given in minute quantities) caused no calcification at the site of injection, but only in the surrounding flare.

CONCEPT: Calciphylaxis is definitely not a simple dystrophic phenomenon dependent upon the degree of tissue injury. Chemical substances can act as local challengers. Mechanical or chemical agents of proven local challenging potency cause no calcification if applied in excess, a phenomenon called *overchallenge*.

Step 9. (1961–1962) SSS: Ti(*Ca*) ← DHT, Vit-D$_2$, Vit-D$_3$, Ptr-E, R-le + *Fe, Cr, Al, Pb,* Fe-Dex, Fe-Din, Fe-OS (i.v.)

> *Not only dihydrotachysterol, but vitamin-D$_2$, vitamin-D$_3$, parathyroid extract or renal lesions (which induce disturbances in calcium and phosphate metabolism) can act as calciphylactic sensitizers. In animals sensitized by any of these agents, not only ferric, but also chromium, aluminum and lead salts act as challengers and, if injected intravenously into the general blood stream, each cause calcification of different tissues for which they have a special affinity. Furthermore, the tissue affinity of a given metal, for example, iron, depends upon the carrier to which it is attached, ferric chloride, ferric dextran, ferric dextrin and ferric oxysaccharate all cause calcification of different tissues when injected intravenously.*

Our next task was to clarify the nature of the calciphylactic sensitizer. We found that among a very large number of agents examined, only indirect calcifiers exhibited this effect. DHT, vitamin D$_2$, vitamin D$_3$, parathyroid extract, and even the renal lesions (produced surgically or by drugs) which destroy kidney tissue and thereby stimulate parathyroid hormone secretion, are all capable of producing nonspecific calcinosis in naturally predisposed organs. These are all indirect calcifiers because, when present in great excess, the compounds of the vitamin-D group—like parathyroid hormone (injected as an extract or produced by the parathyroid glands under the stimulus of a renal lesion)—cause no local calcification at the site of their application, but only indirectly, at a distance, in specially predisposed areas (heart, vessels, kidneys, lungs). However, even when any of these agents are applied in small amounts not conducive to calcification, they sensitize for the subsequent application of a calciphylactic challenger.

What would happen if a calciphylactic challenger were injected intravenously into the general blood stream after suitable sensitization? We found that in this event the various challengers (e.g., ferric, chromium, aluminum, and lead salts) each produce calcification in a different set of organs, thus inducing specific calciphylactic syndromes, each of which is characteristic for the agent injected. Thus, selective calcification of certain skin areas, the salivary glands, the pancreas, the thyroids, or the parathyroids, could be obtained quite regularly and predictably by introducing the appropriate metallic salt into the general circulation of a sensitized rat. These were the most instructive experiments in the entire calciphylaxis project because they revealed the extraordinary spectrum of experimental disease models produced by this technique.

It soon became evident that, in all these inorganic salts, it is the metal part that acts as a challenger. If the same metals are attached (carriers) to various organic substances such as dextran, dextrin, or oxysaccharate, the resulting syndrome changes completely. Apparently, the carrier determines where the metal will settle and cause calcification. Hence, merely by changing the carrier, the entire calciphylactic effect of a metal can be altered at will.

CONCEPTS: Various indirect calcifiers can act as calciphylactic sensitizers. By injecting calciphylactic challengers into the blood stream of a sensitized animal, generalized (systemic) calciphylactic syndromes can be produced. Following intravenous challenge with a given metal, the distribution of organ calcification depends upon its carrier. Thus, different metals attached to the same carrier, may produce the same calciphylactic syndrome, while the same metal, attached to different carriers, may cause calcification in different organs.

Step 10. (1961–1962) SSS: [Ct(Ca) ← *Pb, Cd,* KMnO$_4$]
> *Cutaneous calcification is produced by local treatment with lead and cadmium salts or potassium permanganate, even in the absence of calciphylactic sensitization by dihydrotachysterol or similar compounds. This phenomenon is called "calcergy."*

Are there agents that could cause local calcification even in the absence of any calciphylactic sensitization? Of course, in our work on calciphylaxis we always used controls treated with the sensitizer (e.g., DHT) or the challenger (e.g., FeCl$_3$) alone. During the first year, no challenger was found which would have produced any calcification by itself. It soon became evident, however, that certain compounds, for example, lead or cadmium salts and potassium permanganate, given subcutaneously, produced a local calcified wheal at the injection site. This wheal could not be distinguished from a calciphylactic lesion even microscopically, although it was produced without sensitization by an indirect calcifier. Agents, which cause calcification by themselves without previous sensitization, were designated as *direct calcifiers,* or "calcergens."

CONCEPT: Certain compounds act as direct calcifiers in that they produce local calcification at the injection site even in the absence of any pretreatment with a calciphylactic sensitizer. This direct calcification or "calcergy" must be distinguished from calciphylaxis.

Step 11. *(1961–1962)* *SSS:* [Ct(Ca) ← FeCl$_3$ + Dex, Din] ← DHT

> *Especially intense cutaneous calcification is produced by local treatment with ferric chloride mixed with dextran or dextrin, but only following sensitization with dihydrotachysterol.*

After our brief excursion to identify the phenomenon of direct calcification as distinct from calciphylaxis, we again returned to the latter field. Having seen (Step 9) that intravenous injection of the same metal can produce different calciphylactic syndromes, depending upon the carrier to which it is chemically bound, we wondered what would happen if a metallic salt were merely mixed with potential carriers and then injected either under the skin or into the general blood stream of a DHT-sensitized rat. We found that even when a metallic salt (for example, FeCl$_3$) is mixed with dextran or dextrin and then injected subcutaneously during the critical period after DHT sensitization, the resulting local wheal is greatly enlarged. Indeed, in this case even otherwise ineffective amounts of FeCl$_3$ become effective. The agents that thus enhance the effect of the metallic salts were called *adjuvants of challengers.* They produce no calcification by themselves but enhance the calciphylactic activity of challenging metals. Even when such mixtures are injected intravenously, certain adjuvants can increase, or even qualitatively change, the calciphylactic syndrome produced by a given metallic salt.

CONCEPT: Certain substances, which in themselves cause no calcification even in DHT-sensitized rats, increase the efficiency of subcutaneously injected calciphylactic challengers when mixed with the latter. These compounds are called *adjuvants of challengers.*

Step 12. *(1961–1963)* *SSS:* [Ti(*Ca*) ← DHT + Cha] ← Sr, Hnlib, GC, Hyp-x, PO$_4$, *Ca*, R-xp

> *The calcifications produced in various tissues by dihydrotachysterol plus various challengers are greatly influenced by diverse stressors, histamine liberators, glucocorticoids, hypophysectomy, variations in*

phosphate and calcium intake as well as by partial extirpation of the kidneys (renal tissue).

After identifying the various ingredients necessary for the production of the diverse calciphylactic syndromes, we wanted to learn more about conditioning factors that might affect calciphylactic reactivity as a whole. An extraordinarily large number of experiments was necessary to determine the responsiveness of the various calciphylactic reactions to the many agents suspected of having such conditioning activities. The essence of all these studies may be summarized as follows:

In general, calciphylactic responsiveness is inhibited by pretreatment with various stressors (forced immobilization, exposure to cold, transection of the spinal cord), the so-called histamine liberators (which have definite anti-allergic properties), glucocorticoids (cortisone and similar substances), and hypophysectomy. On the other hand, an excess dietary intake of phosphate or calcium and renal damage (induced surgically or by drugs) greatly increased calciphylactic sensitivity.

There would be no point in evaluating all these observations in detail here. In essence, they led us to the conclusion that the entire calciphylactic system, though very consistently activated by proper sensitization and challenge, is extremely labile and readily influenced by a variety of conditioning factors.

CONCEPT: Various conditioning factors can increase or diminish susceptibility to the most diverse forms of calciphylaxis.

Step 13. (1962) SSS: Tm (Ca) ← DHT + CON

Thymus calcification is produced by dihydrotachysterol plus cortisone.

During the initial stages of our study, no challenger was ever found to produce a systemic calciphylactic reaction without having a direct local challenging activity at a subcutaneous injection site. Hence, we usually tested potential challengers first for their local effect by subcutaneous injection (a simple, very reliable, semiquantitative technique); only compounds active in this test were then examined for all types of potential systemic effects. However, by accident we finally discovered some exceptions to the rule that all systemic challengers must also be capable of producing local calciphylaxis. In a series of experiments in which we wanted to influence calciphylactic syndromes by subcutaneous injection of cortisone, we noted that the thymus underwent such massive calcification that it was transformed into a petrified hard mass. Even in optimally sensitized rats, cortisone produces no local calcification at the injection site, but it does cause sudden thymus involution and the degenerating thymus cells themselves apparently act as local challengers in the thymus.

This was the first example of an indirect challenger, that is, a substance which does not challenge connective tissue directly at the injection site, but acts only at a distance by setting free challenging compounds (here, thymus disintegration products) from the tissues themselves. In subsequent work several additional indirect challengers of this type were found. The hormone serotonin and the antibiotic bacitracin, for example, have little if any local challenging effect, but they act upon the salivary and tear glands, causing them to become calcified.

CONCEPT: There are "indirect challengers" which cause no local calcification at the injection site in sensitized animals, but act only at distant organs where they activate or liberate natural challenging compounds.

Step 14. (1962–1963) SSS: Ti("Premature aging") ← DHT + Fe-Dex + Chron

Production of changes reminiscent of premature aging by chronic DHT-intoxication and their prevention by ferric-dextran treatment.

In the course of our work on calciphylaxis we noted that rats, chronically treated with small doses of DHT, developed a syndrome reminiscent of senility. Not only did they show calcium depositions in tissues which normally calcify at an advanced age (arteries, tendons, rib and larynx cartilages, crystalline lens of the eye), but they also developed other signs of senility not associated with visible calcification, such as wrinkling of the skin, loss of hair, wasting of muscles and sex organs. Curiously, ferric dextran—which, given in a single large dose during the critical period, causes calciphylaxis— here, actually prevented the abnormal tissue calcification, as well as all the other senilitylike changes, when given in very small doses over a long time.

Apparently, when the iron compound is administered chronically, it is taken up by numerous cells throughout the body. It then attracts calcium so diffusely, everywhere, that no single spot can accumulate a large permanent deposit. This phenomenon of calcium deviation by dissemination is apparently the reverse of calciphylaxis. It has accordingly been called *anacalciphylaxis.*

We still do not know why this prevention of calcification is associated with an inhibition of those senilitylike changes that are unaccompanied by mineral deposition.

CONCEPT: Under certain circumstances, calciphylactic challengers can actually prevent calcification through the phenomenon of "ana-calciphylaxis." There may be some causal relationship between calcification and the aging of tissues.

SYNOPSIS. The fourteen principal steps in the elucidation of the calciphylaxis construct have been summarized in tabular form on pp. 256–257.

OUTLOOK. This is the point we have reached in developing the construct of calciphylaxis, at the time of writing these Notes. We have seen that every observation has led to a concept which necessitated the planning of another experiment.

No research project ever reaches an end; no scientific concept can ever be definitive and complete. What we have learned so far about calciphylaxis suggests that this biologic reaction-form is important in regulating the balance between skeletal and tissue calcium, and in producing or preventing the formation of calcific deposits in circumscribed areas. Essentially, calciphylactic responses occur in the connective tissue. They appear to be related to the collagen diseases and even to aging.

We would like to hope that calciphylaxis will teach us something about preventing abnormal calcification in man. It may conceivably also lead us to a better understanding of the basic mechanisms involved in the collagen diseases and in the aging of tissues. It may help us to send drugs selectively to certain organs in order to destroy them without the need for surgery (e.g., by radio-active elements). It may even be possible to send curative drugs selectively to certain organs which need them, without exposing the whole body to toxic concentrations.

It is especially noteworthy that the same substance, say iron, will be deposited in different sites depending upon the "carrier" to which it is attached. It is as though the carrier (chloride, dextran, dextrin, etc.,) would act as an "address tag" which directs the iron to one place or another within the body. This principle may have broader applications in pharmacology as a means of sending drugs to desired target areas.

Meanwhile, these are all only hopes and much painstaking experimentation will be needed to determine to what extent such possibilities are practically feasible. Still, the fourteen steps in the development of the calciphylaxis construct give us a practical example of how a natural phenomenon can be systematically dissected into its constituent parts, thereby giving us power over Nature. Once we know how the parts of a machine interact, we can force the mechanism to perform certain tasks at will.

TABLE SUMMARIZING THE FOURTEEN STEPS

Step	Date	Experiment
1	1927–1928	Ti(Ca) ← Vit-D
2	1929	Ti(Ca) ← Ptr↑:R
3	1932	Ct(Ca) ← Ptr-E
4	1932–1960	Ct-scl ← Ptr-x
5	1957	Ct(Ca) ← DHT
6	1957	[Ti(Ca) ← Ta(hemostat)] ← DHT
7	1961	[Ct(Ca) ← Ta(epilation)] ← DHT + Chron(C.P.)
8	1961	[Ct(Ca) ← Ta(hemostat, FeCl₃)] ← DHT
9	1961–1962	Ti(Ca) ← DHT, Vit-D₂, Vit-D₃, Ptr-E, R-le + Fe, Cr, Al, Pb, Fe-Dex, Fe-Din, Fe-OS (i.v.)
10	1961–1962	[Ct(Ca) ← Pb, Cd, KMnO₄]
11	1961–1962	[Ct(Ca) ← FeCl₃ + Dex, Din] ← DHT
12	1961–1963	[Ti(Ca) ← DHT + Cha] ← Sr, Hn-lib, GC, Hyp-x, PO₄, Ca, R-xp
13	1962	Tm(Ca) ← DHT + CON
14	1962–1963	Ti("Premature Aging") ← DHT + Fe-Dex + Chron

IN ELUCIDATION OF CALCIPHYLAXIS CONSTRUCT

Concept
Indirect calcifiers, Nonspecific calcinosis.
Renal hyperparathyroidism can cause tissue calcification in man.
Parathyroid extract can cause sclerodermalike cutaneous calcinosis in animals.
Parathyroidectomy sometimes ameliorates scleroderma in man.
DHT can cause sclerodermalike cutaneous calcinosis in animals.
Following sensitization with DHT, hemostat-induced mechanical trauma to various internal organs can cause local calcification.
The mild trauma of epilation suffices to cause local cutaneous calcinosis, but only during a *critical period* after acute DHT overdosage. Identification of *local calciphylaxis.*
Calciphylaxis *differs from dystrophic calcification.* Chemicals (e.g., $FeCl_3$) can act as local challengers. *Overchallenge* prevents calcification.
Systemic calciphylaxis. Importance of *carrier* of challenging metal.
Direct calcifiers act without sensitization through calcergy.
Adjuvants increase efficacy of calciphylactic challengers.
Systemic *conditioning factors* can increase or decrease calciphylactic responsiveness.
Certain agents (e.g., cortisone) cause no local calcification in sensitized animals but act as *indirect challengers* by liberating natural challengers from certain tissues (e.g., thymus).
Possible relationship between calciphylaxis and *premature aging. Anacalciphylaxis.*

STATISTICAL TECHNIQUES

Statistics is a science dealing with the collection, analysis, interpretation and presentation of masses of numerical data. There can be no doubt that certain sciences have profited immensely by the application of statistical techniques. In biology, the use of statistics (biometrics or biostatistics) is a comparatively new development, useful especially in descriptive or experimental research where numbers are involved, e.g., in the analysis of complex experiments with more than one variable. Several excellent texts deal with this subject (Snedecor [81], Hill [42], Fisher [36], Cohen & Nagel [20], Carnap [17]), so here we may limit ourselves to generalities.

The first thing to know about biostatistics is the limitation of its applicability. It is significant that the term "statistics" was first applied only to data concerning the state as a whole (e.g., population numbers, birth-rate, mortality, revenue, trade). Let us remember that the method is meant to be used only for the evaluation of group phenomena by an analysis of data supplied by enumeration and measurement. The larger the group and the more precisely the points of interest can be expressed numerically, the more will we profit from the statistical approach. In the study of many public health problems dealing with mass phenomena, statistical research is indispensable. The same is true when it comes to evaluating numerical data pertaining to the bioassay of drugs, the standardization of vaccines, and the like.

It is through its application to such topics that statistics has gained its current prestige as a means of substituting reliable, objective mathematical calculations for notoriously unreliable, subjective impressions. A great deal of harm has been done, however, by the inappropriate use of statistics by dilettantes, often out of ignorance, but I am afraid sometimes only to give a semblance of precision and objectivity.

In experimental biology, the intended use of statistical techniques must be taken into account in planning the work, or else the results will rarely lend themselves to such treatment. Thus, biostatistics deals not only with the interpretation, but also with the design of experiments. We must know which groups can be compared. We must make certain that the individuals in these groups are true samples of an infinitely large hypothetical population. We must consider all the many possible fallacies mentioned in the pertinent texts.

There are several other good reasons for thinking of statistics before we carry out our work—reasons which often escape attention. For instance, it is well known in clinical medicine that, unless we set up a statistically significant test before a drug is generally accepted, its actual value can never be really ascertained. A frequently cited example is Pasteur's rabies treatment which has never been properly proven effective in patients after they have been bitten; indeed, many authorities doubt that it is of any use. But how could we now conduct a proper test by withholding this possibly life-saving treatment from a control group of bitten persons?

Here, a word of warning is also in order about what I call the fallacy of "a posteriori statistics." Suppose that you have tested three chemically related drugs and found that all of them have some retarding effect upon the growth of experimental cancers in animals. Guided by many previous observations, you now hypothesize that a Compound "X" combining the chemical characteristics of the three drugs might be especially potent. Compound X is eventually synthesized and proves to cause complete disappearance of experimental cancers in a group of ten rats. Since it is quite exceptional for such cancers to vanish spontaneously, you can compare your results with an enormous group consisting of the untreated controls in all previous experiments and the results will be statistically highly significant.

Now, assume that another investigator happens to inject adrenaline into a similar group of rats bearing the same kind of experimental cancer, merely because he wanted to explore the effect of this hormone on the blood pressure in the presence of a malignant tumor. Much to his surprise, all tumors vanish just as they did after treatment with Compound X. Statistically, both these tests are equally significant —to the mathematician but not to the biologist. The latter will take into account not only the evaluation of the experiment at hand, but also common sense based on the past experience that does not lend itself to statistical treatment. He will remember that, although these cancers did not disappear in the untreated controls of his experiment, they do so occasionally; there is always the danger of something happening to the cancer graft that kills it accidentally during or after inoculation. He will also remember that three analogues of Compound X were found to be active, while adrenaline and its numerous derivatives have been used for decades in all kinds of experiments involving experimental neoplasms; it is very unlikely that, if this group of compounds had any anticancer effect, it would have remained undetected.

Now, if it is prohibitively expensive and time-consuming to synthesize the new anticancer drug, I believe that a cautiously worded publication on its possible curative effect would be justified on the basis of the one statistically significant test. The experimenter must keep in mind that, by withholding publication, he might retard the clinical application of a drug with potentially immense practical value. Not being a chemist, he cannot synthesize the substance himself. He has no more of it available for a recheck. Furthermore, the chemist who made it in the first place may now be unable or unwilling to spend a great deal of time and money on the preparation of a second sample, merely on the basis of an unpublished and, to him, perhaps unconvincing observation. It may take years to repeat an experiment of this kind; indeed, it may be forgotten as time goes by. On the other hand, the statistically equally significant adrenaline experiment should never be published without ample confirmatory evidence, since the compound is abundantly available.

This kind of consideration does not show any weakness in the statistical method, but only in its evaluation. The fact is that the biologist will unconsciously take into consideration the whole of his previous experience, including vague but valuable memories which are unsuited to precise quantitative evaluation. All our reasoning is influenced by unconscious statistical considerations. Most of these cannot be expressed in numbers; hence, they do not lend themselves to statistical treatment. There will always be room for common sense and an analysis of the experimenter's psychology; his techniques of reasoning are at least as important in biology as the statistical analysis of the result.

The extreme usefulness of statistics in certain fields has created the impression that almost no research should be published without checking the degree of its mathematical probability. Purely qualitative differences and most of the changes in histologic structure, for instance, are not subject to this type of verification. Yet many authors will succumb to the pressure of public opinion (particularly of editors) and use statistical calculations where they have no place. Being primarily a morphologist, I have often experienced difficulties in this respect.

For example, in describing the aggravation or prevention of certain morphologic changes—such as irregular patches of inflammation, necrosis, or calcification in organs—we can at best use a semiquantitative scale of 0–3. Of course, many investigators use more subdivisions, but if you have a scale of, say, ten possible intensities, grading becomes very subjective, while no one has any difficulty in differentiating objectively between: the absence of lesions (0), just detectable changes (1), and the most pronounced alterations that can be observed (3); this leaves only one somewhat ill-defined grade, (2), between the just detectable and the maximal.

If you appraise the lesions in a group of twenty rats by this technique, you may end up with a mean figure of 2.3 for the control group, and 0.2 for the lot in which you think your treatment produced an inhibition. The very nature of certain lesions (e.g., diffuse arteriosclerosis, anaphylactoid swellings, necrotic patches distributed throughout the heart, calciphylactically induced irregular mineral deposits along a nerve) made it necessary for us to use this procedure in publications, but we did not think it would be practical to submit such results to a meaningful statistical analysis. However, since many editors of scientific journals asked us to calculate standard errors, we did so. Yet, once this was routinely done in subsequent manuscripts, just as many other editors insisted that the statistical calculations be omitted as inapplicable. Thereupon I consulted nine of the leading statisticians in the United States and Europe, with the result that four of these vigorously insisted on statistical calculations (though all prescribed different techniques), while the remaining five ruled that this type of material is unsuited to such treatment.

Not being enough of an expert in this field, I have no personal opinion in the matter. Now I blindly follow the desires of the particular editor or reviewer who appraises a manuscript. (Incidentally, it has repeatedly happened to me that even in the same journal, the ruling was contradictory on two successively submitted papers read by different editorial advisers.) Thus, at present the same type of data published from this same Institute at different times and in different journals sometimes is and sometimes is not adorned with statistical calculations, but I cannot say that the problem has ever excited me very much. Frankly, in such cases I personally do not believe the statistics anyway; if they are published, this is done only to please certain readers and editors.

In this type of problem, the solution is found not in the development of ever more cunning statistical calculations but in improving the experimental technique to a point where the results are self-evident. In the case of an inhibition, for example, all animals of the control group should show maximal or near maximal lesions, while the treated group remains unaffected. In other words, such semiquantitative scales of estimation exclude the possibility of using moderate changes as a basis for conclusions; the laboratory procedure itself must be improved until it is essentially perfect.

In our lab, the anaphylactoid reaction—which manifests itself in the form of swelling of the extremities in rats—has also always been estimated simply in terms of a 0–3 scale (with or without standard errors, depending upon the editors). But this did not prevent us from showing that it can be inhibited by cortisonelike compounds or antihistaminics, because when it is inhibited it is just not there in any individual. Some, more conscientious, scientists have developed procedures of different complexity for the quantitative estimation of anaphylactoid swelling. For example, by measuring the weight of the swollen paws after amputation following death, their water displacement or circumference during life, or even the weight of the paper upon which the contours of the paws are drawn with the camera-lucida procedure. Now, all these techniques give a broad range of precise numerical readings which lend themselves excellently to statistical analysis from a mathematical point of view. Yet, I doubt that any of them really represent a great advance over the 0–3 scale procedure with regard to the accuracy of the measurements themselves. Hence, I suspect that the gain, if any, does not warrant the loss of time involved.

In conclusion, statistics is indispensable in some fields, a great help in others, but we must know how and when to use it. Most of all, we must not employ it to give a semblance of great precision to data which do not lend themselves to quantitative analysis.

8. How to Think

It may seem odd to find that the chapter on "How to Think" follows the one on "How to Work." But, as I shall try to show, in basic research most of the thinking comes after a chance observation or after we have done some experiments guided mainly by intuition and by a very superficial (often false) reasoning. Especially in the natural sciences, logic is very rarely at the root of true discovery. It is required mainly for the development—the confirmation—and evaluation of observations. As the saying goes, "You shoot first and ask questions later."

LOGIC AND THE SCIENTIFIC METHOD

"Those who have made the most discoveries in science are those who knew Bacon least, while those who have read and pondered him, like Bacon himself, have not succeeded well."

[J. de Maistre as quoted by Claude Bernard [9]]

"It seems to me that there is a good deal of ballyhoo about scientific method. I venture to think that the people who talk most about it are the people who do least about it ... Scientific method is something talked about by people standing on the outside and wondering how the scientist manages to do it. These people have been able to uncover various generalities applicable to at least most of what the scientist does, but it seems to me that these generalities are not very profound, and could have been anticipated by anyone who knew enough about scientists to know what is their primary objective." [P. Q. Bridgman [13]]

"Everyday experience and history teach us that in the biological and medical sciences reason seldom can progress far from the facts without going astray." [W. I. B. Beveridge [11]]

"Scientific research is not itself a science; it is still an art or craft." [W. H. George [37a]]

263

By "scientific method" we understand those procedures used in the systematic acquisition of knowledge that are based upon: 1. the recognition and clear formulation of a problem; 2. the collection of data through observation and if feasible, experiment; 3. the formulation of hypotheses through logical argumentation; 4. the testing of these hypotheses. A prodigious amount of work has been done by logicians and philosophers ever since Boole [12], to explore the laws of thought [Cohen & Nagel [20], Wolf [91]], and a Herculean effort has been made to systematize the entire technique of theory construction and to arrive at the basis of a unified science [Woodger [90]] solely by conscious reasoning. However, paradoxical as this may seem, the practical value of formal logic, the laws of thought and the scientific method is very limited indeed, both in everyday life and in science.

How often did I really profit by the conscious application of formal logic to my daily problems, either as a private citizen or as an investigator? Come to think of it, there are lots of things that I have learned to do much better by practice than by logic. Walking and talking, for instance. No one would attempt to insure a man against the danger of stumbling by teaching him exactly what muscles he should move, in what sequence, and with what strength. No one learns to speak his native tongue through the conscious application of grammar. The best way to show a child how to walk is to take his hand and pull. After he has listened to your chatter long enough, he also will talk. Knowledge about the physiology of locomotion or the rules of grammar undoubtedly has its uses, but, in practice, unless things go wrong, we can rarely apply this kind of knowledge consciously. Of course, the surgeon who has to repair a damaged limb must know a great deal about the way muscles and bones interact in walking, and it is when a sentence sounds odd or ambiguous that we will consult a grammar book.

I suspect it's pretty much the same with science. Whatever little teaching is possible must be done by taking the novice by the hand and making him walk beside you. We learn both the practice and the philosophy of the biologist's life as we go along, by our own experience and by watching our masters. We would not get far if we were to refer to the rules of logic to check the validity of reasoning at each step. Even in the most simple biologic experiment, our progress would be as slow and hesitating as the walk or talk of a man who insisted on checking, by conscious analysis, the logical sequence of every muscle he contracted and every sound he uttered. As I shall try to explain later, it is pretty much the same with the use of mathematics and statistics in the exploration of life. Logic is the basis of experimentation, as grammar is of language. But we must learn to use such codes intuitively for, as a rule, time does not permit their conscious application to all steps.

It is, of course, tempting to make a logical case for the use of logic and mathematics in science; it is more hazardous to point out its limitations. But let us face facts. The vast majority of the most outstanding experimental physicians know very little about either formal logic or mathematics. The mathematical formulation of biologic laws, the design of experiments (as the statistician understands it), the conclusive proof of the professional logician and the conscious use of the scientific method as outlined by philosophers, played no greater role in the most important medical discoveries of history than did a knowledge of acoustics in the composition of the greatest musical works.

The impression that scientific research is based on the planned application of logic is largely due to the fact that intuitively directed probings into the unknown are forgotten and only the simplest logical road to success is published and remembered. This artificial path is also the only one taught to students. No wonder they come to think of it as the one possible avenue to knowledge. This point is well illustrated by von Helmholtz's description of the way he made his mathematical discoveries:

"I am fain to compare myself with a wanderer on the mountains who, not knowing the path, climbs slowly and painfully upwards and often has to retrace his steps because he can go no further—then, whether by taking thought or from luck, discovers a new track that leads him on a little till at length when he reaches the summit he finds to his shame that there is a royal road, by which he might have ascended, had he only had the wits to find the right approach to it. In my works, I naturally said nothing about my mistakes to the reader, but only described the made track by which he may now reach the same heights without difficulty."

[L. Koenigsberger [47]]

Schiller [62] has expressed this same thought eloquently:

"Among the obstacles to scientific progress a high place must certainly be assigned to the analysis of scientific procedure which logic has provided. ... It has not tried to describe the methods by which the sciences have actually advanced, and to extract ... rules which might be used to regulate scientific progress, but has freely re-arranged the actual procedure in accordance with its prejudices, for the order of discovery there has been substituted an order of proof.... It is not too much to say that the more deference men of science have paid to logic, the worse it has been for the scientific value of their reasoning.... Fortunately for the world, however, the great men of science have usually been kept in salutary ignorance of the logical tradition."

Trotter [84] also emphasizes that logical reasoning has only few discoveries to its credit compared with empiricism; similar views were expressed by Poincaré, Planck and Einstein [W. I. B. Beveridge [11]].

To my mind, logic is to Nature as a guide is to a zoo. The guide knows exactly where to locate the African lion, the Indian elephant or the Australian kangaroo, once they have been captured, brought together and labeled for inspection. But this kind of knowledge would be valueless to the hunter who seeks them in their natural habitat. Similarly, logic is not the key to Nature's order but only the catalog of the picture gallery in man's brain where his impressions of natural phenomena are stored.

It has been said that everybody should have a thorough training in logic and mathematics, because, whatever his job, this will teach him how to think. That I doubt. Indeed, it may even block the free flow of that semi-intuitive thinking that is the very basis of medical research. The study of formal logic or mathematics certainly teaches one how to think about formal logic or mathematics. I question that it helps more efficiently to mold the brain for thinking about histology or for devising a new surgical operation than if the time had been spent in a histologic laboratory or a surgical clinic.

FORMAL vs. "SEMI–INTUITIVE" LOGIC

To my mind, the medical scientist has only two valid reasons for studying at least the rudiments of logic, but these are very good reasons: the inherent beauty of the laws of thought, and their value in helping us to check and repair our largely instinctive "lab logic," whenever it leads us astray. It is for these reasons that I now want to discuss a few problems of logic as applied to medical research, in the form of the "semi-intuitive logic" of the laboratory. For this purpose, I shall try to illustrate certain key patterns of thought with analogies, because we biologists shall have to deal with undissectable, whole complexes of living matter rather than with pure, homogeneous, individual ingredients. I think you will find that this superficial knowledge suffices as a guide in most of the laboratory work you are likely to do.

The semi-intuitive logic that every practical scientist uses in his daily work is a peculiar mixture of rigid, formal logic and psychology. It is formal in that it abstracts the forms of thought from its contents to establish abstract criteria of consistency. Since these abstractions can be represented by symbols, it is even symbolic logic. But, on the other hand, it frankly admits that its idea-units, its abstractions—unlike those of the mathematician or theoretic physicist—are necessarily variable and impure. Therefore, we would only be misled if we consistently attempted to apply the rigid laws of thought to them. In thinking about Nature, we must also assign a prominent place to intuition. That is why psychology has to be integrated with logic in our system of thought.

The following are the foremost problems with which this semi-formal logic will have to grapple:

1. *Formulation of idea-units*
2. *Classification of idea-units* according to
   (a) their characteristics (symptoms)
   (b) their causality (etiology)
3. *Formulation of new questions* about (a) the evolution of the characteristics in time (the types of idea-units that precede them and the types into which they are likely to develop), (b) the mediation of the causality (the antecedents that preceded and the consequents likely to follow the effect of the immediate cause), and, sometimes
4. *The intuitive flash,* the "hunch," which, though inspired by the previous steps, cannot be deduced from them by the application of formal logic.

Diagrammatically, this could be represented as follows:

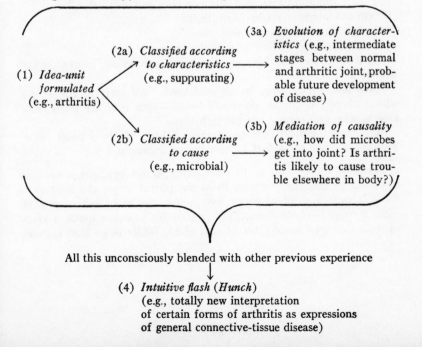

(1) *Idea-unit formulated* (e.g., arthritis)

(2a) *Classified according to characteristics* (e.g., suppurating)

(2b) *Classified according to cause* (e.g., microbial)

(3a) *Evolution of characteristics* (e.g., intermediate stages between normal and arthritic joint, probable future development of disease)

(3b) *Mediation of causality* (e.g., how did microbes get into joint? Is arthritis likely to cause trouble elsewhere in body?)

All this unconsciously blended with other previous experience

(4) *Intuitive flash (Hunch)* (e.g., totally new interpretation of certain forms of arthritis as expressions of general connective-tissue disease)

With a thorough knowledge of the subject, with logic, and with industry, we can guide our path more or less consciously from (1) to (3a or 3b)—that part of the way which is essentially the *development* of a previously formulated idea. But only a flash of intuition, of creative imagination, which occurs in the unconscious mind, can bridge the gap between the whole encircled field and true discovery (4); this intuitive flash is the most fruitful type of achievement, the essence of basic research.

THE THREE STEPS IN SEMI–INTUITIVE LOGIC

Ideas and Idea-Units

It is impossible to understand anything that cannot be expressed in terms of previously known elements of experience. That is why even the most highly educated and intelligent layman is unable really to grasp the quantum physicist's idea of matter or the biologist's delight on discovering a hitherto unsuspected law of living matter. A modification of an old, allegedly Indian, story illustrates this in a simple manner.

A blind beggar asked his friend, "Tell me, what do they mean by white? What is white like?"

"White is a color," he was told. "It is like the snow on the mountains."

"I see," the blind man said. "It is a cold and soft color."

"No, not always; paper is white, too."

"It is a thin and fragile color, then?"

"It need not be. Milk is also white."

"Is it fluid and nourishing?" the blind man asked, somewhat bewildered.

"Not necessarily," his friend explained. "All sorts of things are white: clouds, teeth, an old man's beard—your eyes are white, too, that is why you cannot see through them."

"Oh, never mind!" the blind man sighed. "It is a cruel color. Perhaps it's just as well if I don't try to understand it."

Actually, even those of us who have perfect eyesight never see anything as absolutely white. Even the purest snow, the most perfectly bleached sheet of paper have some shadow or reflection that mars their perfect whiteness. The patriarch's beard, a tooth, a glass of milk fall even more short of that ideal. White is an abstract element of thought; it has no actuality in our daily experience, and yet it would be difficult to get along without it. In real life, things are more or less white, but if we want to point out a white cat, it is not possible or even necessary to describe every speck of dust on its fur or to take the conditions of illumination into consideration; although "In the dark all cats are black," people will understand our meaning. The human brain is so constructed that it refuses to handle thoughts unless they can be wrapped up more or less neatly in individual idea-packages. It is astonishing how much confusion has been caused by the failure to understand the following three simple facts:

(a) Thoughts, like fluids, can be adequately handled (isolated, measured, mixed, sold) only when put up in individual containers.

(b) The thought-packages contain previous experiences; only the selection within the wrapping can be new. We can have no thoughts of things whose likeness we have never perceived before.

(c) The thought-packages, the idea-units, are very loosely bound together and their contents are not homogenous. They are not water-tight compartments that strictly separate pure matter from its surrounding. What they contain is always somewhat variable in amount and impure in composition.

That is all there is to it. No use worrying about these imperfections; we must learn to live with them. We must learn how to use our thought-units, no matter how imperfect they are, because no form of thinking is possible without them. The trouble is that we keep forgetting about these imperfections, and then, we make serious errors resulting in periodic ruts of insecurity and—especially if we are philosophers—pessimism about the power of thought.

That is why we shall have to examine carefully how these units are formed, classified, and used for scientific research.

1. To UNDERSTAND WE MUST FIRST RECOGNIZE UNITS OF CLASSIFI-CATION. We saw that understanding is the establishment of connections between recognized units of Nature. The more connections we make, the better we understand. Therefore, whatever subject we explore, our first questions are: of what smaller units does it consist and of what larger system is it, in turn, one unit? Research in any field is scientific in proportion to the exactness with which it can define its units.

If our object is to understand man, we must first try to determine his constituent units (the organs, cells, and chemicals that make up his body, the elementary ideas and drives that make up his mind); then we must try to classify these constituents and man as a whole in relation to the other units in Nature. Only such a process of unit formation and classification can bring order into our thoughts, by separating the like from the unlike and by arranging things in lawful fashion for the exploration of structural and causal relations between them. Only by recognizing such a dependable lawfulness can we hope to influence Nature at will. Only by establishing such interrelationships in one system will we be able to make theories that can forecast the likely behavior of hitherto unexplored systems with similar units of structure or causality.

In order to learn something about the human kidney we must first recognize its subunits (cells, chemicals) and the role the principal unit (kidney) plays in relation to the other units (organs) in man. Then, comparative studies will show us that, in most of these respects, the human kidney resembles that of other animals. Therefore, by determining how the animal kidney reacts to remedies against certain experimental diseases, we will be able to formulate theories that can forecast, with reasonable probability, what remedies have a chance to cure similar diseases in man.

2. BIOLOGIC UNITS ARE NECESSARILY IMPURE. The imperfection inherent in the formulation of all biologic units is their impurity.

(a) *Other units spill over into the unit in question.* No matter how we formulate a unit, there is always something in it that also belongs to another unit. We dissect an organ and attach a name to it; we call it "kidney." Yet, the urine in its tubules, the blood in its vessels, and even the vessels themselves are hardly "kidney." They are more properly viewed as parts of the units called "urine," "blood," and "vessels," because they resemble other like units outside the kidney more than the remaining structures in the kidney itself. The same could be said about the connective tissue, the nerves, and all chemical elements that make up the kidney—and then, what is left that is really kidney?

(b) *The unit in question spills over into other units.* This is largely a consequence of what we have just said. If a blood vessel that enters the kidney is to be looked upon as part of this organ, at which point does it become kidney? When a chemical is built into the kidney, precisely where does this change occur? What are the limits of biologic units? Where are my own borderlines as far as that goes? What is more I, the tips of my fingernails, which are dead and useless, or the air in my lungs, without which I would die? And, if the air around me is not my substance, when does it become part of me? In my nose, in my lung, in my blood, in my cells? The border-

lines are indistinct and overlapping, even between animate and inanimate Nature. Yet, how could I learn anything about myself without formulating some, no matter how arbitrary, line of demarcation
between my person and the rest of the world?

3. COMPLICATIONS IN THE EVALUATION OF BIOLOGIC UNITS

(a) *Evaluation by analogy.* Evaluation by analogy is based on
the inference that if two or more things agree with one another in
some respects, they are likely to agree in other respects as well. The
metaphor is a figure of speech which, by analogy, suggests such likeness. All generalizations depend on the discovery of analogies in
otherwise dissimilar things.

"Magic is essentially metaphorical. So are dreams. So is most artistic
activity. Finally, theoretical science is essentially disciplined exploitation
of metaphor."   [A. Rapoport [58]]

"Metaphor is the special mark of genius, for the power of making a
good metaphor is the power of recognizing likeness."   [Aristotle]

Originally, the term "analogy" was reserved for quantitative relationships. For example, the relation between two and four is
analogous to that between eight and sixteen, although now this quantitative type of relationship would usually be called "proportion" in
mathematics. In Aristotle, however, we already find the term used
to designate qualitative relationships, as it is currently used today.

The discovery of the analogy underlies all explanation. We consider something explained when we can show it to be like something
else familiar to us. It is by analogy that we can tie a new fact into
the network of our already existing treasury of information.

The danger in reasoning from analogy is that the two pairs of
terms which we compare are always different in some respects; hence,
inference from one to the other is valid only in certain respects. It
helps to understand what we mean by hormones if we compare them
to chemical messengers sent out by a gland of internal secretion to
influence organs at a distance. We immediately think of hormones as
things that must travel through certain routes and that produce an
effect not directly, but indirectly, by transmitting instructions. In
this sense, the analogy is most useful; it helps not only understanding,
but also the prediction, with some degree of probability, of certain
characteristics of hormone actions, because we know that similar
properties characterize the workings of messengers in general. Yet,
we can never foretell how far the analogy can be carried. Messengers
need nourishment, hormones do not. This unpredictability limits the

usefulness of analogies; still, we could not get along without them when we want to explain a novel concept, that is, to translate it into known terms. Analogy can suggest; it is the basis of every hypothesis and theory, but it cannot prove anything.

(b) *Irrelevancies blur regularities.* If you write a word on a typewriter, you can make it illegible without erasing anything, by typing Xs and Ys over it. These irrelevant additions blur the letters and, thereby, make the words meaningless. This is very often the same in Nature.

There is the old story about the fellow who, on Monday, drank whiskey and soda, on Tuesday gin and soda, on Wednesday rum and soda. Since the results were always the same, he concluded that the soda must have been what made him drunk. When a known irrelevant factor runs parallel with an unknown relevant one, this kind of error is extremely common and difficult to detect in basic research. Under "Fallacies," we shall give many pertinent examples (e.g., the "Silent Marker" p. 316 and "Confusing Irrelevancies" p. 319). In these cases the error usually results from the fact that, in a pair of agents (or targets) which are difficult to separate from each other, one is inert but detectable (the silent marker), while the other is active but undetectable. Here, the presence of the active factor is revealed only by the inactive marker, which is then mistaken for the cause.

(c) *Seemingly incompatible theories about relationships between units may be equally correct.* A theory is like a guide; it leads us from one known fact to another. Thereby, it helps us to remember facts and, by an extension of the lawfulness in their connections, it can even enable us to forecast where other interesting new facts are likely to be found.

Assume that two tribes live in valleys to the north and south of a high mountain which neither of them have ever been able to cross. The people in both of these settlements will have a very clear picture of the mountain as seen from their own side. Of course, if the northern slope is rocky and arid, while the southern aspect is covered with flourishing meadows and forests, the two pictures will be totally different. If these people met far away from their home country and spoke of "their mountain," they would never suspect that they were talking about the same thing. This type of misunderstanding is very common in experimental medicine and has been the cause of the most bitter polemics.

The histologist who examines the heart muscle after silver impregnation will clearly see the most minute branches of the cardiac nerves, but no glycogen; his colleague who employs Best's carmine stain will easily detect glycogen, but not nerve endings. If the two use different techniques on purpose, a serious disagreement is not likely to develop. However, often two histologists intend to use the same technique and do not realize that there is a difference in the manner in which they prepare their solutions. Then each of them will be convinced that the other man saw a mirage.

The Idea-Block Analogy

Every animal experiment is essentially a simplified model on which we can conveniently test the possibility of certain biologic interrelations, irrelevant detail having been eliminated. The architect or engineer who makes himself a simple, small-scale model of the complex structure he intends to build, uses this same technique. He has learned from experience that the general laws that regulate the behavior of complex machines are most readily grasped when the system is stripped of all irrelevancies. That is why, to my mind, the most serious handicaps in biologic thinking are the three common sources of error in the formulation and evaluation of units, just mentioned. We must be constantly on the lookout for them as they have an insidious way of slipping, unnoticed, into one's thinking. Let us reexamine them now on the basis of a comparatively simple mechanical analogy.

This block, though composed of many units, is still ever so much simpler than even the most primitive living being:

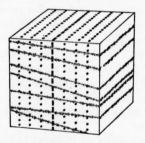

As the earliest explorers approached it from the front they first saw it as an even, flat surface. Then, using crude instruments, they managed to detect the heavy, interrupted vertical line. Having clearly established its position, they concluded that the object consisted of two upright rectangles.

The subsequent discovery of an instrument which detects dotted lines revealed four narrow, upright rectangles within each of the previously detected units. It became evident that the earlier workers were wrong, that the surface consisted of eight symmetrical, elementary parts.

Yet another worker explored this surface with an apparatus that registers only broad crosshatched lines. He agreed with his predecessors, that the surface does, in fact, consist of eight parts, but maintained that these units are quite uneven and, in any event, more or less horizontally arranged. He found this partial disagreement very confusing indeed.

Then, as soon as adapters for investigation in depth became available, both the investigators with the interrupted-line detectors and those who used dotted-line detectors considered the structure as consisting of eight identical, vertical plates. However, the man with the crosshatched-line detector still insisted that the block is made up of eight unequal and essentially horizontally arranged plates.

Meticulous verification of these views subsequently revealed that we cannot speak of units at all because actually, all these lines are discontinuous, so that material along the borderlines of the allegedly separate units cannot be classified with precision.

I need not pursue this frustrating story any further. It clearly demonstrates that, depending upon the point of view and upon the instruments (or sense organs) with which we examine an object, we will form different pictures of it. We may look upon this same cube as composed of different kinds of units; these units overlap, yet, not one of them is more "true" than the others. They are all true elements of the block. Indeed, in any similar case, still further investigation would undoubtedly show that still better instruments can detect even smaller subunits within the smallest that we have so far described. On the other hand, the whole block—like a brick in a house—is merely one unit of a still greater pattern that can be discovered only by exploring its surroundings from a greater distance without the use of any magnifiers.

The moral of this story is that *several, seemingly incompatible theories may be correct.*

The block does not consist of unequal oblique plates *or* of equal vertical plates, but of unequal, oblique *and* equal, vertical plates.

We also note that *all units overlap:* the same matter which forms the oblique plates also forms the vertical plates; consequently, one molecule of it does not belong more to this than to that plate-system.

We see, furthermore, that *irrelevancies blur regularities:* in trying to discover the laws by which the oblique plates are arranged, we will only be misled if in the process we digress and begin to pay attention to the dotted lines.

All the apparently conflicting early theories were correct; the clarity of the final formulation lies only in their summation. The more connections we make the better we "understand." And as for importance, to me the most important fact is the one that made all these observations possible: the discovery that the object exists.

To summarize: 1. It is impossible to delimit units strictly, because no matter how we try to define them their limits will overlap with other possible ways of forming units. Besides, the line of demarcation between two adjacent units is usually hazy and incomplete.

2. Details which are irrelevant from a certain point of view tend to blur the regularities that this approach could make manifest.

3. Several seemingly incompatible theories about the same structure may be correct, if they appraise composition by different criteria.

4. Nevertheless, the formulation of units is indispensable for understanding structure, because this kind of comprehension is precisely the recognition of the role played by the parts in the whole.

5. In biologic systems, these problems are similar, though much more difficult to perceive, because the systems themselves are infinitely more complex. In the formulation of biologic units we must take into account not only shapes but also differences in chemical constitution, color, smell, temperature, consistency, electric charge, the time of appearance and disappearance of transitory units and, alas, virtually countless other factors.

The Idea-Net Analogy

The Idea-Block analogy deals with units as if they were always contiguous. Actually, subjects that are spatially close together may be otherwise quite unrelated (this ham sandwich here on my desk has little in common with the bottle of cortisone that happens to stand next to it). Subjects far apart in space (such as all the samples of cortisone throughout the world) may, however, be virtually identical. These disseminated specimens are welded into a single concept (cortisone) by tying them together in the mind with the threads that consist of our mental pictures of their cognate characteristics.

In the following diagram, things are represented as numbered nodes (circles), their observable characteristics as broad bands of various patterns, and the ideas and memories of these characteristics as thin connecting lines. Our ability to distinguish one thing from another depends upon our capacity to perceive differences in their characteristics:

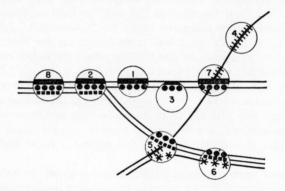

1. Assume that, at first, only node 1 and node 3 are explored. To start with, we note only that both of them have solid and dotted bands. As long as nothing else is known about them, they will seem equal in every respect.

2. Subsequent quantitative studies reveal that node 1 has as much solid as dotted band, while node 3 has less solid than dotted. Now, we can differentiate node 1 from node 3 on the basis of quantitative differences in their composition.

3. Then, the remainder of the field is explored, but with instruments that can detect only solid or dotted bands. The solid-band detector will reveal the additional nodes 8, 2 and 7, while the dotted-band detector also registers 5 and 6. These discoveries will also raise a new point by showing that all the nodes so far seen to have solid bands also have dotted bands (8, 2, 1, 3, 7), but not all those with dotted bands also have solid bands (5, 6).

4. Later, when instruments for cross-striated-, checker-, and star-band detection are developed, it will become evident that node 7 differs from nodes 1 and 3, and that node 5 differs from node 6. At the same time, it will become possible to discover node 4 owing to its possession of cross-striation.

The discovery of additional subjects will depend upon our ability to detect additional characteristics.

5. If a position detector is developed, it will bring a new dimension into our study of the nodes. We will learn that all the solid-band nodes (8, 2, 1, 3, 7) are situated along a straight, horizontal line,

while none of the nodes placed away from this line contain a solid band. This finding leads to the hypothesis that, most probably, additional solid-band nodes will be found by screening along prolongations of the imaginary line connecting nodes 8 and 7.

This simple diagram illustrates the importance of classification as a prerequisite for the formulation of fruitful hypotheses that, by analogy, permit prediction with reasonable probability. It also shows again how relative is the concept of a unit or category. We may speak of "node 1" as a category that encompasses solid and dotted bands in a certain location, but "solid band" itself is also an idea unit, a category, in that it encompasses this pattern wherever located.

In Nature, nothing can be fully characterized, because, in all of its units, no matter how formulated, further details can be detected by additional exploration (e.g., with improved instruments); conversely, the features thought to be characteristic of any one unit may be detected later in another. Hence, no combination of inductive and deductive reasoning can give indubitably valid inferences when applied to natural phenomena. This limitation does not apply to abstract reasoning (e.g., in mathematics), because abstract units can be fully characterized. "2" is only "2." Nothing can be very "2" or slightly "2," and no amount of research can detect anything in any one "2" that could make it qualitatively different from another "2."

What we mean by "understanding" is the process of anchoring something into the idea-net of our memories. The more connections we can find between the new and the previously experienced, the more we feel that we understand it. Yet, understanding is never complete because we always perceive only one segment of the idea-net, and hence, have only segmental understanding of the world [H. Selye [70]].

THE CONSTRUCTION OF THEORIES

"I do not object at all to people who should be accumulators becoming accumulators. When a graduate student tells me that he wishes to make exact measurements, I do not try to show him the error of his ways; I advise him to work with somebody else. I do object, however, to a student, who might have become a guesser, being forced into the ranks of the accumulators because he does not know that there is another and better type of research, and because he does not appreciate the futility of the slogan 'First get your facts.' "   [Wilder Dwight Bancroft [6]]

"While Newton said 'I do not make hypotheses,' he made them nevertheless in almost all his work. Nothing else could be expected, because, without hypotheses, one cannot formulate the laws which experiment confirms by questioning nature, in other words no induction. Not to have seen this is one of the greatest errors with which one must reproach Bacon."   [E. O. von Lippmann]

"No great discovery was ever made without a bold guess." [Isaac Newton]

"First of all, I am blamed for crossing the boundary of experimental evidence. This, I reply, is the habitual action of the scientific mind— at least of that portion of it which applies itself to physical investigation. Our theories of light, heat, magnetism, and electricity, all imply the crossing of this boundary."   [Lord Kelvin]

"The history of science demonstrates beyond doubt that the really revolutionary and significant advances come not from empiricism but from new theories."   [James B. Conant [22]]

Facts vs. Theories

"Learning without thinking is useless; thinking without learning is dangerous" [Confucius]. While it is useless merely to observe and register facts without formulating any ideas about them, pure meditation without any effort to establish the workability of our concepts often results in dangerous misconceptions. During the more than 2,500 years since this thought was formulated, it has been fashionable to express a preference for facts *or* ideas at various times and in various parts of the world. Right now, especially here in North America, we see an entirely unwarranted overemphasis upon fact-finding, accompanied by what often amounts to an actual disdain for theories and interpretations. This has gone so far that most medical journals will reject manuscripts in which important new theories are presented without new facts, although editors gladly accept articles that describe unimportant new facts without any indication of their significance. Indeed, the prejudice against "mere theorizing" has become so serious in the biologic sciences that many an investigator who describes facts, makes a special point of emphasizing, in a self-righteous tone, that he does not attempt to interpret their meaning. What is the value of facts without meaning?

Here, we presumably see a reaction against the sterile dialecticism of the medieval scholastics who were so interested in mental gymnastics that they never bothered to verify the workability of their ideas. It is, of course, futile to construct sophisticated arguments about the number of angels that can dance on the point of a needle, but no more futile than to determine the mean diameter of a cell with greater precision than has ever previously been attained.

Of course, an occasional fact may have some immediate applicability, even if we do not understand it. But random search for data, merely on this off-chance, is hardly scientific. Some time ago, a questionnaire on "Intellectual Immoralities," was circulated by a well-known institution. "Intellectual Immorality No. 4" read: "Generalizing beyond one's data." Bancroft [6] asked whether it would not be more correct to word question No. 4 "Not generalizing beyond one's data."

We have dealt elsewhere (p. 101) with the characteristics of important scientific achievements. Suffice it to point out here that hypotheses which cannot be tested by observation are just as useless as observations that cannot be interpreted by any theory. It is true that the hypothesis which does not lend itself to testing with today's methods may become verifiable tomorrow and that the fact which now eludes interpretation may later become understandable. But such hypotheses and facts are, nevertheless, useless today. If they do acquire importance later, our gratitude belongs, not to the man who originally stumbled upon them, but to the one who succeeds in giving them meaning ("What Is a Discovery?" p. 88).

The importance of facts and theories is interdependent; if a woman wants to wear a string of pearls, it is hardly possible to single out the thread or the beads as more essential. The reason why this problem has so often led to misunderstanding is that the construction of a theory appears to be a more creative accomplishment than mere observation of facts, while a tangible fact appears to have some inherent value, quite apart from its interpretation. This is erroneous. A theory is a bond between facts; it holds them together and guides us to more facts.

Much confusion has arisen from the loose use of the terms, "hypothesis," "theory," and "biologic truth." A hypothesis is a guess; a theory is a partially proven guess; a "biologic truth" is an unscientific exaggeration, for it implies a completely proven theory, and this does not exist in biology. Instead of "truth" let us use the term "fact" in biology, because its derivation from the Latin *factum* (deed or act) implies only the action of having verified a presence.

There is a saying that no one believes a hypothesis except its originator, but everybody believes an experiment except the one who performed it. People are prepared to believe an "experimental fact," but the experimenter is keenly aware of all the minutiae that could have misled him. Hence, the discoverer is rarely as confident as are others. Conversely, the originator of an idea is emotionally attached to it and, therefore, tends to be less critical of his brain child than are others.

It is also important to know when to drop a concept that cannot be confirmed. If a hypothesis does not appear to be consistent with observations, do not reject it either too early or too late. Most investigators will drop other people's hypotheses quite easily if the first few experiments do not support them, yet will go on indefatigably trying to find evidence in support of their own cherished ideas. Of course, it is easier to drop an old hypothesis if we have a better one to replace it.

The Value of Wrong Theories

"We can put it down as one of the principles learned from the history of science that a theory is only overthrown by a better theory, never merely by contradictory facts."   [James B. Conant [23]]

"Each time an experimental result shows some contradiction in an existing theory, progress is in sight, because then a change and improvement of the theory becomes necessary."   [Max Planck [55]]

Even a theory that does not fit all the known facts is valuable, as long as it fits them better than any other concept. It is not true that "exceptions prove the rule," but they do not necessarily invalidate it either. Sometimes facts which at first seem quite incompatible with a theory gradually find their natural place in it when new facts come to light. In other cases the theory is sufficiently plastic to be readily adjusted, so as to cover apparently paradoxical, incongruous new observations. "The best theory is that which necessitates the fewest assumptions to unite the most facts, since it is best suited to assimilate still more facts without damage to its own structure" [H. Selye [69]].

There is a great difference between a sterile theory and a wrong one. A sterile theory does not lend itself to experimental verification. Any number of them can easily be formulated, but they are perfectly useless; they could not possibly aid understanding; they lead only to futile verbiage. On the other hand, a wrong theory can still be highly useful, for, if it is well conceived, it may help to formulate experiments which will fill important gaps in our knowledge. *Facts must be correct; theories must be fruitful.* A "fact," if incorrect, is useless—it is not a fact—but an incorrect theory may be even more useful than a correct one if it is more fruitful in leading the way to new facts.

The development of the Wasserman test for syphilis is an excellent example of the value of a false theory. For technical reasons it was impossible to prepare a pure culture of the spirochete which causes syphilis. Hence, Wasserman used as an antigen (the substance necessary for the "complement fixation reaction" which detects syphilis) an extract of liver of stillborn syphilitic children which he knew to be rich in spirochetes. This preparation worked very well, although it was found later that it is quite unnecessary to use syphilitic liver; normal liver will do. Indeed, equally potent antigens can be prepared even from normal organs of other animals. We still don't know why these antigens give a complement fixation reaction which detects syphilis, although evidently Wasserman's reason for using syphilitic liver was wrong. Yet, we would probably still have no serologic test for this disease but for this false and yet very fruitful idea [W. I. B. Beveridge [11]].

It is quite exceptional that a bold new concept will stand the test of time without any need for modification. In surveying the history of his ideas on evolution, Darwin [26] said, ". . . with the exception of the Coral Reefs, I cannot remember a single first-formed hypothesis which had not after a time to be given up or greatly modified."

But this does not matter. As we shall see later, in "Fallacies" (p. 294), even a theory that postulates the exact opposite of the truth may be very valuable.

The true scientist is just as interested in disproving as in proving his theories; if a theory has real value, it is equally meritorious to show that it is right or wrong. When Magendie found by experiment a result contrary to what he had expected, he exclaimed with delight, "I foresaw a probable and logical fact that anybody could have imagined, and it is the contrary that happened. Now, I discovered an essentially new phenomenon whose importance is proportional to its unexpectedness" [Charles Richet [59]].

Induction vs. Deduction

"A great deal of nonsense is, I fear, uttered in this land of England about induction and deduction. Some profess to befriend the one, some the other, while the real vocation of an investigator, like Faraday, consists in the incessant marriage of both."

[Tyndall, as quoted by Wilder Dwight Bancroft [6]]

"The words inductive and deductive would be useful if people agreed as to what they mean. Most of us would class Bacon as the exponent of inductive reasoning, but Mellor [*A Comprehensive Treatise on Inorganic and Theoretical Chemistry*, Vol. I, p. 17, 1922] reverses this and says that deductive method was favoured by Francis Bacon and the inductive method by Isaac Newton. Mellor goes so far as to say that 'the method of Aristotle was rediscovered and restated by Francis Bacon in his Novum Organum,' a statement which would have surprised Bacon a good deal if he could have heard it." [Wilder Dwight Bancroft [6]]

Induction is the act of reasoning from a part to a whole, from particulars to generals, or from the individual to the universal. On the other hand, deduction is the reasoning from the general to the particular, or from the universal to the individual. The statement is often made, in a dogmatic manner, that in the natural sciences only deductive reasoning is permissible, while the generalizing of inductive thinking should be left to philosophers. Yet others point out that deductive reasoning is sterile because it can give you nothing new. Your conclusions are contained in the premises, which you assume to be known. I must admit that both these views always impressed me as very shortsighted theoretic attitudes, which have never been and should never be applied, in actual practice, to biologic research.

But let us illustrate the use of inductive and deductive reasoning again by an actual problem which I have encountered in my own work.

Desoxycorticosterone is a sodium-retaining or "mineralocorticoid" adrenal hormone and we found that, under suitable experimental conditions, it antagonizes the anti-inflammatory action of cortisol. Another mineralocorticoid, Reichstein's compound "S," also antagonizes these same actions of cortisol. By actual observation, this has been confirmed in a number of individual instances using a series of mineralocorticoid hormones and, hence, we arrived by *inductive* reasoning at the generalization that mineralocorticoids antagonize these properties of cortisol.

Now, after the "natural mineralocorticoid" hormone aldosterone was discovered, we asked ourselves what pharmacologic actions it might possess. It was only then that we could turn to *deductive* reasoning and argue from the general to the particular. We assumed that, since aldosterone is also a mineralocorticoid, it may reasonably be expected to have anticortisol properties. It was on this basis that we actually decided to test the few milligrams of aldosterone available to us for this, rather than for any of the innumerable other actions it might have possessed. In agreement with our hypothesis, aldosterone was found to be a potent antagonist of the anti-inflammatory hormones.

The successive application of both these steps in reasoning was necessary first to propose the "corticoid antagonism theory" and then to verify whether or not the "natural mineralocorticoid" would behave as predicted by this concept. But we may go further. Nothing but a similar combination of inductive and deductive reasoning could have led us even to postulate a relationship between corticoids and clinical rheumatic diseases, merely on the basis of experiments with desoxycorticosterone-treated rats, more than six years before the first rheumatic patient received cortisone.

In biology, both deductive and inductive reasoning have definite limitations, but the limiting factor is the same for both. The smaller the number of individual observations, the greater the danger that generalizations made from them will not hold true. This limits inductive and deductive reasoning to the same extent. When the at first unconnected observations are gradually arranged into a science, *induction and deduction follow each other and depend upon each other*. They are like consecutive steps with the left and right foot in walking; it would be quite false to attribute greater importance to one or the other.

Those who object to inductive reasoning do not realize that what they actually deplore is the unwarranted confidence in a general law. To inspire confidence, a generalization must be based on as many observations as possible. However, once formulated on the basis of a given number of data, it is neither more nor less likely to be correct as a general law than as a guide permitting correct deductions in new particular instances. Of course, such deductions cannot be accepted as equivalents of a proof; their immense value lies merely in singling out, among the infinite number of possible experiments, those few which are worth doing. To scientists accustomed to abstract thinking, these considerations may seem puerile and superfluous, but perusal of the medical literature shows that, in practice, these points are very frequently overlooked.

Pure logic can only establish whether two things are or are not equal. Yet, by doing this from every point of view, we can appraise quantity, quality, and even causal interrelations. Both induction and deduction merely establish juxtaposition for comparison between the particular and the general. Therefore, I see no essential difference between them. To me, a reverse syllogism is still a syllogism. I may say, "All the beads on thread X are iron beads; this bead is on thread X, hence, it is an iron bead." Or I may say, "This bead is on thread X; all the beads on thread X are iron beads, hence, this bead is an iron bead." Actually, experimentation is not based on syllogisms, but on conditional syllogisms. We say that "If all glucocorticoids are anti-inflammatory corticoids and if cortisone is a glucocorticoid, then cortisone is an anti-inflammatory corticoid." Articulated logic is not applicable to biology because neither the major nor the minor premise can ever be completely proven.

How to Question Nature

I have said that all judgment is made up of simple comparisons between two things to see whether there is or is not a variable between them. The question is merely whether or not they are equal, and the answer can only be "yes" or "no." Nature is not loquacious; she merely nods in the affirmative or in the negative. The art is in the formulation of the questions. "What is stress?" is not a question to which she can reply in this way; therefore, it is an impractical question.

Occasionally, if we ask, "What would you do if . . . ?" or, "What is in such and such a place?" Nature will silently show you a picture. But she never explains. You have to work things out for yourself first, aided only by instinct and by the feeble powers of the human brain, until you can ask precise practical questions to which Nature can answer in her precise but silent sign language of nods and pictures. Understanding grows out of a mosaic of such answers. It is up to the scientist to draw a blueprint of the questions he has to ask before the mosaic will make sense. It is curious how few laymen, or even biologists, understand this.

If you want to know whether a certain endocrine gland is necessary for growth, you remove it surgically from the body of a growing young experimental animal. If growth stops, the answer is "yes." If you want to know whether a certain substance extracted from this gland is a growth-promoting hormone, you inject it into the same animal, and, if the latter now begins to grow again, the answer is "yes."

These are the nods of Nature.

If you want to know what is in the fat tissue around the kidney, you dissect it and find the adrenal. If your question concerns the shape, size, or structure of this gland, you just look at it; you can examine even its finest details under a powerful miscroscope.

Such are the pictures of Nature.

But if you now ask, "What is an adrenal?" you will get no reply. This is the wrong question; it cannot be answered by nods or pictures.

Bacon said, "Man can only put things together or asunder." The same is true of ideas. We can only dissect the complex phenomena of Nature into their units and then compare the units of one phenomenon with those of another. Very complex pictures can be built up this way, but they give us the impression of qualitative differences merely by the composite mosaic that results from innumerable "yes-or-no" answers. The electronic brain shows what complex activities can be performed by the innumerable combinations of "yes-or-no" answers. The art lies in knowing what to compare from what point of view, how to bring the twin units together for comparison, and how to arrange the simple answers into the most instructive network of information.

Prerequisites of Good Theories

Theories are the threads that hold our facts together, and, since the units of biologic concepts are impure and overlapping (ideablock, p. 273), it is impossible in medicine to construct completely watertight and unalterable connections between facts—connections which would never require rearrangement. Only when our mind, because of its inherent structure, is automatically led from one point to another, when facts appear to touch each other, are we faced with "self-evident truths" which do not need the support of theory or proof (e.g., the fact that syllogistic inference is true, or that $2 + 2 = 4$). The wider the gap which theory must breach and the more indirect the course of argument, the less the inferences derived from it can be predicted with certainty. In terms of the idea-net analogy (p. 275), the longer the thread we must use to connect two nodes, the more probable it is that the position of one of them may change when new threads are attached, or that intermediate beads will be discovered. All of this makes for uncertainty. On the other hand, the more nodes found and stabilized by verified close cross connections, the greater the stability of the theory regarding a region of the net. In other words, a good theory should unite the greatest number of facts in the simplest (closest) possible way.

In essence, all biologic theories can be fitted into the following three categories: 1) theories of unit formation; 2) theories of classification; and 3) theories of causality.

Theories of Unit Formation

We have used the term "biologic unit" to designate any aspect of life that can be treated as one thing. It may be a target, an agent, or any one quality of targets and agents (color, age). Complexes are combinations of smaller units, but they themselves are also units within a still larger structure. Cells are units of the liver, the liver is a unit of the body, the body of the species. The delimitation of units is only a convenient abstraction. Like the symbols of algebra, units permit us to handle cognate things as single packages. This makes the handling easier. Instead of always having to remember and enumerate everything in the unit, we can discuss it merely by mentioning the name of the whole package, as if it referred to something simple, unchangeable and clearly demarcated from everything else. Of course, no biologic unit is like that, but it is convenient to nail down the essentials by saying, for instance, that "Starchy foods cause adiposity," before we turn our attention to such details as the fact that not all quantities of all starchy foods cause adiposity in everybody.

Ever since the dawn of recorded history, perfectionists have been indefatigable in assailing the very principle of unit formation, yet we could not make a single statement about biology without making use of them. Biologic units, like most concepts in Nature, have only statistical meaning: when we say, "Starches make fat," we mean that most starches make most people fat; when we say, "Pregnancy lasts nine months," we mean that in most women pregnancy lasts approximately nine months.

The unifying theory acts like a magnet. It gathers the cognate from random distribution among the irrelevant, so that related data may be used and transmitted (taught to others or stored in memory) in one convenient package.

Theories of Classification

Classification is the oldest and simplest of scientific methods. It is a prerequisite for all types of theory construction, including the complex procedure of establishing causal relations between classified things. Without classification, we could not even speak, for every common noun (man, kidney, star) is based on the recognition of a class. To accept the existence of a class (e.g., vertebrates) is to recognize the essential characteristics (vertebrae) that its subunits have in common. Hence, classification presupposes the recognition of smaller units which are common to a larger unit (the class itself). All classification is based on the discovery of some order in things. Science is not concerned with individuals as such but with generalizations, that is, with classes and with the laws according to which the members of these classes are arranged in orderly fashion. That is why the process of classification is fundamental. It is usually the first step in the development of any science.

We have said that the best theory of classification is that which connects the largest number of facts in the simplest possible manner. Let me illustrate this graphically. The next diagram shows the *initial confusion* that exists when apparently unrelated subjects are discovered. Seven of them have something in common: they all contain solid black lines. We may call them the "black-striped class," to distinguish them from all other subjects that do not contain black lines. Within this class we can also recognize subclasses with dots and a black stripe, checkers and a black stripe and only a black stripe. This leaves us with one unit (No. 3) which does not fit into any of these classes, as it contains two black stripes, dots and checkers. Such a classification is not based on any theory but merely on observation.

If an observer met some such problem in Nature, he would soon wonder whether, on the basis of size, shape and pattern, he could not fit all these units into a single system. He might guess (hypothesize) that thereby he could reveal new principles of order between the individual items. After trying to put them together in various ways, he hits upon an arrangement based on the hypothesis that all these units possess characteristics which naturally fit them into *two parallel lines*.

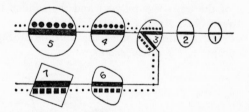

If he is bold, he may even postulate a direct transition from the large round circle (No. 5) to the small ellipse (No. 1), and a second system in which the large square (No. 7) transforms itself into the smaller, curve-cornered figure (No. 6).

When so arranged, certain new regularities do, in fact, become obvious. For example, measurement shows that the longest diameter of successive units in the top row decreases from left to right by exactly the length of the smallest diameter (breadth) of No. 1. Furthermore, all the units in both rows can now be connected by simple, straight lines (black, dotted or checkered) which are projections of the inherent, "natural," pattern of the units.

Still, this classification is, on the whole, unsatisfactory. The dotted and checkered unit, No. 3, does not fit naturally into either series and the connecting link between the top and bottom row is artificial: nothing in the units themselves suggests such a long, angular connection between No. 3 and No. 6 as postulated by the hypothesis of arrangement. Finally, several units cannot stand upright if their stripes are arranged horizontally. This hypothesis does not offer a simple, harmonious order of connection between the units; yet, although it is bad (can we say false?), it does call our attention to certain unexpected regularities.

Now, another investigator wants to bring more order into this pattern by arranging all units in a *single line.*

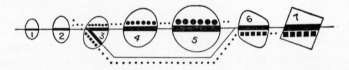

This pattern is perhaps a little simpler. For one thing, the numerical order is natural, from 1 to 7. But one unit, No. 3, now still creates an irregularity in the arrangement, the numbers are still crooked, the connecting lines still contain purely hypothetical kinks (the existence of which is in no way implied by observable characteristics of the units themselves) and the sudden break in size and shape between Nos. 5 and 6 is artificial.

Then a third investigator classifies the units according to an entirely novel concept: the Y *arrangement.*

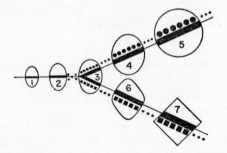

This classification is clearly superior to all others. It connects the seven units in a simple, orderly manner, and uses a minimum of perfectly straight connecting lines (assumptions) all of which are implied by the observed patterns of the units themselves.

At about this point, the hypothesis becomes a theory, especially if it possesses the power of prediction. This would be the case, for example, if exploration beyond the left of unit No. 1 succeeded in finding smaller, black-striped ellipses or if, to the upper right of unit No. 5, larger, dotted-and-black-striped circles were discovered, in agreement with expectations.

Once so far verified, this theory could inspire new hypotheses. It brings up the possibility that all the units may have developed from a common ancestor to the left of No. 1 (theory of evolution) or that all units tend to become simplified into ever smaller black-striped ellipses, like No. 1 (theory of dedifferentiation). Like any pure theory of classification, it cannot be verified except by the order it creates, including its power of predicting future orderliness (e.g., by showing where and what kind of additional units of this type might be expected). It does not attempt to reveal causal relations between the units, but furnishes a base line for this usually later step. The orderliness itself suggests cause-and-effect relationships. For instance, if in Nature we saw some units arranged in this Y pattern, we might suspect that some local factors along the branches of the Y cause the appearance of black lines, dots or checkers. Alternately, we might also feel that the possession of such patterns forced the units into Y shape.

All this becomes even more evident when illustrated by an actual problem of biology. The relationship between bone, cartilage and connective tissue has long been puzzling. If various regions of skeletal structures are examined under the microscope at random, we see cells of the following types:

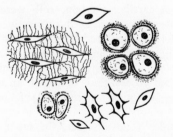

It is evident that all these shapes have certain characteristics in common; for example, they all contain central dark nuclei. But in other respects they are quite dissimilar: some cells are small, others large; some are isolated, others form groups; some are naked, others are covered with branching processes or are surrounded by dense capsules. This confusing lack of orderliness could be dispelled only by studies which eventually permitted us to classify these cell types as shown in the next diagram.

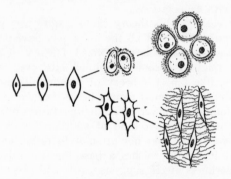

From left to right we note that first, "undifferentiated" connective tissue cells grow until the third stage (middle of the Y), then they increase in number by division and at the same time differentiate either into roundish, encapsulated cartilage cells (upper branch of Y) or into elongated, slender bone cells with branching extensions (lower branch of Y). Finally, in the four-cell stage we see the typical microscopic aspect of mature cartilage (top) or bone (bottom).

The hypothesis that led to this classification was confirmed by: (1) the resulting orderliness (demonstration of an uninterrupted line of transitional stages from left to right); (2) the power of prediction (wherever cartilage or bone cells were found it was possible to demonstrate undifferentiated connective-tissue cell precursors); (3) the orderliness-inspired fruitful hypothesis (evolution of connective-tissue cells into cartilage or bone cells, role of local factors in this transformation). These hypotheses became theories when it was proven, by actual observation, that such an evolution can occur and that local (e.g., chemical, mechanical) factors are able to induce it.

These two examples (one abstract, the other actual) show how mere classification can help us to formulate a theory which reveals order and has predictive value. But the most useful biologic theories deal directly with causality.

Theories of Causality

The mere inspection of natural events will not reveal causal connections. These can be inferred only from lawful connections between certain physical antecedents and consequents. The general procedure for establishing causal connections has been formulated in the "Canons of Induction," also known as *The Five Simpler Inductive Methods* [A. Wolf [91]].

If it were possible to formulate pure units in biology, the construction of theories about causality could become a standardized process, subject to mathematical analysis. In his classic work, *The Laws of Thought*, Boole [12] outlined this method. It rests on the assumption that the symbolic processes of algebra, which had been invented as tools of numerical calculation, should also be competent to express every act of thought. This type of procedure has been applied, for example, by Woodger [90] in *The Technique of Theory Construction*. Here, every observation and every act of reasoning is denoted by a simple symbol, so that the validity of any conclusion can be checked by following it backwards through the whole chain of antecedents and consequents on which it was based. This analysis of the laws of thought through symbolic logic is one of the greatest accomplishments of the human intellect. Yet, as I have said so often, in biology its applicability is extremely restricted, because our units cannot be sharply delimited and, hence, their designation by simple symbols creates ambiguities. Worse than that, it gives a wholly fictitious impression of precision and certainty; it makes us forget that inference valid for the symbols is not necessarily valid for what they are intended to symbolize.

Some simple symbolism can help us to understand the procedures of causal theory construction, but only if we always remember that our symbols—just like the words in our language—have only statistical validity. The idea of a dog is symbolized by the word "dog," not because all dogs are absolutely equal (which would imply that whatever we say about one dog is true of all others), but because most dogs are similar in most respects. Hence, it is statistically probable that whatever we find out about one dog—or better, about many dogs—will be true of most other members of this species. (Evaluation by analogy, p. 225.)

An exhaustive philosophic discussion of causality in relation to Heisenberg's principle of indeterminancy would be beyond the scope of these Notes. But, whatever we may think of causality, scientific research would be impossible without the assumption of causal connections between antecedents and consequents. The human mind cannot embrace and handle complex events unless their parts are connected by causality threads. The first aim of science is orderly simplification. The mere recognition of innumerable natural phenomena is of no use if we cannot return to them at will through the mental labyrinth of all possible connections.

Ariadne, daughter of Minos, King of Greece, fell in love with Theseus and gave him a clew of thread to guide him out of the labyrinth in case he should slay the Minotaur. Causality may have no more inherent value than Ariadne's thread, but, without it, in research we could not find the way through our labyrinths any more than Theseus could have through his. Perhaps causality is no more than the mind's habit of connecting regularly recurring sequences of events in terms of cause and effect. But the biologist is less preoccupied with the epistemological justification of this way of thinking than with its dangers.

In "Fallacies" (p. 294) we shall analyze the sundry errors committed by biologists because of the difficulty of distinguishing the *post hoc* from the *propter hoc*. The fundamental difficulty here is well illustrated by a striking if imaginary example, brought up by one of my students at a staff meeting some years ago. People on Mars watch us through strong telescopes. They note that each time a traffic light turns red, all automobiles stop and do not move again until the light turns green. Some Martian scientists concluded that, strong and speedy as our cars are, a red light paralyzes their mechanism. However, this theory was soon attacked by scholars who argued that the motion of cars causes the light to turn green. Now, all astronomic research concentrated on the accurate measurement of time relations between the changing of the lights and the motion of the cars to see which comes first, since only this type of study could distinguish between cause and effect. Actually, there is no causal relationship between the color of the traffic light and the functioning of the motor ... or should we say that there is—indirectly?

Theories of Teleology

"Teleology is a lady without whom no biologist can live. Yet he is ashamed to show himself with her in public."

[Von Bruecke as quoted by Walter Cannon [16]]

An allegedly still more disreputable sister of causality is teleology. Causality only states that a change is produced by an agent, but teleology suggests purposeful causation, the intention to achieve an aim. When two creations fight, how do we know which is the Creator's favorite? The problem is neatly put in P. Schwartz's essay on inflammation. He says:

"One should think that the exalted Law of Nature—to vary a famous saying of Anatole France—recognizes no difference between microbes and man. One cannot consider inflammation as a specific 'cleansing' measure, that is, one for the conservation of tissues, any more than one can envisage malignant neoplasia (cancer) as having the 'purpose' or 'duty' to destroy organs: both processes are—just as all manifestations of Nature—in themselves aimless and purposeless phenomena."

The great danger in the interpretation of creation with a purpose is what I call the "post factum teleology." The patterns of living beings, as established by evolution, are certainly useful—they are useful in making and maintaining those living beings as they are. The question is, who wants these creatures to be just the way they are? Think of a complex inanimate structure such as the St. Lawrence River. From its many sources to its broad estuary, every rock in its bed, every island and tributary is precisely so arranged as to give it the form it has. If the river were alive, it would undoubtedly consider itself desirable. It would stand awestruck before the carefully planned lawfulness that has, throughout the ages, directed all elements of Nature to act in perfect harmony to perform the billions of tasks necessary to carve this particular river bed just as it is. But if the river had any other shape, would it not think the same? It has to have some shape! Teleology assumes that whatever happens to exist was the purpose of the forces that brought it into existence.

We sense a Creator mainly because we and our surroundings seem complex, and during his short life span man sees no really complex structure built up by chance without the purposeful influence of a maker. But could not the organizing effect of a centralizing teleology be our view of the maker? Could it not—in the span of aeons—eventually build up awe-inspiring complexities, such as a planet, a tree, or even a man?

Having been built and being capable of building are the most inherent characteristics of our every part. We, therefore, see everything through an atmosphere of building which tinges all our perceptions, just as a red crystal ball—were it alive and capable of perception—would see everything red, inside and outside itself. Teleologic thought does not necessarily have to lean upon an individual, purposeful Creator; nor should it do so, even on religious grounds, since faith does not need the support of understanding.

What we must clearly realize in biology is that teleologic analysis is applicable to every unit of creation.

Science cannot and should not attempt to embrace the purpose of the original Creator; but it can and must constantly examine teleologic motives in the objects of creation. Only by doing this can science progress from the mere accumulation of unintelligible facts to what we call understanding.

That is why, despite all the invectives heaped on teleology, I still agree with Cannon [16] when he says: "My first article of belief is based on the observation, almost universally confirmed in present knowledge, that what happens in our bodies is directed toward a useful end."

FALLACIES

"Nature will tell you a direct lie if she can."
[Charles Darwin, quoted by Walter Cannon [16]]

In logic, fallacies are usually classified as material (misstatement of fact), verbal (misuse of terms) and logical or formal (misjudgment of inference). The classification used in Aristotle's *Organon* (*Sophistici elenchi*) distinguishes the following eight basic types:

1. *Fallacy of accident,* confusion of an accidental fact with what is essential (e.g., hormones are white substances).

2. *Secundum quid,* erroneous argument from the general rule to the particular case, or vice versa, without regard to modifying circumstances (e.g., if stress causes thymus involution, exposure of an adrenalectomized rat to stress must cause thymus involution. Actually, stress acts on the thymus through the adrenals; hence, its effect is inhibited by adrenalectomy).

3. *Irrelevant conclusion,* special pleading by diverting attention to some irrelevant fact (e.g., instead of proving that the theory is false, attack its proponent).

4. *Begging the question,* arguing in a circle by means of premises which presuppose a conclusion (e.g., condemning an argument because it is "unscientific").

5. *Fallacy of the consequent,* arguing from a consequent to its condition (e.g., parathyroidectomy causes convulsions, therefore, convulsions indicate lack of parathyroid hormone).

6. *Non sequitur,* basing a conclusion on insufficient or false evidence (e.g., cold is a stressor, cold causes shivering, hence, shivering is a nonspecific effect of all stressors).

7. *Post hoc ergo propter hoc,* if a change follows treatment with an agent, it must be caused by this agent (e.g., if an experiment succeeded in the spring but not in the fall, its success must depend upon seasonal variations).

8. *Fallacy of plural questions,* in which several questions are improperly grouped in the form of one (e.g., why is cortisone the most useful of all corticoids? Here, the admission that this is, in fact, the most useful corticoid, is smuggled into the question by making it appear to be a proven fact).

Such a systematization of all possible fallacies into a finite number of groups is very tempting but quite fallacious in itself; the groups overlap and very little assistance is given to the scientist in his daily work by the mere classification and naming of erroneous interpretations. As Claude Bernard [9] says in the concluding passage of his classic, *Introduction to the Study of Experimental Medicine:*

"When philosophers, such as Bacon or other more modern thinkers, wanted to offer a general systematization of precepts for scientific research, they may have seemed seductive to people who see the sciences only from afar; but such undertakings are of no value to already trained scientists, nor to those who intend to dedicate themselves to science; in fact, they confuse them by implying a false simplicity of things; in addition, they encumber the mind by a mass of vague and inapplicable precepts which must be rapidly forgotten if one wants to enter into science and become a true experimenter."

Still, traps in reasoning continually lurk in every corner of the lab and it may be useful to call the attention of the young scientist to the most common among them.

I have no illusions about being able either to classify these fallacies into non-overlapping categories or to exhaust the list. Here, I only want to enumerate a rather respectable number of the traps into which I personally have fallen, or was in danger of falling, at one time or another. By recognizing the prototypes, we are alerted and, as the French say, "L'homme averti en vaut deux" ("The forewarned man is worth two").

Before I embark on this enumeration, a word of warning is necessary in case these Notes should fall into the hands of a reader not particularly conversant with my field of interest. To him I say, just glance through the following pages superficially or skip them completely, for it will take some effort to think your way through these traps. I could have used simple, imaginary examples (arrows shot at apples, instead of hormones acting on glands and the like), but if these Notes have any virtue compared with the customary theoretic discussions of logic and psychology, it is that they are based throughout on personal experiences. As I have said before, the highly simplified, abstract laws of thought are not easily applied to the practical problems of the lab. By contrast, the prototypes of traps that we have actually encountered in one field of research have a practical reality about them which makes their applicability to other areas of science, and even to everyday life, rather self-evident.

To me, the most striking thing about the errors made even by the most eminent scientists is their naïveness. It seems almost inconceivable that highly gifted, great thinkers could fall into these simple traps. In retrospect, once the mistake is explained, even the most primitive intellect can easily recognize it. Yet all my examples are real. They are all taken from the actual history of biology, they are *mistakes actually committed by experienced career scientists*. Most of these mistakes are due to the fact that, once we look upon something from a certain point of view, psychologic blocks develop which prevent us from seeing the subject in another perspective. All our interpretations depend upon past experience, but, as much as our memories can assist the thinking process, they can also impede it. We develop blind spots for the unusual which seems improbable, but it is the richest source of great discoveries.

THE ERROR OF THE OMITTED CONTROL.   This is the most common error in biologic experimentation. Everybody knows that if you want to study the effect of a treatment you need an untreated control for comparison. However, in actual experimentation, many other forms of controls may be necessary to provide a meaningful framework of reference. For example, if we want to establish the specific effects of an injected drug, the proper control is not an animal given no injections, but one given similar injections of the solvent in which the treated animal receives the drug. Thereby, any nonspecific action of the solvent and of the injection procedure, itself, can be eliminated as sources of error.

The need for such controls is usually recognized, but more hidden sources of error are often overlooked. For example, if the drug to be tested is a diuretic, an anesthetic, or simply a very toxic substance, controls are necessary which possess equal diuretic, anesthetic or toxic effects, before an observed change can be attributed specifically to the drug under investigation.

No wonder I am particularly conscious of the need for this type of control because, without it, the stress concept could never have been developed. When adrenal hypertrophy and thymus atrophy were produced by formaldehyde injections, it was only too tempting to conclude that these effects were due to formaldehyde. Actually, they are and they aren't. It is true that formaldehyde produces such changes, but so does atropine, morphine, adrenaline, cold, heat, and every other stressor. Hence, it is misleading to state the conclusion in terms implying that adrenal hypertrophy and thymus atrophy are characteristic actions of formaldehyde, just as anesthesia is a typical action of ether. We now know that the stress of formaldehyde treatment—like that caused by any other agent—produces adrenal enlargement and thymus atrophy. But, in order to justify this formulation, a great many controls were necessary; for example, we had to show that various agents, otherwise unrelated to formaldehyde (e.g., other drugs, trauma, changes in temperature) produce the same changes and that formaldehyde elicits them in proportion to its other stressor actions.

A few years ago I came across a paper stating that, some days after removal of the kidneys (bilateral nephrectomy), rats no longer respond with the usual anaphylactoid reaction to egg white. It was concluded that the presence of renal tissue is indispensable for this reaction. Although I doubted this interpretation, repetition of the experiment fully confirmed the published findings. By that time, we already knew that all severe stressors can prevent the anaphylactoid reaction; hence, we performed control surgical operations, comparable in severity to the removal of the kidneys. These interventions were ineffective, and now it seemed even more justified to conclude that renal tissue is, in fact, indispensable for this anaphylactoid response. However, in the absence of the kidneys, a severe uremic intoxication gradually develops which adds to the stress of the operation itself. Appropriate additional control experiments showed that immediately after ablation of the kidneys, rats do react normally with an anaphylactoid reaction to egg white. It is only a few days later, when uremia sets in, that they become refractory. This control experiment proved conclusively that exactly the contrary of the published original interpretation is correct: renal tissue is not necessary for the anaphylactoid reaction. We therefore assumed that the unusually intense stress of uremia blocks this response, but still further controls were required to prove that uremia acts only by virtue of its stressor effect.

INTERSECTING DOSE-EFFECT CURVES. So accustomed are we to finding that large doses are more effective than small ones that our mind is ill prepared for observations contradicting this general rule. Often an investigator, failing to confirm the work of a colleague, emphatically points out that he could not reproduce the reported finding "although" he administered many times the dose used by his predecessor.

Some time ago, we found that the male sex hormone, testosterone, causes adrenal atrophy. This was contested by others who obtained no such change, "although" they administered several times as much testosterone as we did. A repetition of those experiments showed that the observations of our critics were correct. But so were ours. Owing to a specific effect of this compound, small doses of testosterone cause adrenal atrophy, while large doses induce adrenal hypertrophy, presumably because their stressor effect overcompensates this specific adrenal-atrophy-producing action of the hormone. It was this work that first called our attention to a very general pharmacologic phenomenon, which we called the "law of the intersecting dose-effect curves." It can explain many apparent paradoxes in pharmacology.

In endocrinology, it is a widely accepted axiom that, if a crude glandular extract can be partitioned into two fractions having qualitatively different effects, this constitutes proof that the impure original preparation contained two chemically distinct, active principles, now separated from each other. In the case of glands, e.g., the pituitary and the placenta which produce several hormones, this axiom has been, and still is, the basis of every discussion concerning the alleged discovery of new hormones. Yet it is false, and this is how we proved it:

If we prepare a solution containing a fixed proportion (say 1:1) of two chemically pure, but pharmacologically antagonistic, hormones, we may obtain qualitatively different (indeed, sometimes diametrically opposite) effects with the same solution given at low and at high dose levels. It had long been known, for instance, that in the rat a folliculoid or "estrogenic" compound (e.g., estradiol) causes cornification, while a luteoid (e.g., progesterone) produces mucification of the vagina. When low doses of estradiol, just sufficient to cause vaginal cornification, are given conjointly with high doses of progesterone, the cornifying effect of the former is totally abolished by the latter compound and the vagina becomes mucified. However, we showed that a solution, containing a mixture with a fixed proportion of estradiol and progesterone, causes cornification at low, and mucification at high dose levels. Presumably, very small doses of estradiol are capable of producing a virtually maximal effect which is not inhibited by small doses of progesterone. But, as the dose of both compounds is raised, the blocking action of progesterone gradually comes to predominate because it continues to increase in intensity as the dose is increased, while the opposite effect of estradiol does not increase.

To show the wide applicability of this concept, let us take yet another example from a different field of endocrinology. It is well known that in the adrenalectomized rat an experimentally produced inflammation can be inhibited by an anti-inflammatory corticoid (e.g., cortisol), and that this inhibition is, in turn, blocked by a pro-inflammatory hormone (e.g., desoxycorticosterone acetate, or "DCA"). It is possible, however, to prepare a mixture (containing both these hormones in a fixed proportion) of which small amounts stimulate, while large doses inhibit, inflammation. Indeed, if we now take this solution and dilute part of it, the pro-inflammatory effect of the dilute portion can be antagonized by the simultaneous administration of the more concentrated original solution. This phenomenon is, again, explicable by the "law of the intersecting dose-effect curves" as illustrated in the following picture.

Illustration of the "Law of the Intersecting Dose-Effect Curves"

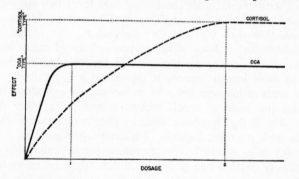

We note that the effect of DCA rises very sharply, but it rapidly reaches a plateau at dose level "1." The effect of cortisol increases more slowly, but eventually reaches a much higher plateau at dose "2." These curves also fit the previously mentioned antagonism between estradiol and progesterone except that, there, the "target" is not inflammation, but vaginal cornification.

We must keep in mind that the "law of the intersecting dose-effect curves" does not deal with mutual chemical neutralization between two compounds, but with antagonistic interrelationships between two pharmacologic properties. This is why it can manifest itself even with different doses of a single compound, if the latter possesses two independent and potentially antagonistic pharmacologic properties. Testosterone is such a compound, since it produces vaginal cornification at low, and mucification at high dose levels. We have seen that testosterone also causes adrenal atrophy at low, and hypertrophy at high dose levels for similar reasons.

From what has been said so far, the impression might be gained that the phenomenon of the intersecting dose-effect curves could be misleading only when the pharmacologic properties of one preparation reverse those of another substance. Actually, it can even create qualitatively new effects. For example, as seen from the preceding graph, neither the pro-inflammatory nor the anti-inflammatory effect of the corticoid mixture is evident at the point of intersection, so that, here, this one action is selectively removed from the total picture. Other properties of DCA and cortisol are not mutually antagonistic (e.g., the liver-glycogen-depositing effect of cortisol is not depressed by DCA at any dose level on the above curve), and yet, other effects (e.g., the life-maintaining power of corticoids in adrenal insufficiency) are mutually enhanced. It is easy to see how an investigator, furnished with several vials containing only these two steroids in the same fixed proportion, but at different dilutions, could come to the conclusion that each vial contains altogether different hormones in the pure state or, at least, different proportions of many hormones.

I have discussed the phenomenon of the intersecting dose-effect curves at some length because it represents a particularly common cause of error in my own fields of endocrinology and stress research. It is also the basis of much misunderstanding in other domains. But, despite all that has been said, separation of crude extracts into fractions with pharmacologically distinct properties is an important step. It furnishes a very legitimate reason for believing that a crude material *may* contain two principles which might be separated from each other. Yet, the possibility of such separation merely furnishes a logical reason for suspecting the presence of several hormones. Thus, it justifies further chemical work to attempt complete isolation and identification, the only definite proof for the existence of a new biologic principle in an impure extract.

DISSOCIATED TIME-EFFECT CURVES. A somewhat similar kind of problem arises when the various actions of the same agent do not manifest themselves simultaneously.

To illustrate, in our studies on stress and the general adaptation syndrome (p. 97), it was noted that the transition between its three typical stages (the alarm reaction, the stage of resistance, and the stage of exhaustion) is not sharp. Often there is some dissociation in the manifestations, with certain signs of two stages simultaneously in evidence. This is so, no matter what stressor agent is used to elicit the syndrome, and we may, therefore, take the following schematic drawing as an illustration of dissociated time-effect curves during stress in general.

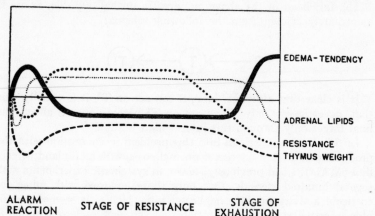

EDEMA-TENDENCY

ADRENAL LIPIDS

RESISTANCE
THYMUS WEIGHT

ALARM
REACTION STAGE OF RESISTANCE STAGE OF
EXHAUSTION

Here, the edema-tendency, the adrenal lipids, resistance to stress, and thymus-weight (given as illustrative examples selected at random) do not traverse simultaneously from the alarm reaction to the resistant stage and, subsequently, to the stage of exhaustion. This has been ascribed to different degrees of "inertia" in the various targets affected by stress.

It is evident that if any agent produces such dissociated time-effect curves in different targets, the over-all pattern of response may be totally different in two experiments, merely because they have been terminated and analyzed at different times. Of course, the development of the whole syndrome at a given time also depends upon a variety of other factors which are not always easy to control or even to recognize (e.g., state of nutrition, dosage, and speed of absorption of an injected stressor substance, influence of uncontrollable contaminants, surrounding temperature).

THE RELAY STATION. Let us assume that it has been shown by actual observation that both the stimulus S and the hormone of an endocrine gland T can act on a target T^1. It seems rather obvious that, in this event, the theory which holds that *only* T can act on T^1 is necessarily false.

If the problem happens to present itself in this formulation, it is very tempting to consider the above statement as self-evident. Yet it overlooks the possibility of complications due to a relayed effect through T. Any endocrinologist knows that all the final effects of gland-stimulating ("glandulotrophic") pituitary hormones are thus mediated; nevertheless the error is quite common in actual practice.

The falsehood of the above, apparently unchallengeable, axiom is immediately evident from the following schema:

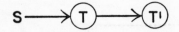

It is clear that although, here, S can act on T^1, it is equally true that, nevertheless, only T can act on T^1 because even S affects the final target only through this intermediate station.

In this Institute, we ran into this problem in connection with the production of a renal disease, nephrosclerosis, with methylandrostene-diol (MAD). I had previously shown, in systematic experiments with several hundred steroids, that only those endowed with mineralo-corticoid activity produce nephrosclerosis. Hence, it seemed justifiable to arrive at the generalization that the nephrosclerotic action is closely related to the mineralocorticoid effect.

Then, one of my former students (Floyd Skelton) published a most interesting paper in which he showed that MAD also produces nephrosclerosis. This compound is a testoid or male sex hormone. It certainly possesses no mineralocorticoid properties; indeed, it has no corticoid activity at all. Even chemically, it is quite different from all cortical hormones.

This fact puzzled us for quite some time, until (in collaboration with Ernesto Salgado) we noted that MAD has no nephrosclerotic action in adrenalectomized rats—although its testoid activities (stimulation of the male accessory sex organs) remain uninfluenced by adrenalectomy.

It thus became evident that, although adrenalectomy does not interfere in any way with the activities characteristic of this compound itself, it prevents the compound from producing nephrosclerosis. This is presumably so because the compound exerts this latter effect through the induction of some "metabolic error" in the adrenal cortex itself; under its influence, the cortical cells produce predominantly mineralocorticoid-like hormones.

THE ALTERNATIVE PATHWAYS. This fallacy is frequently due to a phenomenon which I have called "conditioning," the dependence of a certain action upon modifying agents. Here, the typical reasoning is the following: if a stimulus S acts on a target T^1 only in the presence of an endocrine gland T, then it is highly probable that S acts on T^1 through T. If it can be shown, subsequently, that hormones of T act on T^1 (in the same sense as S acts on T^1 in the presence of T), then it may be taken as virtually certain that S acts on T^1 through the intermediary of T (as depicted in the schema on p. 302).

This conclusion is also false, as shown by the following diagram.

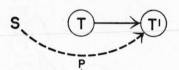

It is evident that, under such circumstances, S may act on T^1 directly, through the pathway P, but the effect of P can become manifest only in the presence of the hormones of T. In this case, we say that P conditions for the hormonal actions of T, but is in itself ineffective.

The study of the corticoids has given us innumerable examples of this type of relationship. For instance, in the adrenalectomized (as opposed to the intact) rat, treatment with a stressor agent (e.g., formalin, cold) does not cause acute accidental thymus involution. On the other hand, cortisol induces thymus involution even in the adrenalectomized rat, and subthreshold doses of cortisol (which would be in themselves ineffective) can be rendered effective by simultaneous treatment with stressors even in the absence of the adrenals. In a case like this, we may say that the stressors conditioned or sensitized the target (thymus) to cortisol. Virtually the same interaction between stressors and cortisol has been demonstrated to hold true for the catabolic, anti-inflammatory, and many other effects of this steroid.

There are several modifications of this type of interaction. For instance, a certain response of T^1 (in the preceding diagram) may not occur under the influence of the hormones of T, nor under the influence of the stimulus S if the gland T is absent. In such cases, the response may still be obtained if both the hormones of T and the stimulus S act simultaneously.

A pertinent example which has come up in the course of my own work on corticoids is the production by DCA of the type of renal lesion called nephrosclerosis. In a normal rat, kept on a low sodium diet, it is virtually impossible to produce nephrosclerosis with DCA.

A moderate excess of sodium chloride alone likewise fails to produce nephrosclerosis under these conditions. Yet, simultaneous treatment with DCA and small dietary sodium chloride supplements invariably produces intense nephrosclerosis.

THE BRANCHING PATHWAYS. The general principle of the most common fallacy, occasioned by a branching of the pathways between stimulus and target, is illustrated as follows:

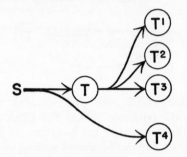

Supposing that, when the actions of the stimulus S are first submitted to study, all the initial investigations happen to be concerned with its effect on T^1, T^2, and T^3. Much effort is devoted to determining exactly how S acts and eventually it can be definitely established for each of these targets that all actions are mediated through the relay point T. As the years go by, it becomes classic textbook knowledge that S can act only through T. If it is now discovered that S also acts on the target T^4, there is a very great temptation to assume that, here again, the action was mediated through the same relay point. Actually, S could still exert this effect directly (as indicated in the drawing) or through some relay station other than T, but by now there is a psychologic block for even considering this possibility.

We ran across this particular problem in connection with our work on the direct actions of ACTH preparations. When we began to study these, it was generally thought that ACTH acts merely by stimulating the corticoid production of the adrenals, since all its known effects could be abolished by adrenalectomy. It then turned out that even the most purified ACTH preparations stimulate the preputial glands of the rat. These structures, being accessory sex organs, are regulated by the gonads. Hence, we repeated our work on castrated animals to check a possible transgonadal mediation. No such action could be demonstrated since ACTH retained its activity in the absence of the gonads. Hence, we silently assumed that we must be dealing with an ordinary, that is, adrenal-mediated, effect of ACTH itself, not with an action due to contaminating gonad-stimulating substances.

It took some time before we realized the necessity of verifying whether or not this particular action of ACTH is actually dependent upon the presence of the adrenals. Finally, when the experiments were repeated on adrenalectomized animals, we found that, curiously, the preputial gland-stimulating effect, unlike all other known actions of the hormone, was not abolished by this operation. Thus, we proved that ACTH itself (or some principle present even in the most purified ACTH preparations) possesses an extra-adrenal direct effect.

Here again, in retrospect, it would seem elementary to check adrenal-mediation. However, among the many previous publications describing the preputial-gland-stimulating effect of ACTH, not one reported any data on adrenalectomized animals. It was considered so self-evident that ACTH could act only through the stimulation of corticoid production, that other possibilities just had not come to mind.

I committed the same error again in connection with the production of nephrosclerosis by large doses of somatotrophic hormone (STH). It had been definitely established by innumerable observations, that STH does not act through the adrenals upon any tissue previously examined. Then, when we observed that, in suitably sensitized rats, large doses of STH can produce nephrosclerosis, the question of a possible adrenal mediation did not even enter my mind for quite some time. However, eventually, we did consider this possibility and found that, in adrenalectomized animals, STH does not cause nephrosclerosis at any dose level. In this respect, even therapy with various corticoids fails to substitute for the missing adrenal. Apparently, the nephrosclerotic action of STH (or of some principle inseparably attached to all available STH preparations) is mediated through the adrenals.

The so-called feedback theory of ACTH secretion during stress, which had been so popular even as late as a few years ago, was based on this same fallacy. It had first been definitely established that, during the alarm reaction, the pituitary secretes ACTH which, in turn, stimulates corticoid production. Conversely, corticoids had been shown to produce "compensatory atrophy" of the adrenals through a diminution of hypophyseal ACTH secretion. Evidently, here, we are dealing with a feedback arrangement. In view of all this, it was tempting to assume that, during stress, ACTH secretion is stimulated through the same mechanism in that the utilization of corticoids is so much increased that a state of functional hypocorticoidism results. This deficiency could then become the stimulus for an increase in ACTH production.

Actually, there is no factual evidence for an increased utilization of corticoids with a consequent hypocorticoidism in the alarm reaction. Indeed, the corticoid concentration in the blood is greatly augmented during stress. We had also demonstrated many years earlier that, even in animals heavily overdosed with various corticoids, stress can still stimulate the adrenal. These findings led us to conclude that "the blood-corticoid level regulates ACTH secretion only at near-physiologic levels." It is actually as a prerequisite for a normal stress reaction that this feedback mechanism must be, at least partly, inactivated. Otherwise, the characteristically great increase in corticoid production could not occur. Nevertheless, the psychologic block to the consideration of branching on alternative pathways was so great that the "tissue utilization and feedback theory" remained popular for many years.

A rather instructive application of the "branching pathways principle" came to our attention in connection with studies on inflammation. Here, the situation was greatly complicated by the fact that it was not the branching of the pathway between stimulus and target, but the uneven distribution of factors influencing target responsiveness that led to confusion.

Two completely independent foci of inflammation—the previously described granuloma pouches (p. 208)—were produced in the same adrenalectomized rat, which was maintained on a medium dose of cortisol. Into one of these foci we introduced a high, into the other a low concentration of irritant (croton oil). Under these conditions, the inflammatory focus containing the high concentration of the irritant underwent complete disintegration (necrosis), because the development of a protective inflammatory barrier or granuloma between tissue and irritant, was insufficient (too much cortisol). The other focus, which contained the lower concentration of irritant, underwent an excessive degree of inflammation without there being any necrosis (too little cortisol).

Thus, the same amount of circulating cortisol resulted in a coexistent hypo- and hypercorticoidism in two foci of inflammation within the same animal. Or, to put it differently, a given blood level of cortisol may be too low to maintain normalcy in one focus, and yet, too high in another location within the same individual.

The principle of these somewhat complex interrelations is illustrated by the following diagram.

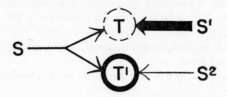

Here, S is the circulating cortisol, S^1 the high concentration, and S^2 the low concentration of croton oil, while T and T^1 are the two inflammatory foci, treated with these different concentrations of the irritant. At T, there results a relative hypercorticoidism manifested by necrosis (disintegration of the barrier), while at T^1, there is a relative hypocorticoidism manifested by excessive inflammation (undue thickening of the barrier).

I believe there are many applications of this same principle that have not yet received the attention they deserve. We are accustomed to thinking of hypo- and hypercorticoidism as conditions which could never coexist in the same individual, because the cortical hormones are necessarily distributed evenly, throughout the blood stream. With this picture in mind, we are ill prepared to think of the eventualities just outlined.

It would be well worth while to explore further the role such conditions play in clinical medicine. For instance, in severe diabetes a large amount of cortisol must be produced in order to maintain life and combat the stress effect of the metabolic derangement. On the other hand, the rise in cortisol production necessarily aggravates the diabetes and the predisposition for infection. Although, here, there are no circumscribed foci with different corticoid requirements, the over-all situation is, again, such that, from a certain point of view there is too much and, from another, too little cortisol in the body.

THE CLASS NAME OR EXTRAPOLATION TRAP. Evidently, there is a certain overlap between the various problems we have considered so far under different headings. However, as I have indicated, my purpose in presenting these fallacies is not so much to arrive at their clear-cut classification as to present them in the way they usually present themselves. We are most likely to avoid such traps in the future if we acquaint ourselves with their manifold camouflages.

For instance, the particular fallacy in thinking which, in our lab we call "the inflated authority of a class name," overlaps, to some extent, with the "branching pathways" and the "alternative pathways" fallacies. Yet, I believe it is instructive to reconsider it specifically in relation to the importance of class names because, so frequently, it is actually a term, itself, which seems to be the immediate cause of error.

Their general principle is illustrated by the next schema.

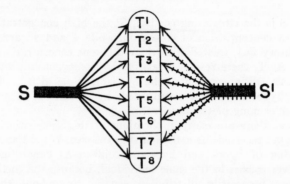

Here, the whole target (represented by the rod-shaped central structure) has many characteristics in common. That is the only reason why we can refer to it by a single class name, say, the "T-rod," instead of having to enumerate each of its parts from T^1 to T^8 every time we mention it. These common characteristics are not necessarily due to an anatomical proximity of the parts; they may have a purely functional basis (e.g., the almost ubiquitous cells of the reticulo-endothelial system which, nevertheless, usually react as one unit).

Such class names are convenient, but they may become misleading. Let us assume that, in our schematic model, an investigator first proves, by actual observation on seven points, that S stimulates (T^1–T^7), while S^1 inhibits (T^2–T^7) the development of the T-rod. Let us assume, furthermore, that by the time he gets that far his supply of S^1 is exhausted. In a case like this, the temptation is great to say that, of course, on T^1 and T^8, the actions of S and S^1 would also mutually neutralize each other. The reason for this is that we come to think of S as a single stimulator (solid common part of the arrow at the left) and of S^1 as a single inhibitor (crosshatched common part of the arrow at the right). Actually, when we examine the schema more closely, it turns out that on T^1, both S and S^1 stimulate, while on T^8, S stimulates but S^1 has no influence in either sense. Here, the formulation of the three class names (and concepts), S for *the* stimulator, S^1 for *the* inhibitor, and T for *the* target, is justifiable and convenient. However, these collective designations themselves became the very reason of a psychologic block which prevents us from seeing such exceptions as may occur at individual points (namely, at T^1 and T^8).

To take an actual example, the male (primary and secondary) sex organs represent a composite target which consists of many structurally quite dissimilar tissues (the testis and beard of a man, the antlers of the stag, the cock's comb, etc.). We refer to them by the single class name "male sex organs" because, despite the diversity of their appearance, function, and site, they are characteristically well-developed in males and not in females. Furthermore, they are generally stimulated by the testoid "male" hormones (e.g., testosterone) and inhibited by the folliculoid "female" hormones (e.g., estradiol). This leads us, in turn, to think of a whole group of other male hormones as stimulators (androsterone, methyltestosterone), and female hormones as inhibitors (estrone, estradiol) in this same sense. The growth of the cock's comb, is in fact stimulated by testosterone, androsterone, and methyltestosterone and inhibited by estradiol, estrone, and estriol. After a similar antagonistic interaction has been established on numerous other male sex organs, the concept of a hormonal antagonism in the genital sphere becomes so firmly established in our mind that exceptions are not readily noticed. Yet, the mammary glands of the male rat are stimulated by both types of hormones, while the preputial glands are stimulated by testoids, but not inhibited by folliculoids.

The discovery of such exceptions invariably induces some critics to question the wisdom of establishing class names for the conjoint consideration of the various parts of a target or for the diverse individual actions of the stimuli. This criticism is quite unjustified. To take the above example, it would be very awkward to get along without the concept of the "male sex organs" or of the "male hormones," despite the exceptional, unusual behavior of certain individual components which the class name tends to unite. It would obviously be impossible, for instance, to enumerate every known (and, indeed, every as yet undiscovered) male hormone whenever we wish to say that a certain organ is stimulated not only by testosterone, methyltestosterone, and androsterone but, as far as we know, by all the male hormones. The human brain itself is so constructed that, in most of our thinking, *we must use symbols* which act as shorthand descriptions for entire classes of related entities. Otherwise, we would be lost in the mass of details with which we have to deal. The solution is not to abandon class names, but to recognize their limitations and to avoid inflating them with an absolute authority which they do not possess. A good class name will serve us well, but only as long as we realize that it refers to similar, not to identical things.

In the course of my own work on the adrenal cortex, I had to face a somewhat different problem, arising from the misunderstandings likely to be caused by class names. When I proposed the terms "mineralocorticoid" and "glucocorticoid" for the two major classes of the life-maintaining adrenal hormone actions, I took great care to emphasize that the same chemical compound may exhibit both these activities, although generally not to the same extent. The terms were, therefore, meant to designate *actions, not chemical compounds*.

Ample experimental data subsequently confirmed the fact that these actions are distinct and, indeed, in many respects actually antagonistic. In practice, it then became customary, for the sake of convenience, to refer even to compounds as "mineralocorticoids" or "glucocorticoids" if their activity was quite predominantly of one type or the other. This is undoubtedly justified and in agreement with common usage in endocrinological terminology. No one would question the wisdom of calling cortisone a "corticoid," although it does possess slight virilizing effects (hirsutism), nor would one want to reject the term "male hormone" because cortisone also acts in this way. Nevertheless, in the intervening years, more than fifty authors claimed that the subdivision between mineralo- and glucocorticoids is not tenable because certain compounds possess both these actions. The virtually unanimous acceptance of our classification by all other investigators demonstrates quite clearly that such class names are useful, if not indispensable, as long as we merely keep in mind that the members of a class are similar, but not identical.

Another error of extrapolation that has recently crept into the literature was based on the following argument: reserpine discharges catecholamines from the heart. Resperine prevents certain forms of cardiac necrosis. Hence, these cardiac necroses depend upon the presence of catecholamines in the heart. Actually, pretreatment with any stressor inhibits these cardiac necroses, and reserpine is a strong stressor. The specificity of the reserpine action and its dependence upon an effect on cardiac catecholamines has never been tested.

Perhaps the most commonly committed extrapolation error consists in the uncritical assumption that the effective dose of a drug, determined per kilogram (kg.) of living tissue in one species, permits inferences concerning the dose needed to produce similar effects in another species. Here, the argument usually runs somewhat like this: The dose of cortisone necessary to produce a certain change in a rat weighing 100 grams is 1 milligram. It is concluded that, in a man weighing 70 kg., seven hundred times this amount would have to be secreted by the adrenals to produce this change. Since such an enormous amount is unlikely to be produced, these observations on rats have no possible implications in clinical medicine.

Actually, this argument is quite false; per weight of living tissue, a man may be much more or less sensitive to any drug than a rat. Indeed, extrapolations made on a weight basis are not even applicable to young and old individuals of the same species. Per kg. of body weight, a child is much more sensitive to morphine than an adult, and a rat much more resistant than a human being of any age.

WHAT IS NOT THERE CANNOT ACT.   At first sight, it appears to be a self-evident fact that an agent which is not there cannot act. Actually, this assumption has led to innumerable errors in interpretation, some of which have become classic in the history of medicine.

It will be recalled that, during the earliest stages of the development of modern bacteriology, Robert Koch formulated his famous "postulates," outlining the conditions that must be fulfilled before a disease can be ascribed to the actions of a microorganism. The first and most essential postulate of this kind was that the microbe must be demonstrable in every case of the disease.

In the words of Koch [46]:

"A thoroughly satisfactory proof (of the parasitic nature of a disease) can only be (obtained) when we have succeeded in finding the parasitic microorganisms in all cases of the disease in question, when we can further demonstrate their presence in such numbers and distribution that all the symptoms of the disease may thus find their explanation and finally when we have established the existence for every individual infective disease of a microorganism with well-marked morphologic characters."

Actually, subsequent work has shown that, in many instances, the manifestations of a microbial disease are present only after the microbe is no longer demonstrable. Indeed, in some cases (botulinus toxin) the disease may occur in individuals who were never infected with the microbe itself, but merely ingested material containing toxins of the microorganism. Conversely, highly pathogenic microbes may be present in healthy carriers who happen to be resistant.

The so-called metacorticoid lesions are another case in point. Suitably sensitized rats, treated with large doses of DCA for a comparatively short period, may manifest no evidence of nephrosclerosis, hypertension or periarteritis nodosa during the hormone treatment or even immediately after its interruption. But weeks or months following discontinuation of the DCA treatment they will develop all these changes. Thus, here again the effect is manifest although the original cause is not present in the body.

The principle of this trap may be illustrated by the following diagram.

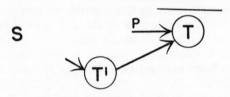

Here, the stimulus S can act upon the target T through the direct pathway P. The resulting change may not have been manifest while the stimulus was actually present in the body, but its results are nevertheless the consequence of this action. (This eventuality was not covered by Koch's postulates.) On the other hand, the stimulus S can act upon the target T^1 and cause delayed changes in it, which secondarily affect the target T at a time when the original stimulus is no longer present. (This is apparently the explanation of the "metacorticoid" vascular lesions, secondary to delayed nephrosclerosis.)

There are innumerable additional examples illustrating this point —the delayed effects of X-irradiation, of anaphylactic sensitization, or of emotional experiences which occurred in early infancy, and, indeed, every experience which leaves a potentially traumatic "scar" in the broadest sense of the word.

Now, in retrospect, the causal relationship between all these stimuli and their delayed effects is so clear that it may seem superfluous to mention this source of error. However, as we have seen, medical history shows that, in practice, the axiom "What is not there cannot act" is so generally accepted as self-evident that it misled even a Robert Koch. It has handicapped medical research in many other ways as well. The correct interpretation of vitamin deficiencies—such as rickets, pellagra, beriberi, and scurvy—was greatly delayed by the stillborn search for a positive cause in some kind of a poison. The alternative possibility, the absence from the food of a vitally important material, suggests itself quite naturally today, in retrospect. But I insist that it took great genius to think of it for the first time. Simple as the solution may seem, the fact is that it did not occur to any among the numerous eminent scientists who studied these nutritional diseases throughout the centuries.

The same problem arose repeatedly in endocrinology. It has long been known that various poisons can cause convulsions. When the disease now known as parathyroid tetany was first observed, physicians considered it self-evident that the violent convulsions characteristic of this malady must be due to some intoxication. The discovery that parathyroid removal causes tetanic convulsions obviously suggested a deficiency, but the specialists did not look at things that way. For years, they continued to search for some convulsive metabolic poison that might be produced or insufficiently detoxified by the body when the parathyroids are absent. Despite the immense amount of work performed along these lines, this theory proved fruitless as no such poison could be found. It did not occur to anybody, at that time, that these cramps are not caused by any excess but by the lack of something: namely, calcium.

In nutrition and endocrinology, we are now accustomed to thinking of deficiencies as probable causes of disease. Yet the habitual suppression of any thought suggesting that the absence of something is a causative agent continues to interfere with fruitful thinking in biology. In my own field, the "first mediator of stress," the hypothetical agent that initiates the entire general adaptation syndrome, occupies a central position. Innumerable efforts have been made to identify some toxin or metabolite (histamine, products of proteolysis, etc.) which might act as first mediators. But our suggestion that exposure to stress may cause a depletion in some vitally important metabolite and thereby initiate defense phenomena, has never been taken up seriously. We still do not know the nature of this first mediator. Hence, both approaches hold equal promise, but it is instructive that only the search for a positive agent is actively pursued.

These are the considerations that lead me to think that, as compared to experience and common sense, great familiarity with the complex laws of logic and psychology have little to offer to the biologist. It takes no great erudition, no intimate knowledge of the intricate laws of thought, to think of the possibility that a disease may be caused, not only by an excess, but also by a deficiency. Yet, the latter possibility is commonly neglected, perhaps because in everyday life, things usually seem to happen because of positive reasons. Hence, we are conditioned to think of these first. The statement of these facts in the abstract and their illustration by some simple mechanical analogy is of little value to the scientist. But I do believe that a survey of actual experiences, showing when and how often we are likely to overlook negative causes, may help to overcome this handicap by calling attention to its high incidence.

OPPOSITES ARE NOT UNLIKE.   Hardly anyone will take exception to the statement that opposites are about as different from each other as any two things can be. No point on earth is further removed from the North Pole than its exact opposite, the South Pole. If our intention is to cool an object to as low a temperature as possible, nothing could serve our purpose less than if we heated it as much as we can.

Yet, here again, we are faced with one of those self-evident facts which is altogether false. The North and the South Poles are farthest removed from each other in one sense; yet they are actually quite alike in many more respects. Similarly, whether we are to heat or cool an object, we will have to know the same principles of heat regulation. In general, the changes produced by heat will be of the same kind as those evoked by cold. They are opposite only in their direction.

Almost any other example taken at random will illustrate this close similarity between opposites. The negative of a photograph, the mirror image of a picture, are extremely close to the original. If you start traveling westward on the surface of the earth, the faster you go the sooner you will be east of your initial position. A perfect mirror image is the exact opposite of the original, yet it would be difficult to imagine anything resembling the latter more closely. Stereoisomers are nearly identical opposites. There are many parallels to this in biology. Anesthesia and excitation can be caused by different doses of the same drug. Stimulation and paralysis of a muscle can result from different degrees of mechanical trauma to the same nerve, etc.

Now, the proposition that opposites are quite alike has become so self-evident as to be unworthy of further discussion. However, the history of medical research shows that the ambivalent mental attitude toward the problem of opposites is very likely to create psychologic mirages which can mislead the greatest masters in the art of clinical observation.

Take the case of Pierre Marie, who first observed patients with the disease he called "acromegaly" toward the end of the nineteenth century, at a time when nothing was known as yet about any relationship between the pituitary and growth. These people showed excessive growth and, at the same time, their pituitaries were replaced by tumor tissue. It is only natural that Marie thought the *pituitary may produce some growth-inhibitory substance,* since destruction of the gland resulted in uninhibited growth. In the light of his own later writings and of modern endocrinology, this interpretation seems to be just about as wrong as possible. Actually, being its mirror image, it is quite close to the truth. Functionally, the pituitary is not destroyed here, but replaced by overactive tumor tissue. We must look out for this type of error, but, because of its close proximity to truth, the perfect opposite of the correct interpretation can nevertheless act as a most fruitful theory. After all, Marie's initial observation was still the first suggestion of a causal relationship between the pituitary and growth. Probably many previous autopsies had revealed pituitary tumors in giants and acromegalics, but it took the genius of Pierre Marie to suspect an interrelation between them.

Here again, I could cite several instances where this problem turned up in my own work. DCA happened to be the first corticoid to become available by synthesis in amounts adequate for systematic experimental investigations. Since an excess of it produced a variety of inflammatory changes in the connective tissue (periarteritis, myocarditis, arthritis, etc.), we concluded that *corticoids can predispose tissues for inflammation* and that, therefore, the adrenal presumably plays a role in the causation of various inflammatory diseases.

I had learned, several years earlier, that adrenalectomy does not diminish the inflammatory potential and, indeed, that the anti-inflammatory effect of stress (e.g., in anaphylactoid inflammation) is blocked by the ablation of the adrenals. This had suggested that during stress the adrenal exerts an anti-inflammatory effect, but, curiously, when it came to the interpretation of the DCA experiments, I failed to take these earlier observations into consideration. The resulting hypothesis concerning the action of corticoids in inflammation was not actually the opposite of the truth, but only half of it. It could have been formulated much more completely had I remembered that often opposites are not far apart and that the authority of the class name "corticoid" should not be overrated. Only later, when we took this into consideration, did it become possible to complete the hypothesis and arrive at the conclusion that the adrenal can both increase and decrease the inflammatory potential and that some corticoids are pro- others anti-inflammatory.

The so-called *asbestos suit theory* of cortisone action was based on an altogether different kind of misconception, but it had its origin in the same psychologic mirage and it applied to almost exactly the same topic. It will be recalled that soon after cortisone became available for clinical use, the hypothesis was formulated by clinicians that it acts in so many different inflammatory diseases because it puts some kind of an "impenetrable barrier," an "asbestos suit," between the potential pathogen and the sensitive living tissues. Actually, the anti-inflammatory hormones act mainly by interfering with the development of the inflammatory granulomatous barriers, whose chief vital function is to effect such a separation between tissues and irritants. They do not prevent the irritating pathogen from attacking tissues. On the contrary, cortisone facilitates the production of tissue disintegration (necrosis) by irritants (e.g., croton oil) and the spreading of infections (e.g., tuberculosis). Its rather non-specific beneficial effect in so many inflammatory diseases is precisely due to the fact that, in most of these, the formation of inflammatory barriers between the pathogen and the tissue is excessive. Indeed, here, inflammation is the disease or, at least, the cardinal disease manifestation the patient experiences.

Whenever you formulate a theory, remember that opposites are not far apart. It is often well worthwhile to consider the possibility of interpreting our data in a way which is exactly opposite from what our first inclination would dictate.

THE SILENT MARKER. This trap essentially corresponds to the "fallacy of accident" in Aristotle's Organon. The problem is well illustrated by the fatal error of the gentleman who decided to avoid soda water because it was the only detectable common factor in all the drinks that gave him trouble.

Bancroft[6] cites a more serious story, showing that even great scientists are prone to fall into this simple trap of logic. For many years investigators believed that ultraviolet light kills bacteria only in the presence of free oxygen. This error persisted until it was traced to misleading observations. Early experimenters used two methods to prove the indispensability of oxygen for this effect of ultraviolet light. 1. They enclosed the test culture in an evacuated glass tube. Now, we know that glass absorbs all but the longest of the ultraviolet rays and, although the investigators had eliminated oxygen, they inadvertently simultaneously shut out the active rays with their glass screen. 2. They allowed the ultraviolet rays to fall upon the surface of a culture on a solid medium, in the presence of air. Since they found that, in this case, only the upper layers were sterilized, they concluded that the deeper strata were protected by the absence of free oxygen. However, we know now that the active rays cannot penetrate deep into films of organic matter and that this is the true explanation of the fact that the deep layers were not sterilized. It is now generally accepted that the germicidal action of ultraviolet rays is just as effective in the absence of free oxygen as in air.

The silent marker can even confuse the identification of anatomic structures. For example, when early surgeons observed that removal of the thyroid (complete thyroidectomy) leads to tetanic convulsions, it was assumed that these are due to thyroid deficiency. The subsequent discovery of the parathyroids revealed, however, that: (1) thyroidectomy causes convulsions only if the parathyroids (situated in and around the thyroid) are, accidentally, also removed; (2) parathyroidectomy alone causes convulsions even if the thyroid is left intact; (3) after parathyroidectomy the convulsions can be suppressed by parathyroid hormone, but not by thyroid hormones. These findings proved that, in relation to convulsions, the large, easily detectable thyroid was merely a silent marker for the active, but not readily detectable parathyroids.

Three years ago, on a European lecture tour, I witnessed a rather amusing instance of the silent marker fallacy. While visiting a particularly well-equipped institute for the study of the nervous system, I met an investigator who was working on conditioned reflexes with the most modern, complex electronic equipment. He was so meticulous that, for example, in an experiment which happened to be underway on a dog, the animal was kept in a lab on the second floor, while the observer followed its reactions from a room on the first floor through telecommunication, to avoid any disturbance of his canine subject. The investigator told me, however, that this particular experiment was of only minor interest to him, because he had recently made a very startling discovery which occupied most of his time. He had found that the "well-known" trophic necrosis that follows denervation of the leg, depends upon the activity of the adrenal glands. It had been "proven" long ago by several scientists that, if the sciatic nerve of a rat is cut, the paw becomes necrotic and is spontaneously amputated; adrenalectomy prevents this phenomenon while cortisone treatment restores it. Thereupon, the following conversation ensued:

H.S.: This is peculiar, I have denervated many a rat's leg and never noticed any spontaneous amputation of the paw. Did you cut the animal's teeth?

INVESTIGATOR: The teeth?! Why the teeth? I'm talking about necrosis of the leg.

H.S.: Well, rats often eat their own legs after denervation. The limb can feel no pain and, I suppose, rats just like rat meat. If you don't cut their incisor teeth, they also eat dead rats that happen to be in the cage.

INVESTIGATOR: Ah, but how come adrenalectomy protects them?

H.S.: Loss of appetite.

INVESTIGATOR: But what about the effect of cortisone?

H.S.: Return of appetite.

This experiment has since been repeated with the result that, whether or not the adrenals are there, cutting the incisors completely inhibits these "trophic disturbances." The investigator in question was no beginner, in fact, he is quite an expert in neurophysiology and I know him as a highly gifted, intelligent man. Yet, I submit that no amount of familiarity with electronic equipment—or, as far as that goes, with the writings of Bacon, Hume, Boole, and the other giants in the exploration of man's mind—could have done him as much good as a little more familiarity with the rat's mind.

MULTIPLE CAUSES.   In our discussion of the alternative pathways fallacy we have already touched upon errors due to the disregard of multiple causative factors in the production of a biologic change. We saw how the latent activity of an agent can be made manifest by simultaneously acting, conditioning factors. We spoke of the tendency to be satisfied by the demonstration that a change is produced by an agent, without checking whether this is the only (specific) agent capable of producing this change. Stress research is based upon a dissatisfaction with this kind of experimentation. Almost every known effect of stress had been described before, but as a specific property of one agent or another. The essence of the stress concept is to point out that certain changes (e.g., adrenal-activation, shock, inhibition of inflammation) are nonspecific phenomena which can be produced by many agents and by their many combinations.

There are various diseases which develop only if several causative factors are simultaneously present. These we have called the "pluri-causal diseases." The various forms of cardiac necroses that can be produced in animals by combined treatment with certain electrolytes, steroids and stressors develop only if two or more in themselves inactive factors are applied in a certain sequence. The same is true of all forms of calciphylaxis. Such conditions are difficult to study because of the complexity of the underlying pathogenic situations. Yet, it is well to be aware of the pluricausal diseases, for they are probably quite common in man and no amount of search for "a cause" in the usual sense, that is, for a single specific eliciting factor, can help us to understand them. Unfortunately, we are so accustomed to think that every specific disease must be due, or at least very predominantly due, to a single particular cause (e.g., a special microbe or poison) that we often neglect the possibility of multiple causation.

When two factors cause a disease and one is universally present, it is usually concluded that the other is "the causative factor." In the nineteenth century, unsanitary conditions were thought to be the only cause of enteric fever. At that time, the causative microorganisms were universally present and the development of the disease was determined by the conditions of sanitation. Most diseases are "pluricausal," and infectious diseases depend not only upon the presence of the causative microbe, but also upon conditions necessary for its transfer from one host to the other and upon factors influencing the disease susceptibility of the host. In such instances, we are tempted to single out as "the cause" whichever factor is not commonly present.

CONFUSING IRRELEVANCIES (THE RED HERRING). In discussing the fallacy of the silent marker, we spoke about the danger of confusing an irrelevant fact with the actual cause (e.g., soda water with alcohol as the cause of intoxication). However, there, the ancillary factor was merely an inactive silent partner of the active cause. Irrelevancies which blur the picture in a positive way are even more likely to cause a confusing interference. They act as red herrings by diverting attention from the real issue.

An example of this kind is furnished by the discovery of the insulin-antagonizing hormone, glucagon. All early insulin preparations tended to raise the blood-sugar slightly before producing the typical drop. This initial rise was considered to be part of the insulin effect, until it became possible to separate the blood-sugar-raising factor, glucagon, from the blood-sugar-depressing insulin. Then it became obvious that the former was the active blood-sugar-diminishing principle in the early insulin preparations, while insulin itself merely acted as a more readily detectable marker of blood-sugar active preparations in general.

Noguchi isolated a spirochete from cases of leptospiral jaundice and concluded that it was the cause of yellow fever. This understandable mistake greatly delayed the exploration of yellow fever and led to Noguchi's suicide owing to his Japanese sense of honor [W. I. B. Beveridge [11]].

John Hunter deliberately infected himself with gonorrhea to determine whether or not this disease is different from syphilis. Unfortunately, the material he used to inoculate himself contained also the germs of syphilis; consequently he contracted both diseases and so established for a long time the false belief that both were manifestations of the same malady [W. I. B. Beveridge [11]].

I still remember my perplexity when I first looked at a spleen under the microscope. I could not see anything that I was supposed to see. The professor told us all about the various structural elements that make up a human spleen, and all I could see was millions of little blue and red dots intermixed in complete disorder. The white and red blood cells are so preponderant and so diffusely arranged in the spleen that, although there is an order to their arrangement, this is difficult to see. The lawfulness in the organization of the connective tissue and vessels is even more completely masked before the inexperienced eye. Here, practice, practice and more practice seems to be the only remedy.

THE GROUP-SPOILAGE PHENOMENON (THE CAGE FACTOR). This very common fallacy in the reasoning of medical investigators may be illustrated by the following case.

Each of five groups of animals are treated in a different manner, but in only one of these is there a striking change in the target organ under examination. In this group, however, every individual animal shows this change and there can be no question about the statistical significance of the difference between this and all other groups. Under such circumstances, the experimenter is very likely to conclude, without hesitation, that the treatment was the cause of the change. Experimental medicine is based upon the principle that, if a change occurs only in those individuals receiving a certain treatment, the latter must be regarded as the cause of the change. Here, the important fallacy is that *what you gave is not necessarily what acted.*

Fallacies of this type are extremely common, but often quite difficult to detect. For instance: if we are using small laboratory animals (rats, mice), usually the whole group receiving the same kind of treatment is kept together; therefore, they are likely to be affected by the "cage factor," which means anything that is peculiar to their cage. An infection may thus be transmitted from one animal to all the others. One particularly aggressive individual may fight with his cage mates and thus interfere with their well-being and food intake. The water bottle may be blocked. The metallic grill, which acts as a floor in most of the common types of animal cages, may be corroded and produce traumatic lesions that are falsely ascribed to the treatment. One cage of animals may have received a wrong injection, etc.

This possibility of error is so evident that many readers will consider its discussion superfluous. Yet, for the benefit of the younger investigators, I would like to point out that, despite all my experience, hardly a month goes by when I am not fooled by one or the other camouflages of this vicious trap. Fortunately, being particularly aware of it, I take the most elaborate precautions to ascertain that such sources of error be discovered before accepting the results as due to my treatment. Of course, even the most careful statistical analysis of the data will not help here. The apparent differences are undoubtedly significant, but they are not due to the agent listed on the experimental protocol.

To avoid this type of error, it is necessary for the investigator always to watch experimental animals personally and not to confide their supervision to technicians. Furthermore, whenever possible, each experiment should be repeated several times—even if only on small groups of animals. From the mathematician's point of view a group of thirty rats treated in a given manner simultaneously is the same as six groups of five rats receiving the same treatment at different times. The true biological significance of the latter experiment is, however, infinitely greater than that of the former. In rats kept in different cages and observed at different times, any one of the errors mentioned above is quite unlikely to occur six times in succession always with the same treatment, by sheer coincidence.

However, not only the cage but the climate of the lab and the habits of technicians may introduce undetectable sources of error. I have come to be so afraid of the group-spoilage phenomenon that I have had two floors of this Institute identically equipped so that every experiment may be repeated under the supervision of two entirely separate teams working in different locations. Since we have made such duplication of work mandatory, we have noted with surprise how often two animal experiments, performed with the greatest care in the most comparable manner, nevertheless give different results. The procedure is costly, but it calls attention even to errors in the human and climatic elements of a lab which could not be detected otherwise by any number of repetitions.

Of course, there are many other reasons why we must constantly keep in mind the rule that "What you gave is not necessarily what acted." For instance, a compound injected may be metabolized into an altogether different substance, so that the effects observed are actually due to the latter (experiments with MAD, p. 302). The injection of a drug may cause much local irritation and inflammation under the skin, and associated organ changes may well be the result of this local damage, rather than of any specific pharmacologic property of the substance given.

Those who consider it unlikely that such evident possibilities could be overlooked by an experienced investigator should peruse the voluminous literature of the last few years on the assay of anti-inflammatory drugs in rats. We have done this rather carefully and repeated many of the published observations with various popular drugs of this class. Our results were quite unexpected.

Most of the published work was performed with the three routine techniques developed at our Institute (the "anaphylactoid inflammation" produced with egg white or dextran, the "formalin arthritis," and the "granuloma pouch") as indicators of inflammation. The supposed anti-inflammatory drugs were injected subcutaneously; and curiously, at the high dose levels given, most of them are toxic or have an intense local irritating effect upon connective tissue: they produce widespread local tissue damage with consequent systemic stress. However, all these tests are of relatively short duration; hence, the necrotic tissue in the resulting abscesses does not actually perforate to the outside. The tissue damage can readily pass unnoticed, unless the skin is removed from the underlying tissue. The tissue damage, however, is so widespread that the resulting intense stress (shock) can inhibit inflammation at a distance from the injection site, even in adrenalectomized animals.

This does not mean, of course, that the drugs employed are not anti-inflammatory—some of them undoubtedly are—but the experimental arrangements used could not have revealed such an activity, as this would have been masked by the much more intense systemic stress effect. Here, again, it was not the agent given, but a secondary, irrelevant side effect of the subcutaneous injection technique that caused the observed change.

THE CUMULATIVE ERROR. In general, the fewer intermediate stations there are between an agent and its target, the more certain and reproducible is the result. There are many exceptions to this rule. But it is well to keep in mind that a biologic chain reaction may be blocked by a disturbance anywhere along its pathway—and particularly at each of the specially fragile relay points.

Usually, the direct application of an agent to its target organ gives the most consistent results. To illustrate, stimulation of the cock's comb by the local application of testosterone will most reliably stimulate the growth of this structure, even if the bird is ill or mutilated by the removal of various organs. The cock's comb also grows after injection of testosterone into other parts of the body, but much larger doses are required and the response is more easily prevented by the presence in the body of antagonistic hormones. Gonad-stimulating pituitary hormones likewise enhance the growth of the cock's comb, but their effect is still more indirect and, hence, still more variable. The pituitary hormones can act only by stimulating the testosterone secretion of the testis; any serious interference with this gland—particularly castration—will block their effect.

Cumulative errors affect not only the transmission of stimuli in the body but also the stringency of complex arguments, because exceptions to the postulated rule can affect each link in a chain of thoughts. For example, the statement: "Removal of the parathyroids causes convulsions by creating a state of parathyroid hormone deficiency," is in no great danger of being incorrect. On the other hand, many exceptions can interfere with the validity of our conclusion, if we say: "Removal of the parathyroids causes convulsions because, in the absence of parathyroid hormone, the blood calcium drops; and, in the absence of calcium, certain enzymes necessary for muscular contraction cannot properly exert their effect." Removal of the parathyroids does cause a drop in blood calcium, but it also increases the blood phosphate level and produces many other metabolic changes which might modify muscular contraction. Although enzymes play an important part in convulsive muscular contractility, many additional factors are likewise involved and, besides, disturbance of the nervous system probably also influences the convulsions induced by removal of the parathyroids. Because of the cumulative corruptive effect of exceptions that can affect each point in a complex train of thought, involved dialectic arguments are rarely of great value in biology. The simplest theory that can explain a phenomenon is the best, even if it does not try to explain everything.

FAULTY TECHNIQUE. Errors in experimental design or procedure play some part in almost every fallacy, but this is not the place to discuss the purely technical aspects of methodology. Two examples will suffice here, to illustrate how hidden simple errors in technique can lead to confusing interpretations.

The early literature on the adrenals was replete with contradictory reports concerning the importance of these glands for various vital functions. Some investigators even went so far as to maintain that, in certain species, the adrenals are not necessary for life. It turned out that some strains of rats and rabbits possess minute accessory adrenals at varied and unpredictable locations, some distance from the two normal glands. If only the latter are removed, the accessories undergo hypertrophy and are then perfectly capable of maintaining normalcy.

Incomplete removal of the normal adrenals is simply bad technique, but failure to remove a sometimes hardly visible accessory adrenal, which may be situated virtually anywhere in the abdominal cavity, is an unavoidable source of error which often remains undetected, even at autopsy. Hence, we must choose strains of experimental animals which do not possess accessory adrenals.

An unforgettable incident in my own career was precipitated by a technical error which, despite its primitiveness, proved difficult to identify. A few years ago, speaking about anti-inflammatory hormones before a very large audience at an International Therapeutics Congress in Rome, I mentioned the "granuloma-pouch" technique which I had devised for the quantitative study of inflammation (p. 208). To recapitulate briefly, in this test, a little air is injected under the skin of a rat and then an inflammatory irritant such as 1 per cent croton oil (diluted in olive oil) is introduced into the resulting air pouch. The irritant that comes in contact with the connective tissue wall of the pouch produces an inflammation whose fluid and solid parts can be quantitatively determined under strictly reproducible circumstances. The inflammatory fluid (exudate) accumulates in the cavity and its volume can be measured, while the solid, inflammatory tissue barricade (granuloma), which develops from the connective tissue of the pouch wall, can be weighed.

I took great care to explain the manifold advantages of this test, but the ensuing discussion was opened by the rather terse remark of an investigator who said that he had repeated my experiments exactly as I had described them, and had found the test useless. As soon as the croton oil is injected, he claimed, the skin simply disintegrates as a consequence of necrosis so that the fluid perforates to the outside and the pouch becomes infected.

There is not much time for discussion at such large meetings and I had to think quickly of possible errors my critic might have made; the effect of his remark on the audience was quite dramatic. I asked what kind of rats he used, how much croton oil he gave, whether the irritant was diluted to 1 per cent and so forth, but he assured me, somewhat impatiently, that he had read my papers and that, in all these respects, he had followed my prescription to the letter.

Discussion time was running out and I was just about to give up when, in desperation, I added one last question concerning the kind of oil he employed as a diluent. The solvent might have had some particularly irritating properties. "Oh, no," he replied, "on the contrary; to make sure that the diluent would not be irritating, I simply put the croton oil into water." Now, this explained everything. Croton oil is not soluble in water, but merely floats on top of it, hence, the rat's skin had come in contact with concentrated croton oil. Besides, unlike olive oil, water is almost immediately absorbed from the injection site so that nothing but concentrated croton oil remains in the pouch. No wonder the skin disintegrated. This explanation saved me from a very embarrassing situation, but I must admit it would never have occurred to me to ask whether water was used as a "solvent" for the water-insoluble croton oil. This fault in technique was revealed only accidentally by my question about the kind of oil employed.

Incidents like this—like so many of the examples cited in the preceding pages—show that in actual practice, simple oversights, due to absent-minded negligence or to lack of experience, are much more common and dangerous than errors in logic due to lack of intelligence or to unfamiliarity with the fundamental laws of thought. There is no point in arguing that anybody should know oil is not soluble in water; my critic knew that as well as I did. Still, the fact remains that he did not think of this as an important consideration. The incident is not a hypothetical example, it did actually happen.

FAULTY LOGIC. As a young boy, I was much impressed by the paradoxes of Zeno, the Greek philosopher usually recognized as the father of the dialectic method of argumentation. Best known among his many intriguing mental contortions is the famous argument about the race between Achilles and the tortoise. It goes something like this: If the tortoise gets a head start, Achilles can never catch up with it because, while Achilles traverses the distance from his starting point to the starting point of the tortoise, the latter advances a certain distance and, while Achilles traverses this distance, the tortoise makes a further advance, and so on ad infinitum. Consequently, Achilles may run indefinitely without ever overtaking his competitor.

Now, I must make two admissions: 1. As a boy, I couldn't find out for myself where the error lies in this argument. 2. When I remembered this story yesterday, again I couldn't detect the error. It is true that, when I first heard this story, I immediately understood the teacher's explanation. Apparently, in this respect, I have not yet deteriorated because, when I looked it up in the book yesterday, again I understood the explanation. The error, here, lies in the confusion of the "infinity" of possible subdivisions of a finite distance as stated in the premise, with the "infinity" of the conclusion which refers to this distance. In other words, the paradox does not distinguish between an infinite distance and a finite distance infinitely divided. In essence, this is merely a semantic trap, but a rather cunningly designed one.

I must also admit that it is somewhat humiliating for a career scientist to realize that he cannot find the error in an argument that is dished out as compulsory, routine mental nourishment to high school boys throughout the world. But I like to learn from my humiliations; therefore, I tried to analyze the possible reasons for my deficiency. It may be that I am just not bright enough. It may also be that this kind of dialectics irritates me so much that I cannot concentrate on the solution. Finally, both these factors may be at play simultaneously. In any event, the hell with dialectics!

Even after I was told, and understood where the error lies, the solution did not satisfy me. Zeno was a great philosopher, and yet he couldn't find the error in his paradox. And I have a sneaking suspicion that my high school teacher may not have detected it by himself, either. Of course, some professional philosopher did find the solution, or else it wouldn't be in the book. I do not know who this philosopher was—it may have been Aristotle because he liked to talk about Zeno's paradoxes. But, whoever it was, I doubt that he would have made much headway in medical research. The biologist knows from experience that fast-moving objects overtake slow-moving ones. He is so sure that Achilles could catch up with that tortoise that he just cannot work up enough enthusiasm to worry about how Zeno got himself tied up in knots. Perhaps this comparative indifference is no drawback, because if the biologist did spend his energy on the problems of Zeno, who would explore the biology of the tortoise?

EPILOGUE.   By now it must be quite obvious that, in my opinion, the fallacies most likely to handicap the biologist in his daily work can be avoided more easily through simple common sense and experience than through profound logical meditation. Therefore, I selected for special consideration a series of dangerous traps in scientific reasoning, illustrating the sad but actual stories of authors who were caught (usually myself). As we look back upon these manifold fallacies we realize that, in the final analysis, all of them fall into one of the three groups, which might be described as: 1. the "upside

down mirage," 2. the "mirror image," and 3. the "red herring."
Hence, my advice is this:

Learn to concentrate—despite all traps, pitfalls, and mirages—
first upon the selection of a truly meaningful topic and then, after
your work is completed, upon the appraisal of its true meaning.

Remember that it is so easy to underestimate these traps, and when
it presents itself, to miss the discovery of what is clearly before you,

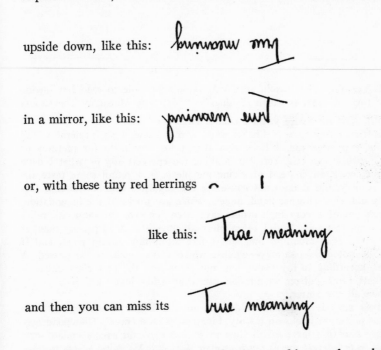

upside down, like this:

in a mirror, like this:

or, with these tiny red herrings

like this:

and then you can miss its

All these weaknesses in the evaluating machinery of our brains
have long been known to psychologists but, like some other more
pleasant weaknesses of the flesh, they continue to create havoc because of their almost irresistible temptation. To avoid them, knowledge is not enough. Only if the horrible fate of those among us who
have fallen into these traps can deter others, will we be able to say:
"We did not fall in vain."

9. How to Read

"Education ... has produced a vast population able to read but unable to distinguish what is worth reading."   [George Macaulay Trevelyan]

"But now for many years I cannot endure to read a line of poetry: I have tried lately to read Shakespeare, and I found it so intolerably dull that it nauseated me. I have also almost lost my taste for pictures or music. Music generally sets me thinking too energetically on what I have been at work on, instead of giving me pleasure. I retain some taste for fine scenery, but it does not cause me the exquisite delight which it formerly did. On the other hand, novels, which are works of the imagination, though not of a very high order, have been for years a wonderful relief and pleasure to me, and I often bless all novelists. A surprising number have been read aloud to me, and I like all if moderately good, and if they do not end unhappily—against which a law ought to be passed. A novel, according to my taste, does not come into the first class unless it contains some person whom one can thoroughly love, and if a pretty woman all the better.

"This curious and lamentable loss of the higher aesthetic tastes is all the odder, as books on history, biographies, and travels (independently of any scientific facts which they may contain), and essays on all sorts of subjects interest me as much as ever they did. My mind seems to have become a kind of machine for grinding general laws out of large collections of facts, but why this should have caused the atrophy of that part of the brain alone, on which the higher tastes depend, I cannot conceive."

[Charles Darwin [26]]

"A classic is something that everybody wants to have read and nobody wants to read."   [Mark Twain]

Technical Literature

Just how much technical literature you should read depends on your subject and on your personality—in the final analysis perhaps only on your personality.

It would seem that the scientist, interested in a small, strictly limited field, would have less literature to cover than his colleague who studies a very broad subject. But in science there are no small, limited fields; only small, limited scientists. In Nature, every field flows right over into all adjacent subjects, and it depends only on you—largely on your reading capacity—*just where the limits of your interests must stop.*

In 1937, when the anaphylactoid inflammation was first described, it was easy to cover the entire world literature on the subject— there was no relevant publication. Now, more than a quarter of a century later, there are still only about five hundred papers specifically dealing with this reaction. A scientist who would have made it his research subject in 1937 would certainly have had no difficulty in keeping up-to-date with this small volume of publications over so many years. Even with only five hundred papers well digested, he could have made some interesting contributions. But the scope of his research potential would certainly have enlarged immensely had he also followed the subject as it spilled over into adjacent territories. As the years went by, it turned out that anaphylactoid inflammation can be elicited by many agents. We may ask, what are the essential pharmacologic properties of these "anaphylactoidogens," what chemical or physical properties do they have in common that might explain their singular action? It turned out that the mast cells are severely damaged in the shock organs affected by anaphylactoidogens. We immediately ask, what else is known about these mast cells? This question alone sends us on a literary search that must go back to the time when Ehrlich discovered the mast cell a century ago. We learn that histamine, serotonin and heparin are produced by mast cells, and begin to wonder whether these compounds might not also play a role in anaphylactoid inflammation. What is the relationship between anaphylactoid inflammation and anaphylactic shock, or between anaphylactic shock and other hypersensitivity reactions?

There is no end to the concatenation of questions raised by a single new observation, and—since "chance favors only the prepared mind"—the more you know, the more likely you are to make significant discoveries. To a great extent, nontechnical, philosophic and belletristic literature—and even technical literature far outside your specialty—is apt to sensitize your mind for the discovery of important things.

But, just as in the lab excessive preoccupation with the preparations for discovery creates the gadgeteer (who constantly improves his instruments for the research he never gets time to do), so in the library, endless preoccupation with the perfection of erudition creates the bookworm (whose continual drive to improve his mental machinery prevents him from ever making creative use of it). Indeed, extreme erudition can seriously interfere with inventiveness. There is a popular saying about "the fool who didn't know it couldn't be done, so he went ahead and did it."

Where should we draw the line between too little and too much reading? Although many psychologists do not agree with me, I firmly believe that the human brain has only limited storage space for memory—space which soon gets awfully crowded, at least in front where one can get at things easily. After this place is full, any new fact that you push in forces another out of reach into the dark background, whence only strong demands can bring it forward again. I know, for example, that in my memory one language can displace another. I speak both Spanish and Italian reasonably well, even if I don't have any occasion to speak either of them for long periods. But, if I have to give a series of lectures in Italian, my Spanish slips out of reach and I can recall it only by practice. Similarly, my Italian becomes rusty if I practice Spanish too much. (Curiously, this is much less true of two wholly unrelated languages; for example, lecturing in Russian does not seem to do any great harm to my fluency in Hungarian or German, but it ruins my Czech, a related Slavic language.)

Just as in eating, the feeling of satiety should be our guardian against excess in reading; different people have different capacities and should gorge themselves with literature accordingly. All you need do is watch for symptoms of overindulgence, and when they appear—stop. Fortunately, memory storage can be greatly aided by the various tricks one learns with time. Here are a few:

Don't try to remember things that you will not need immediately; just remember where you can find them. If you come across a review or monograph on histamine at a time when you are not actually working on this compound, just leaf through the pages sufficiently to see whether or not the text would be worth reading. If so, jot down the reference in SSS ("Hn/Rev") for your files and forget that you ever saw it. If, in a week or in ten years, you will need a general survey of today's knowledge on histamine, you will find it anyway by turning to the corresponding section of your file.

I strongly recommend this technique not only for the storage of published information but for remembering anything. My assistants and I always carry a notebook and pencil in the breast pockets of our lab coats, and whenever anything comes up that cannot be handled immediately without unnecessarily interrupting what we are doing, we just write it down. For example, during conversation on our daily rounds, we may make a note to have a drug ordered, to verify a sentence in a manuscript, to start an experiment, or to read up on a subject; we let the notebook do the storing for future reference. It does so more reliably than the brain and without interfering with other activities.

Either read or skim through literature, but do not try to read quickly. Nowadays, in American schools, students are taught to read as quickly as possible. This is supposed to save time, but I am afraid it also saves learning. Being a hopelessly slow reader, I am probably prejudiced. Yet, I have discussed the matter with many scientists and find that most of them complain of the same weakness in quick reading—perhaps it is not a weakness at all. If I am interested in a text, reading, meditating, and even dreaming about its subject are all one. I do not think that enforced speed helps the quality of the reading capacity or the enjoyment of our meditations and dreams. You might as well ask a man to increase his musical capacity by learning how to take in records at five times their normal speed. My advice is: *never try to read faster than you find natural,* always allowing time to stop for daydreams on related subjects. I use my reading largely as a scaffolding for meditation on research and the planning of experiments. It is very difficult to sit down and tell yourself, "Now think about an interesting experiment," but ideas come automatically as you mix someone else's thoughts with your own by reading his text at leisure.

On the other hand, if you want to keep up-to-date (or if at least you want to keep your files up-to-date) you must indulge in mass reading, but this is an entirely different mental process: you merely *skim through the pages to scan them for information* that might be of use. For example, you take an original paper and just look at the title. If this does not give sufficient information you read the summary. Then, if a method interests you, turn to the section "Materials and Techniques." But never try to read the whole paper at great speed. Whatever is important can be taken down in seconds on a filing card in simple SSS symbols, ready for consultation whenever it will be needed.

This is the type of mass reading that we teach our codifiers who keep the Institute's library up-to-date. They put it to great advantage although most of them are not even physicians and could not possibly be expected to understand all the implications of the material they make available for our scientific staff. They need a kind of understanding very similar to that of book-index makers who may become astonishingly proficient at spotting key words without making any effort to understand the text. To learn this art take an abstract journal and try to skim through a page from top to bottom by following a filing card that you slide down to cover the text as yet unread. Here, speed is of the essence and you can learn to do this rapidly, without losing an indexable key word. We can apparently sensitize our mind for certain words that are important to us, and these register selectively as we skim along the text. Some codifiers learn to do this without a card, by "diagonal reading," slowly moving their finger from the left upper to the right lower corner of the page.

In addition to slow reading for understanding or as a guide for meditation, and diagonal reading for indexing, I believe it is good for any investigator always to peruse recent editions of textbooks on subjects only remotely related to his own. Textbooks usually contain the cream of the most important and best-established facts in a broad field; they are excellent means for maintaining the general medical culture of those who specialize in a restricted field. Here, diagonal reading will suffice for the major part of the book, while certain passages that are new and especially interesting to you should be read at leisure.

Belles Lettres

No generalizations can be made about the nontechnical reading of scientists; most of them read what other educated people read. Unfortunately, research is such an absorbing task that many investigators simply never read anything but technical texts. Some do not even read the daily newspaper; others will go so far as to take a magazine or a thriller to bed in the evening as a tranquilizer and soporific. To my surprise, I have learned from some of the greatest scientists of our time that, apart from the technical literature, they read nothing but detective stories from which they derive much amusement and relaxation. I have tried it, but unsuccessfully. Other scientists are voracious readers of poetry or the classics but tastes differ enormously. I have been unable to find any correlation between the type of scientific accomplishment and the literary tastes of an investigator.

The biographies of great scientists and even fictional works about science can be very stimulating, especially to young investigators. I shall never forget the enormous emotional stimulus that I derived from reading Pasteur's biography by Vallery-Radot, Claude Bernard's analysis of his approach to experimental medicine—which is essentially an autobiography of his intellect—or Sinclair Lewis' *Arrowsmith*. From discussions with colleagues, I am convinced that the latter has been one of the greatest stimuli to young scientists throughout the world to enter a scientific career, although the author was not a scientist, himself, and the story is purely fictional.

Personally, I read nontechnical literature only in bed before going to sleep, but this I have done every day throughout my life. I can take poetry only in small doses, but I am very fond of good novels, biographies, autobiographies, philosophy, and—as you may have noticed—aphorisms. I have a strong aversion to translations (perhaps because some of my own books were pretty badly translated); hence, I read whatever I can in the original language. This practice affords me additional amusement, just because I like languages for their own sake. I find that nothing can bring me a greater variety of thoughts, emotions and entire foreign cultures, than reading authors, or talking to people who express themselves in their own tongue. Often I catch myself having the feeling of intimately belonging to a foreign nation in reading an anecdote, a pithy popular expression or a joke especially characteristic of its people and culture; I think of it as "that's just how we are."

10. How to Write

"He does not write at all whose poems no man reads."   [Martial]

"... for it is clear that I failed to impress my readers; and he who succeeds in doing so deserves, in my opinion, all the credit."
[Charles Darwin [26]]

"Writing maketh an exact man."   [Francis Bacon]

"The essence of style is the avoidance of (1) wind, (2) obscurity."
[W. R. Bett [10]]

In this section I shall try to make a few suggestions about the effective use, by scientists, of the written word and the picture. My remarks will be based mainly on personal experience in medical research, but essentially the same principles are applicable to other sciences and, to a lesser extent, even to nonfiction writing in general.

Generalities

There are many detailed publications on the technique of medical writing which may be consulted elsewhere (Albutt [1]; Almack [2]; Anderson [4]; Alvarez, Clegg, Marti-Ibañez, Selye, Sigerist [3]; Bett [10]; Fishbein [35]; The University of Chicago Press [85]; Cochran & Cox [19]; Nelson [51]; Trelease [83]). Here, I should merely like to discuss the points that have come up most frequently in my own writing and in that of my pupils.

For whom are you writing?   Whenever you decide to write anything, be it only a letter or an entire encyclopedia, the first thing to ask is: Who should and will read this? There is no such thing as a perfectly written piece, at best it can be perfect only for a certain type of reader. It is a common mistake for beginners to send articles to the wrong journals or to adjust the general tone of their communication to a level quite different from that of the probable reader. The usual errors are to talk down to the audience; to be too far above their heads; to use a chatty narrative tone when dry conciseness is desirable, or vice versa. We shall have more to say about this in connection with the various media available for scientific expression.

Once you have decided upon the proper public for what you want to say, try to follow the traditional style of the medium you have chosen, especially in abstracts of papers for oral presentation, in original articles for technical journals, or in Ph.D. theses. Much less conformism is expected in review articles, and still less in books that do not form part of a series.

When should you write? Of course, you should write when you have something to write about. But the problem is not quite that simple. Unless you have made a startling, entirely novel and simple observation which is easy to describe, a great deal of tedious preparation is needed before the actual writing of a technical text can begin. All the experimental protocols have to be gathered, the results correlated and tabulated, charts and photographs prepared. During this preliminary work it invariably turns out that some data are incomplete; hence, additional experiments are required before the material can be published.

My advice is to describe the essential results of each experiment —successful or unsuccessful—as soon as it is completed, and to file them properly so that they can be easily retrieved when needed. Even charts, graphs and photographs of interesting but still unpublishable data should be prepared as you go along. This is especially true of photographs which may help to illustrate a particularly "photogenic" experiment that would be time-consuming and costly to repeat later just for the sake of a suitable illustration. Granted that if you proceed in this way, there will necessarily be some waste of effort because not everything registered will eventually be used for publication. Still, this systematic procedure is well worthwhile. You will be richly rewarded for keeping your records neat and up-to-date by the ease with which they can be transformed into a manuscript. Perhaps even more important, this constant bookkeeping helps to direct research by giving you a perfect picture of where you stand at any one moment.

I get very tired of the author who continually complains that he has accumulated material for umpteen papers but just can't find time to write them up. He implies that he cares only for science and not for fame. Actually, in most cases, he just cannot face the task of bringing order into his sloppy notes.

better than any other in expressing what you mean. "Meretricious" is a word rarely used by the man (or woman) in the street, but if I were to write about a scientist who accepts a position as a promoter of drugs just because it pays well, I could think of no better term and would not hesitate to use it.

Even colloquialisms are acceptable if they are particularly descriptive; but jargon, including clinical and lab jargon, should be avoided though perhaps not at the cost of extreme redundancy or obscurantism. An "acute abdomen" is a linguistic horror, but if I had to refer to it many times in a passage, I could think of no substitute without sounding specious and pedantic.

Here are a few commonly used examples of grandiloquence, pomposity, exaggeration, vulgarity, or just simply bad English, that should be avoided:

DON'T	DO
Has been engaged in a study of ...	Has studied ...
It is my carefully considered opinion that ...	I believe that ...
All the accumulated available evidence tends to indicate that ...	The evidence suggests that ...
The kidney showed no structural evidence of pathology;	The kidney was structurally normal;
He was a complicated case of typhoid;	The patient had a complicated form of typhoid;
Let me call your attention to the fact that this is not always so;	This is not always so;
The experiments were performed on rats. In the animals treated with cortisone, the adrenals were atrophic, while in those given ACTH they were hypertrophic;	In rats, cortisone caused atrophy, ACTH hypertrophy of the adrenals;
We have made the interesting discovery that A acts on B.	A acts on B.

Also to be avoided are various habitually used forms of exaggeration, for example, the description of every significant change as "marked" or "pronounced." Likewise, do not speak of "careful inspection" or "meticulous weighing" when the inspecting and weighing were merely done under the usual conditions.

Driven by commendable modesty, some authors will go to the oddest extremes in their desperate efforts to avoid the use of the pronoun "I." It seems to me that it all depends on how often and in what connection the "I" is employed. "The author of the present communication was wrong" sounds genteel but is hardly more modest than "I was wrong."

Neologisms.   Too many scientists "love not the flower they pluck, and know it not, and all their botany is Latin names" [Ralph Waldo Emerson].

Neologisms are standard constituents of scientific language; hence, they deserve special attention. Every new material or conceptual entity must be named, as it would be too awkward to redefine it, whenever mentioned, through an exhaustive description of its typical characteristics. For example, it would be quite impractical to define the carotid artery or the concept of calciphylaxis each time we speak of them. This is rather self-evident; still, there exists a widespread and quite unreasonable aversion to the use of neologisms in general. Especially those who never had the occasion to learn a foreign language find it difficult to get used to new terms. These strike them either as ridiculous merely on account of their novelty, or as "fancy," because in medicine most terms have Greco-Latin roots which may make them seem grandiloquent.

Undoubtedly, the coining of new names can create confusion. Having been responsible for quite a few of them (both terms and confusions), I am well aware of this. Indeed, in "Fallacies," we have already seen how certain class names can be the source of serious misunderstandings.

Of course, new terms should be coined only if they are really indispensable. A great deal of legitimate aversion toward neologisms has been created by authors who introduce them merely to leave their personal signature on a subject that did not deserve a special name. The many clinical syndromes which represent minor modifications of well-known diseases, illustrate this point. A syndrome, hitherto characterized by three cardinal symptoms, if observed in association with a fourth, rarely needs to be renamed.

When new names are required they should be coined in consonance with certain well-tested linguistic principles. Arbitrary combinations of letters or the name of the discoverer are to be avoided in favor of some self-explanatory term, preferably one easily understandable to foreign authors and translatable into foreign languages. That is why it is best to begin by searching through dictionaries for familiar Greek and Latin roots commonly used in biology. Some purists violently object to compound terms made up of Latin and Greek roots. If it is convenient, hybrids should be avoided, but not at the cost of speciousness; I prefer "appendicitis" to "perityphlitis" and "adrenotrophic" to "epinephrotrophic."

Sometimes we find that the name which best reflects our meaning has been used before in a different sense. This rarely creates confusion, however, if the term is slightly modified (e.g., "anaphylactic" becomes "anaphylactoid"), or if the suggested new use is clearly defined. For example, I proposed to designate as *"conditioning"* the provision of the conditions necessary for a hormone to exert certain effects. Pavlov had spoken of "conditioned reflexes" in an altogether different sense, but no one is likely to confuse these totally unrelated concepts. It would be difficult to restrict the use of such common and descriptive terms as "conditioning" and "conditioned" to one particular biologic phenomenon. These words are successfully employed in even more fundamentally different senses (e.g., physical conditioning for fitness, air conditioning) without any danger of creating confusion. Here, the advantage of a self-explanatory term (easily translated into any language by just appropriately changing the Latin root) greatly outweighs the farfetched possibility of a misunderstanding. Much more confusion has been created by the purists who attempted to replace this expression by such terms as "permissive" or "supportive" hormone actions, at a time when these effects were already known under the label "conditioning." The new terms suggested nonexistent differences in meaning.

I encountered even more opposition to my use of the words *"stress"* and *"stressor"* to designate respectively "the sum of all nonspecific changes caused by function or damage" and the agent which elicits such changes. It was pointed out that "stress" had already been used in physics in a somewhat different sense; it is also currently employed in conversational English, to denote almost anything that causes fatigue. However, the fact that the term was so rapidly and generally accepted in its new, strictly defined, biologic sense makes it dubious whether another designation would have been more satisfactory.

Yet, perhaps even here it might have been better to select a term of Greco-Latin derivation. Unfortunately, in 1935 when I began my work on stress, I just did not think of the problems which translation into foreign languages might raise. The result was that some French authors used such words as *stimulation* (stimulation) or *agression* (aggression); Germans spoke of *Anstrengung* (effort) or *Schaden* (damage); and the Spanish edition of my own monograph "Stress" was printed—much to my surprise—with the subtitle *Sufrimiento* (suffering). All of these terms have entirely different connotations. In any event, it has become customary in all languages to use the word "stress," without attempting to translate it. Had we chosen a term derived from Greek or Latin, all this confusion could have been avoided. Actually, I learned later that, as usual, the Greeks had a word for it. *Pónos* corresponds almost exactly to "stress," but by now the English designation is far too generally in use to warrant any change.

Some years ago, I proposed the term *"corticoid"* (derived from "adrenal cortex" and the Greek suffix "oid," meaning "similar to") as a class name for "those hormones which imitate the physiologic function of the adrenal cortex." For this I have been reprimanded on the more general grounds that ". . . the invention of technical terms by those not born in the language is very dangerous. . . ." I tried to point out innocently in self-defense (Selye [65]) that it would greatly handicap the progress of science if only those who could call both Latin and Greek their native tongues were considered competent to coin Greco-Latin technical terms—but I got the implication.

One last warning, which may be in order here, is to observe, as much as possible, a uniformity among terms referring to related topics. This is particularly important when it comes to teaching. For instance, it is easy to explain to our students that ACTH is the abbreviation for the *a*dreno*c*orti*c*o*t*rophic *h*ormone, just as LTH stands for *l*uteo*t*rophic *h*ormone, but when it comes to TSH for thyrotrophic hormone, we run into difficulty. Of course, we can point out that this principle had first been designated as the *"t*hyroid *s*timulating *h*ormone" but the student wonders why, even in recent papers in which the authors usually speak of "thyrotrophic hormone," they nevertheless use the abbreviation TSH, when *TTH* would be so much more logical. The beginner continues to worry about the possibility that there may be some fundamental difference between the trophic and the stimulating hormones of the pituitary.

The "growth hormone" furnishes us with an even better example of how important these apparently insignificant terminologic considerations can be. In English medical literature, the most current abbreviation of growth hormone, GH, was self-explanatory, but when an English-speaking investigator tried to work his way through the foreign literature he ran across the abbreviations WH (*Wachstumshormon*) in German, HC (*Hormone de Croissance*) in French, and RH (*Růstový hormone*) in Czech and the meaning of these symbols was far from evident to him at first sight. There was also much confusion with the "growth hormones" of plants and insects which are totally unrelated substances.

The "growth hormone" had been discovered, more than a quarter of a century ago, by H. M. Evans, and most of its fundamental properties on growth and allied phenomena had been adequately studied by numerous investigators. Our only contribution to this field was the demonstration that "growth hormone" does not produce growth under all circumstances; while, on the other hand, it can exert actions quite independent of growth in length, owing to its powerful effect upon connective-tissue reactions, particularly inflammation. Nevertheless, the abbreviation we suggested, *STH* (for *somatotrophic hormone*) was immediately accepted throughout the world. This was hardly due to the importance of our modest research with STH, but to the fact that the term (being of Greek derivation) was readily understandable to workers of all language groups and corresponded to the general trend of naming trophic hormones by designations ending in "TH."

You may say, "What's in a name? A gene by any name would be as great," but this is not so. Imagine if it had been called a "catalytoid auto-perpetuating chromonematoblast." The entire progress of genetics could have been retarded through such an unmanageable and incomprehensible (though logically correct) linguistic horror!

Of course, the popularity of technical terms depends primarily upon the importance of the subject they designate and upon the existence of a real need for a specific appellation. If the thing already has a well-known name it should not be rechristened, except when the old term is so bad that it causes even more confusion than would the introduction of a new one. This is rarely the case, because well-established language habits are notoriously difficult to break. For example, among the terms that I have proposed for steroid hormone actions *"corticoid,"* as a class name (with the subgroups *"gluco- and mineralocorticoids"* or *"pro- and antiphlogistic corticoids"*), was rapidly accepted because no other terms had been previously in use, while the expressions "estrogenic," "progestational," and "androgenic," though inconsistent and objectionable in many ways, were already too well established to be easily displaced by *"folliculoid," "luteoid"* and *"testoid."*

There are several technical terms and symbols whose fate I followed with special attention, having been responsible for them myself. Among these, in addition to the ones just mentioned, are:

Alarm reaction
Anacalciphylaxis
Anaphylactoid inflammation

Calcergy
Calciphylactic adjuvant, challenger and sensitizer
Calciphylaxis
DHT
Direct calcifiers or calcergens
ECC-syndrome
Electrolyte-steroid-cardiopathy with calcification (ESCC)
Electrolyte-steroid-cardiopathy with hyalinization (ESCH)
Electrolyte-steroid-cardiopathy with necrosis (ESCN)
Endometrial mole (as distinct from hydatidiform mole)
General adaptation syndrome (G.A.S.)
Hyalinosis syndrome
Mastotaxis
Metrial gland
Neurolathyrism
Neurotropic calciphylaxis
Osteolathyrism
Pseudopregnancy of lactation
Siderocalciphylaxis
Stage of exhaustion
Stage of resistance
Steroid anesthesia
Suckling reflex
Vasotaxis

The subsequent history of these terms reveals certain characteristics which are responsible for their success or failure. It seems to me that neologisms should be:

1. Necessary, because of the novelty and importance of their subject.
2. Brief and, if possible, of Greco-Latin derivation, to facilitate international understanding.
3. Descriptive and self-explanatory.

Tables. Arrangement in the form of a table is one of the most effective means of preparing data for comparison and evaluation. Tables should be constructed with the greatest economy of space, not only because they are much more expensive per page than text, but also because their chief purpose is the condensation of data. The general principles of table construction are discussed in standard texts (e.g., Trelease [83]).

Drawings and photographs. Tables, curves and columns are supposed to give accurate information to prove quantitative relationships. Most drawings and photographs on the other hand are intended to illustrate quality rather than exact quantity, and they may quite properly do this by a certain exaggeration which em-

phasizes the most important points. For example, a schematic drawing illustrating the effect of a certain hormone upon various organs
need not, and should not, be made to scale. An atrophic organ should
be drawn proportionately much smaller, a hypertrophic one much
larger, than it actually is in order to make the differences more
obvious. The drawing merely helps to visualize facts or interpretations already proven by the text and by the quantitative data given
in the form of tables, curves or columns. Therefore, there is rarely
any need to show the same material both in tabular form and in
curves or columns, but quantitative data thus represented may still
be advantageously summarized in a drawing which, like a caricature, puts emphasis on particularly characteristic features.

Almost the same can be said of photographs. The photograph need
not represent the mean change, but the one that best illustrates what
happens, as long as this is made clear by the text. For example, in
illustrating a cardiac infarct, we need not take the average type, out
of a misplaced sense of honesty, if its color and position makes it
quite unsuitable for photography. It is much better to take a specimen in which the change is best seen. Drawings and photographs
cannot possibly prove anything in quantitative terms since they
represent selected, individual cases. But both have the great advantage that they depict complex structural relationships that could
not be shown otherwise, and the photograph does this more accurately
than the drawing. In other words, both drawings and photographs
are primarily supposed to teach, not to prove. The only thing they
prove is that such and such a change can happen; they say nothing
about mean intensity, frequency or constancy.

Because of their cost, colored photographs should be used only
when they are definitely superior to black-and-white halftones; for
example, in the illustration of differently colored cell granules which
would come out in an equal grey tone on black-and-white pictures.

References.   Except in review articles and books meant to act
as guides to the literature, references should be kept to the minimum
necessary for the proper acknowledgment of earlier related investigations and as a background regarding the implications of the new
work. References should also be given instead of lengthy descriptions of complicated experimental procedures previously described.
Only beginners are awed by their ability to collate monumental
bibliographies which the readers of the original articles rarely consult anyway.

The Technical Paper and the Thesis

There are five customary media for the publication of technical information:

1. Printed abstracts of papers presented orally at meetings of scientific societies.
2. Original papers for technical journals.
3. Theses submitted for the obtention of degrees.
4. Review articles.
5. Books.

Here, we need not discuss the first-mentioned three media, since these form the main topic of most books that deal with medical writing (p. 348). In this connection suffice it to say a few words about two points that have rarely received adequate attention: the choice of journal and that singular phenomenon, the "Thesis Neurosis." Later we shall deal at greater length with the more complex tasks of how to write a detailed review article or a scientific book. Finally, we shall also have to speak about parascientific writing: in particular, the vexing problems of how to beg for money by applications for grants and fellowships; how to write reports to subsidizers of research, and how to cope with the often voluminous general correspondence of the scientist.

CHOICE OF JOURNAL. Some journals specialize in brief communications; others publish only detailed studies. Indeed, there has been much controversy about the perennial problem of several short articles versus one long paper. The decision depends so much upon the subject and the individual taste of the author that generalizations are impossible. Personally, I prefer the short paper on the one hand, and the review or monograph on the other. In view of the currently enormous volume of medical research, it becomes increasingly more difficult to collate the literature on a certain subject; therefore, it is of great assistance if the contents are clearly expressed in the titles of papers. To make this possible, I believe that when a study has led to definitive, well-supported conclusions, it should be published as a separate paper under a telling title. As soon as the investigation branches out to a point where its contents can no longer be revealed by a title of manageable size, the material should be split up into several publications. On the other hand, the naïve but quite prevalent practice of judging a young investigator by the number of papers he has written must be broken, because it creates a temptation toward excesses in this direction. It is quality, not quantity that counts. Once this is well understood there is no need—out of a misplaced sense of modesty—to bury more and more data under a single title that can no longer cover them. The coordinating of larger fields of research is not the function of original papers but of reviews and monographs.

In its general structure, the detailed article need not differ essentially from shorter communications. Expose your aims, methods, results and conclusions clearly and concisely without using flowery language, dramatization or special pleading; the facts themselves must convince without appeal to feelings. Even in brief communications some speculation is quite in order, indeed desirable, as long as theories and plans for future work are clearly presented as such. Just how far we should go in the discussion of implications is difficult to say. "Don't never prophesy—onless ye know" [James Russell Lowell] is undoubtedly the safest but not the most stimulating attitude. The ultimate aims and the applications an author has in mind are not always evident from a mere factual presentation of his data; personally, I like to read papers that are not mere catalogues of facts, but also give some indication of what the data might be good for.

It is often advantageous to publish the different aspects of an extensive series of investigations in journals devoted to the corresponding specialities. A scientist who discovers a new hormone is well advised first to publish it in an endocrinological journal. But then, as he goes on to study, say, the metabolic or cutaneous manifestations of overdosage with this hormone, his work will probably gain in usefulness if called to the attention of those who read journals specifically devoted to metabolism or to dermatology. For the same reason, it is an advantage for those authors who can do so to present their data at the meetings and in the journals of those countries which most actively participate in cognate research. Today, English is by far the most generally used language in medical research, and a scientist of a different tongue should attempt to describe at least his major results not only in his native langage but also in English. However, a great many outstanding investigators are not sufficiently conversant with English to follow all its fine points easily. Hence, it is well for English-speaking scientists to publish some of their findings in other tongues as well. If the author cannot do this himself, he can have his paper translated.

THE ETIOLOGY AND PROPHYLAXIS OF "THESIS NEUROSIS." If experimental work is poorly directed and continued during the writing of a thesis, the repeated interruptions and the uncertainty of the outcome almost invariably bring about a serious mental derangement commonly referred to in our lab as "thesis neurosis." The candidate loses confidence in his work and in himself; he becomes depressed, nervous, irritable and irritating owing to ever more frantic and, hence, unsuccessful efforts to complete the work by the end of the academic year. In this desperate state of mind, he loses his objectivity in the assessment of results, especially of those that threaten to invalidate large portions of his laboriously prepared manuscript.

Another important factor in the development of "thesis neurosis" is the beginner's inability to concentrate on writing and to persevere at it until the lengthy text is completed. Whenever he hits upon any unforeseen difficulty in putting his thoughts on paper, he takes flight in yet another experiment, a chore he promised to do for relatives, a comradely favor he suddenly feels he owes a colleague, or anything else that could serve as an excuse to get away from the desk for a while.

The compilation of a thesis not only teaches self-discipline in all these respects, but it also gives the young scientist his first opportunity to learn something, by personal experience, about the administrative aspects of writing. It takes experience to prepare dictation for tape or for a rough draft on paper, so that a typist can follow it without having to interrupt you constantly with questions. If a typist is assigned full time to your work, it is difficult to see that she is always occupied, yet not overworked by impatient requests for some pages that you urgently need to continue the text. It takes time to learn how to draw a rough sketch of a graph or diagram which the draftsman can interpret, or to prepare a specimen properly for the photographer. In earlier years, our Institute assumed the entire cost of thesis writing with disastrous results; each job had to be repeated umpteen times, to the great irritation of all involved. Despite fantastic waste of time and money, the candidate learned nothing about these important administrative aspects of writing. Now, postgraduates receive more substantial fellowships, but the entire cost of preparing the thesis must be borne by them. What they waste is their personal loss; what they save is their own gain. This experience is just as valuable to a future chief of a research unit as that gained earlier in directing the work of technicians.

My recommendations for profitable postgraduate work and the prophylaxis of thesis neurosis are that the candidate should:

1. Learn to do, himself, everything needed for research, including the choice of a problem, the planning of experimental techniques and the organization of lab and office work.

2. Not be asked to do too much monotonous routine work himself.

After he has proven that he can perform a task perfectly, it is much more important for him to learn how to direct the work of others.

3. Prepare and submit a detailed plan of the proposed thesis for careful criticism by his chief and colleagues.

4. Complete all experimental work and describe each experiment separately as soon as it is terminated, before beginning to write the definitive text.

5. Be relieved of all other duties for several months so that he may devote himself uninterruptedly to writing.

6. Be personally responsible for the direction and cost of all the work connected with his thesis.

Apart from the points just mentioned, the problems encountered in writing a thesis or a monograph are essentially the same. We shall discuss them conjointly under the latter heading (p. 349).

REVIEW ARTICLES.   The purpose of a review article is to present a critical survey of the literature on a subject. It has a dual function: it must be an index of references not otherwise easily accessible as well as a guide to their interpretation. Thus, the objectives of a review are essentially the same as those of a monograph, except that the latter usually deals with a broader subject. In any event, the technical aspects of preparing reviews and monographs—collection, abstracting and the harmonious arrangement of the material—are virtually identical.

A review is usually written by invitation; therefore its style should conform, as far as possible, to that of the journal which solicited it. To act as a useful key to the literature, the review should discuss all or at least most of the relevant publications objectively, irrespective of whether the reviewer approves of them or not. But by "objectively" I do not mean uncritically. It is a common error merely to tabulate all publications "objectively" according to the easy formula of: "Blank says yes, Doe says no; while Smith says sometimes yes, sometimes no." This style is both boring and uninformative. It offers not much more than a simple list of references, arranged according to subject, since each of the original papers must be looked up and evaluated by the reader before forming an opinion. We look to the reviewer for a competent, personal evaluation, even if we may disagree with some of his conclusions.

Books

Matters related to science are described in a great variety of essentially different books: monographs, textbooks, encyclopedias, procedure manuals and nontechnical or semitechnical books about science. Each of these media poses unique problems, but one rule applies to all: they must bring out something new in a readable manner.

Therefore, as soon as you feel like writing a book the first thing to do is to find out whether there is any need for it, that is, whether the book you have in mind would be sufficiently new and different from existing publications to interest a significant number of readers. Then, make sure that you have the talent and facilities to collect, digest and present the relevant material in a readable manner.

Few scientific books are supposed to be read avidly from cover to cover; most of them are meant for consultation of individual sections; but even a procedure manual or an index is highly readable if its style brings otherwise inaccessible material within easy reach. The structure must be adjusted to the type of information you want to convey; anecdotes, drama and humor are assets to an auto-biography, but not to a procedure manual intended to give rapid information on how to use a machine or file. Whatever the subject, the most of the best pertinent facts must be brought to the reader in the least tiresome manner. In other words, the author must do all the predigesting and rearranging of data himself, so that the reader gets the essence with a minimum of effort. To do this well the author, who is always enthusiastic about his subject (or else he would not expose himself to the grueling task of writing the book), must visual-ize his reader as blasé, lazy, and none too bright—one who will follow only as far as he is carried. This assumption is not easy to make because you love your readers and like to think of them as a very distinguished lot. Of course, you must never admit publicly to such a derogatory assumption (as I do in these confidential Notes) —but it does improve your style.

THE MONOGRAPH. *Generalities.* The monograph (mono = one, graphein = write) is a scholarly and thoroughly documented treatise, exhaustively covering a single area of a field of learning. To my mind, this is the highest medium for the expression of scientific thought because it best permits the integration—indeed, often the creation—of a new field. A monograph may be short, if not much is known about the subject, or extremely voluminous, if the relevant literature is extensive. In any event, it should cover all the important aspects of the topic indicated by its title.

My monograph, *On the Experimental Morphology of the Adrenals* (Selye and Stone [75]) consists of only 105 pages, while *Stress* (Selye [68]) takes up 1,225 followed by five volumes of addenda, in the form of the *Annual Reports on Stress,* each of which again comprises an average of about 500 pages (Selye et al.[69]). *The Chemical Prevention of Cardiac Necroses* (Selye [71]) and *The Pluricausal Cardiopathies* (Selye [73]) were based mainly on experiments previously described by our group; while *Calciphylaxis* (Selye [74]) was published so soon after formulation of its basic concept that most of its experimental foundation had never previously been published in journals.

Since integration of data from a novel point of view is its principal object, the monograph is almost invariably written by a single author. The responsibility of compiling a textbook or an encyclopedia may be shared by a group, each author writing one chapter. But such collective efforts can never hope to achieve the harmonious unity of the ideal monograph that creates a new concept by the thorough integration of many subjects in a single mind. That is why the monograph is the most personal form of scientific expression.

Probably the only generalizations that can be made about the preparation of monographs are that: (1) the author must be well acquainted with the field from personal experience; (2) there must be a real need for correlation of the field from a new viewpoint; (3) the general rules about good scientific writing (as outlined at the beginning of this section) should be observed.

Tricks. In the course of writing monographs, I have learned a few "tricks of the trade" some of which may be worth mentioning here, especially since they are useful also in preparing other types of books.

While *compiling material* for a book, don't worry about order of presentation and phraseology. Just accumulate notes on anything that seems relevant: brief abstracts of papers written by others, summaries of your own experiments, theories. Structure and style are very important, but when the time comes, the pieces will fall into order of themselves and it will be easier to give the whole its final form and polish then.

The brief notes are typed out on slips of paper about $6\frac{1}{2}$ inches wide and stuck with scotch tape on what we call *"rail paper."* The latter is a standard size ($8\frac{1}{2}$ inches wide by 11 inches long) perforated ring-binder loose-leaf page whose two lateral margins are covered by a double width of scotch tape, thus forming a plastic "rail." The narrower paper slips containing the loose notes can be attached easily and even detached again for transposition to another place on the rail paper without tearing its plastic-protected surface. This simple procedure is very helpful because it permits rapid rearrangement of passages for insertion of new remarks between the old, without time-consuming retyping or splicing.

When the plan of the book has matured to the point where at least a preliminary table of contents can be made, index tabs, bearing abridged section-headings, are stuck to the margin of the rail paper at appropriate points. Now the pages are arranged to form chapters and any new material can readily be inserted in its proper place.

For example, the rough preliminary manuscript of these Notes which I hold in my hands at this moment, consists of thousands of these paper slips stuck to rail paper pages. These are held together in a ring binder in which the position of the material for each chapter is already identified by a marginal index tab.

After this, it is very easy to prepare a chapter for dictation: you merely open the ring binder at the corresponding index tab, take out all the rail paper pages in that section, lay them out side by side on the table for survey and rearrange the individual slips in the desired final order. Some slips carry only a reminder of what has to be discussed (for example: for what I am dictating now, I had a reminder saying "Describe rail paper technique and illustrate it with a picture"), but others are more complete. One slip fully describes a particularly instructive event that happened in the lab ten years ago and was intended to illustrate a point in the psychology of research; another brings back to mind a beautiful passage from a book I read long ago and which I want to quote in a certain connection.

In the case of purely technical books, of course, most of these slips carry concise abstracts of scientific papers or descriptions of personal observations. But, whatever the subject, it is most useful to have such slips conveniently arranged; the system relieves you of the need to search for data at the time of dictation when you want to concentrate uninterruptedly on the most taxing task in book writing, namely: synthesis. Naturally, the loose notes cannot be copied as such; they still need to be modified and connected by text to give unity to the presentation. But this is usually not too difficult after such preparation.

Now, just a brief note about the use of *dictating machines*. Some authors write their text (from notes, abstract cards or memory) by longhand or, if they have learned the art, on a typewriter; others dictate to a secretary-stenographer. But the mere mechanical work of writing by hand or on a typewriter is distracting. So is a secretary. She may never break the point of her pencil or ask you to repeat a word; she may never sneeze, yawn or have to go out for a moment just when you have collected your thoughts to deliver a difficult passage—but, when you can't think of the next sentence, her mere presence is a reproach which blocks your thinking. Besides, some finicky secretaries dislike coming in at five o'clock in the morning when I happen to be in the best form for dictation. Even at other times of the day their alertness may vary, while the machine to which I am confiding these thoughts now is always receptive, quick and faultless in registering my every word; never at a loss in reading its own notes back to me; never annoyed if my wandering memory makes me ask it to repeat the same sentence too often.

It is true that authors, used to typing or writing out their own text, find it difficult at first to use a machine because they do not see what they have done and cannot polish it immediately. But, with the preliminary notes on the rail paper before you as a rough guide, you soon learn to remember pretty accurately what you have said, and it will rarely be necessary to play back long sections. As for the final polishing, it is much more easily done on a neat first draft (with a wide margin) typed from the tape by an expert at her leisure, uninterrupted by your hesitations, undisturbed by your physical presence.

The insertion of last minute additions to an almost finished manuscript often causes confusion by changing the *pagination*. To obviate this, we devised a "decimal point system," which permits the unlimited insertion of additional pages at any point if you proceed as indicated by the following example:

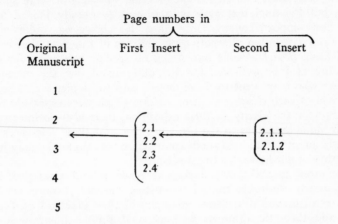

We have used this system successfully even for the insertion of printed pages in the loose-leaf *Encyclopedia of Endocrinology* (Selye [67]).

In summary, my recommendations on the mechanics of book writing are: make abundant notes long before you start to think of a structure, then get yourself a ring binder, some scotch tape and a dictating machine. The rest is easy.

THE TEXTBOOK. Textbooks are primarily meant for students. They usually deal with a broad and well-established field of learning, covered by a regular lecture course which the textbook is meant to complement. The textbook should contain more information than can be given in a lecture course, yet not so much as to confuse a beginner.

In writing a textbook, the author must constantly keep in mind the probable background of his readers and the amount of time they can reasonably be expected to devote to his particular subject. Hence, standard textbooks should not present too many unsolved problems; references to conflicting views imply that the reader should look up the original text and make up his mind himself. In theory, it seems attractive to stimulate independent original thinking in this manner. In practice, however, students rarely have the time to look up textbook references or the experience to evaluate them.

For this reason, in preparing the *Textbook of Endocrinology* (Selye [66]), I tried to do as much as possible of the reading and evaluating myself; then I discussed each section with one or more specialists, but the final text gave only what I eventually judged to be the best supported views. Only when this choice was quite impossible did I mention alternative possibilities of interpretation briefly indicating pros and cons but giving no specific references for each shading of interpretation. On the other hand, for the occasional reader who may want to delve deeper into the topic, I attached to the end of each chapter a list of articles which were especially noteworthy for the clarity of their exposition, their historic interest, or their value as guides to the literature. Each of these references was briefly annotated to indicate its contents, so that the reader may judge whether or not he wishes to consult it.

In order to make even textbooks readable and attractive, it is particularly desirable to use interesting anecdotes concerning the history of certain discoveries, examples of their practical applicability and theoretic value as well as good simple illustrations and diagrams.

NONTECHNICAL AND SEMITECHNICAL BOOKS ABOUT SCIENCE. Most scientists are so deeply involved in their work that they never write about science, except in the technical language of their specialty. I think this is a pity. Such outstanding investigators as Bernard [9], Richet [59], Poincaré [57], Darwin [26], Einstein [32], Carrel [18] and Cannon [16] have written interesting and stimulating books about the general problems of the scientist in the form of diaries, biographies, or essays on the philosophy and psychology of research. There is no reason why science and the personalities of scientists should always be brought before the public only as seen by professional men of letters. Most scientists will not write so well, but they can compensate for this lack by a more intimate knowledge of themselves and their work. Probably the greatest value of this kind of contribution is that it stimulates and helps to orient those who are just about to enter a scientific career. These young people are especially interested in the opinions and experiences of those who preceded them in their chosen field. I think it is almost an obligation to gratify this need. Besides, in the years to come, as Bertrand Russell put it:

"Not only will men of science have to grapple with the sciences that deal with man but—and this is a far more difficult matter—they will have to persuade the world to listen to what they have discovered. If they cannot succeed in this difficult enterprise, man will destroy himself by his halfway cleverness."

Of course, a scientist who has never written other than purely technical texts runs into a great many difficulties when he first tries to address a more general public. Here, even more than in other forms of writing, he must constantly keep in mind for whom he is writing. Well do I remember my difficulties in this respect when I wrote my first semitechnical book, *The Stress of Life* [70]. In dictating the rough manuscript, I continually found myself wavering between baby talk, which would have been below the level of any individual likely to pick up a nonfiction book, and highly technical language meant only for specialists.

[*In dictating the present Notes, it helps me a great deal to think of you, John, whose picture is very clearly before me. Sometimes, I may be a little dry and matter-of-fact, when I want to teach you a procedure. At other times you may think of me as a maudlin sentimentalist far too romantic about research, or as one who is far too blasé, critical, and sarcastic about conventional values. Indeed, looking these Notes over, I see that they have no style, each section having been written at a different time, in a different mood. Only one thing unites them: they are all meant for you. I imagine you as a young and intelligent person, willing to take science and scientists unretouched as they actually are, and, if my sales talk is convincing enough, perhaps willing to join our club. On the other hand, if there should be someone apart from you who also wants to read these Notes but is not particularly interested in one or the other of our problems, he can skip the odd bit here and there without losing continuity. These loose slips of paper have no unifying principle anyway, beyond the fact that they are written by a very peculiar fellow for the likes of him.*]

Book Reviews

The first object of a book review is to state the contents of the book. It should also mention such salient technical facts as: number of pages, quality of illustrations and price. A personal evaluation is extremely useful, but only if the reviewer is an authority in the field and has actually read the book carefully—which is not always the case.

Book reviews are usually written by invitation; they are therefore difficult to reject even if they are unsuitable. Hence, it is particularly bad form to use them as a forum for the popularization of the reviewer's pet views or the advertising of his own publications on related subjects—unfortunately a rather common practice.

Begging for Money

In discussing this important topic, I shall try to be calm and just. It won't be easy, but I shall try.

Most granting agencies supply pamphlets describing their aims, together with *standardized application forms*. Usually, they ask you to state your previous training and to explain, in detail, just how you plan to go about discovering whatever you are after. If you are a beginner, applying only for a fellowship, you may be asked to visit an approved expert in some other city, who will talk to you for an hour or so, and then report his impressions of your research potential to the granting agency. If you are the head of an institution and ask for a great deal of money, a whole group of such approved experts will come to make a "site visit," to appraise not only you, but also your coworkers and facilities (p. 196).

Frankly, all this is not very satisfactory; it is difficult to appraise either people or projects on the basis of a written report or a brief interview. The talents needed to do good research are quite different from those necessary to obtain subsidies. These latter gifts, collectively referred to as "grantsmanship," are not particularly endearing; I do not recommend that you spend much time cultivating them, but you should know what they are and how they function.

In applying for a grant, you must *describe your plan* in great detail, with special emphasis on materials and techniques, so that the judges may see that you are familiar with the subject and that you have worked out your plan with care. It is well to include a number of investigations that require thorough familiarity with complicated procedures (preferably micro-) and apparatus (preferably electronic), since the man who takes the trouble to learn a refined methodology is judged more deserving of help than the one who can use only his head, hands and eyes.

By anticipating how the work will go you must work out a budget, clearly indicating in advance how much of the total sum awarded will be used for assistants' salaries, experimental animals, instruments and other supplies. Only thus will the judges be able to see whether you are worldly enough to know how much things cost and whether you can plan a reasonably proportioned distribution of funds.

Most important of all, you must apply for a study that falls within the donor's field of interest. Some granting agencies are supposed to subsidize purely basic research which has no obvious immediate application; others are intended primarily for applied research, likely to be immediately useful, say, to clinical medicine or agriculture; yet others like to provide "a public service." The latter may, for example, support library research only if it is to furnish an information service available to many people. Or they will provide funds to create a center designed to serve as a nucleus for clinical research, or as a school for postgraduate training. Conversely, some agencies are specifically prevented by their regulations from giving assistance to a project that provides a public service, because it may compete with private enterprise.

Of course, it is difficult to put all the shadings of these policies clearly into a pamphlet or an application form, but a candidate who asks for a considerable sum might well be expected to make a little effort to understand. He should carefully read even the small print in the documents sent him; if need be he can also discuss the matter orally with officers of the granting agencies or their scientific advisers, who devote much of their time to these problems—often without remuneration. The choice of a topic, suitable from the point of view of grantsmanship, may take a good deal of time and know-how, but the procedure is obviously necessary, since no granting agency can legitimately subsidize work in contravention of its own rules. Officers of agencies administering governmental funds or moneys collected by foundations through public campaigns, must be particularly careful in these matters. Private philanthropists and philanthropic foundations have much more latitude in distributing their funds; but here, everything may depend upon the candidate's ability to convince one or a few individuals—often laymen—whose opinion has a decisive influence upon applications.

Fortunately, most donors insist upon all these points only before they make a grant. *Once the award is approved,* they allow you to deviate from the stated program just as you see fit. If your project was good enough to be selected for a grant, they realize that you, who are doing the work, are the best judge of how and with what tools it should be done. I would not be surprised to learn that some of the less scrupulous investigators foresee the possibility of such future deviations from their stated program, even as they include in their application some impressive but actually impractical studies, or some popular but, to them, useless piece of machinery.

The unfortunate thing about all this is that you must have grantsmanship to obtain the grant in the first place, and the acquisition of this talent is not only time consuming but quite unrelated to scientific competence. Indeed, it seems to me that the development of the kind of worldliness needed to get a grant is actually harmful to the scientific spirit.

The question of *how to subsidize research intelligently* is one of the most important in our contemporary society. There is no point in complaining about things as they are, because under existing conditions, the officers of granting agencies cannot act otherwise than they do. Indeed, once you have made a name for yourself and your project is really promising, one or other agency will usually find some loophole in its regulations to help you, even if your application is not quite appropriately worded. But could all this not be simplified?

I have given the matter a great deal of thought and was very gratified to learn that at least one of the major granting agencies, the John Simon Guggenheim Memorial Foundation saw fit to approve my recommendations as shown by the following excerpt from its published 1957–1958 report [49]:

"There was unanimous and enthusiastic agreement with the point of a letter by Professor Hans Selye, Director of the Institute of Experimental Medicine and Surgery in the University of Montreal, published in the *New York Times* of 27 October 1957, as follows:

" 'A great deal has been written about the relative merits of subsidizing practical (applied) research, whose immediate aim is to cure a disease, or fundamental (basic) research, whose only concern is to acquire knowledge, irrespective of its immediate practical use.

" 'In either case, the funds are distributed to those applicants who submit the most promising research program. This is as it should be when it comes to the development and further evaluation of previously made discoveries.

" 'But who subsidizes original discoveries? Wholly original, first observations cannot be planned in advance. Yet they form the basis of all premeditated research projects. Most of the completely new leads are accidental discoveries made by men who have the rare talent of noticing the unexpected. Would it not be reasonable to endow this type of discovery too?

" 'It may be argued that the unexpected cannot be appraised in advance and that hence it would be risky to select recipients for such grants. This is quite true. But would the hazard be greater than that taken when funds are allotted on the basis of a detailed plan?

" 'In the former case the risk is that nothing may be found; in the latter that the conscientious pursuit of an approved project may stifle the imagination of a truly talented scientist and prevent him from following up hunches and unforeseen observations. Besides, it is in the nature of things that grants given to execute specific plans must be awarded to those who can prepare the best applications. These men are not necessarily the most gifted scientists.

" 'Scholarships and fellowships are usually awarded to junior investigators, chiefly or entirely on the merit of the personal characteristics and over-all accomplishments of the candidates, not on the basis of any research plans they may be able to submit. This method carries a risk, but it can be a carefully calculated one.

" 'Why not do the same with career investigators? They can be judged, even more objectively than beginners, by their longer record of scientific achievement. Why not give them research grants outright, with the approval to follow their own instinct in appraising the importance of whatever finding they may stumble upon? Would the risk be really too high a price to pay for the advantages to be gained by ridding the creative spirit of the elite among a nation's scientists of the shackles of predetermined routines?

" 'Would it really have been too hazardous to have given a personal grant, without restrictions, to Pasteur "for research on bacteria," to Fleming "for work on antibiotics," to the Curies "for investigations on radioactivity" or to Pavlov "for the study of conditioned reflexes"?

" 'Would it have been desirable to have made these scientists submit detailed plans about the manner in which they wanted to perform their task, and to spend much of their time writing annual or semi-annual reports on their activities?

" 'It may well prove profitable for those who subsidize research to examine not only applications, but also applicants (their way of life, their technical skills, their power of observation and even their vague hopes which cannot be put into writing), to see whether quite a few among the nation's top scientists might not do better with less supervision.'

"It was deemed by the Committee of Fellows that Dr. Selye's letter indicated an even better and bolder course for the Foundation than we hitherto have taken with respect to our new type of Fellowship.

"For to search out scholars of distinction, and those with high promise of distinction, and to make them free grants of considerable magnitude for their studies, without reference to a specific formulated project or specific time, was deemed a most daring and most worthy proposal. The spirit of freedom for the scholar to follow his own ideas, or to start out on a new line, was thought the nub of the proposal; for often, nowadays, the scholar has to tailor, or even distort, his research plans to fit a project that commands the support of some other agencies. Often the project that will receive support from those other agencies is not close to his own interests or abilities, or by the time funds are made available to him he may have found new research leads or developed other interests.

"The safety and progress of the nation, it was stated by the Committee of Fellows, comes from having at hand a supply of trained, first-class scholars and creative workers in all fields—men and women who are alert to the nation's, and the world's welfare. Dr. Selye's proposal to endow 'original discoveries' was judged feasible, in view of the Foundation's principles of giving complete freedom to its Fellows; and a plan by the Foundation for doing it would be likely to add greatly to the common strength and welfare."

After the publication of my suggestion in the *New York Times*, and in the Guggenheim report, I received numerous letters from scientists, educators, and donors of many countries (particularly the United States), expressing their agreement. Nowadays, the principle of giving grants on the basis of past accomplishments is receiving ever wider acceptance. [*I hope, that when the time comes for you, John, to apply for a major institutional grant, it will be awarded solely on merit, without the need to reread this depressing passage on how to beg for money.*]

Reports to Subsidizers of Research

All granting agencies must, of course, receive reports on what you have accomplished with the money entrusted you. If you haven't succeeded in anything, you will need a great deal of grantsmanship to report this well. In order to camouflage your failure, you will have to write pages and pages of text, difficult to compose. Don't look to me for advice on how to do this.

If you have done something worthwhile, you will publish it in a technical journal. In this case, the task is easy: you send in the manuscripts or reprints (which you have written by then, anyway), with a brief synopsis of the whole work, based on the summaries; to this you attach a financial account, prepared by the treasurer of your institution. And that is all there is to it.

General Correspondence

A letter should reflect the personality of the sender; hence, few general rules can be formulated about correspondence. All I can do is to say how we handle the problem here, although our case is perhaps unusual because of the extraordinary volume of mail we receive. Just answering requests for reprints keeps one secretary occupied full time. I cannot even read all my mail personally, yet, with the help of efficient secretaries, we usually manage to answer every letter within twenty-four hours of receipt.

At 9 A.M. the mail is delivered from the University post office to my personal secretary. She reads all English, French and German letters first and makes any marginal annotations that I shall need for my answers; for example, whether or not a suggested date for a visit or lecture is open on the agenda; whether a drug, histologic slide, or book, mentioned in a letter, has arrived. If I am supposed to comment about anything sent separately (e.g., a manuscript, reprint, or histologic slide) she waits until the material arrives before submitting the letter.

Only letters marked "Personal" are brought to me unopened. These I answer myself together with those in languages unfamiliar to the secretary and those that deal with subjects requiring a personal reply or, at least, decision. I then dictate the full text of my answer to certain letters, but things are so arranged that the major part of the correspondence can be dealt with by more or less standardized form letters.

If the answer to a letter is merely "yes" or "no," I simply dictate "yes" or "no" into the machine and the secretary does the rest according to stereotyped forms. For example, if I am asked to give a lecture I cannot accept, I just say "no" and the secretary puts this into the proper, courteous form according to standardized samples. The same procedure is used to answer requests for writing a book review, an introduction to a book, judging a thesis, receiving a visitor, etc.

Requests for positions or postgraduate fellowships are referred to one of the assistants. He again answers with form letters, which indicate whether there is an opening and what additional information or documents might be needed before we can reach a decision.

Most of the other routine mail is also handled by members of the staff. For example, reprints and books received are sent to the library for codification and filing. Letters from patients who want medical advice are answered by mimeographed form letters explaining that I do not practice. A request for reprints from any colleague is always granted (as long as copies are still available) and is automatically sent to the secretary in charge of mailings. Even if a request is made for all our reprints on a certain subject (e.g., steroid anesthesia, calciphylaxis), she can handle the problem by using previously prepared lists of the corresponding publications.

Letters from well-meaning people who wish to donate or sell items which I cannot use (e.g., their bodies for dissection after death or for experimentation right now, "cancer cures," lay suggestions for the improvement of our research, honorary membership in dubious societies, etc.) are gratefully but firmly refused and advertisements discarded.

I am afraid all this looks like a very impersonal way of dealing with correspondence, but in view of its volume, no other way is open to us. Whatever time I have for letter writing, I reserve for the comparatively small percentage of personally or scientifically interesting items. In a similar spirit, I do not write Christmas cards to everybody who has crossed my path during the year, but spend a fair amount of time writing long Christmas letters to a few close friends.

11. How to Speak

"If you your lips would keep from slips of five things have a care:
to whom you speak, of whom you speak, and how, and when, and where."
[Anonymous]

"A man may speak very well in the House of Commons, and fail very
completely in the House of Lords. There are two distinct styles requisite:
I intend, in the course of my career, if I have time, to give a specimen
of both." [Benjamin Disraeli]

"The more that, which one says, is great and difficult, the more is it
necessary to be simple and without pretensions in style." [Stendhal]

"You have not converted a man because you have silenced him."
[John, Viscount Morley]

The art of effective discourse is of immense value to any scientist.
Not only is it indispensable for lecturing to students and colleagues
or to satisfy the inevitable demands for addresses to the public at
large (clubs, radio, television), but it is a powerful asset at scientific
round tables and for contact with assistants in the laboratory and
office. Few scientists like public speaking because it is so often abused
as a means for self-advertisement and as an obligation imposed by
organizers of "worthy cause" campaigns or of lecture courses on
boring subjects. Yet, as an instrument for mutual understanding, the
art of speaking is at least as important to scientists as the art of
writing—and it is perhaps even more difficult to learn. The written
text can be reread and polished until it satisfies the author, if not
the reader. But the spoken word, once uttered, cannot be erased even
if it does not satisfy either. Speaking is a much more impromptu art
than writing; it depends to a great extent on an ingrained fluency in
the language and even on such personal stamina as self control,
pleasing diction, and freedom from mannerisms. It also requires a

363

certain sense of mass psychology to judge the silent reactions of the public and a talent for on-the-spot thinking if the audience's response —particularly unexpected questions—necessitate rapid deviation from a prepared text.

Much of what has been said about writing holds also for speaking and, unfortunately, the latter art depends even more upon innate qualities that cannot be taught, although they can be greatly improved by experience. Therefore, my first advice to the beginner is that he should use every opportunity to speak in public because he needs an audience for his training. Some practice in front of a mirror helps to check your appearance and possible mannerisms while lecturing, but this is of limited value. On the platform, what you will see before you is an audience which likes or dislikes you; it reflects interest or boredom, understanding or perplexity, and the art is to adjust your remarks accordingly. To do this well is no easy matter. You must learn to make close contact with your listeners, although usually you know almost nothing about them, and they cannot direct your speech by continual questioning. There they are in front of you, enigmatically silent and you need more than lip-reading, you need face-reading, to learn what they think. This art can and must be acquired. If you publish a text, the readers cannot direct your explanations by questions either, but they have more time to think about each point; they can adjust their speed to your own; they can even make you repeat a difficult passage by rereading it. Besides, the audience of printed words is not limited to a roomful of people who happen to belong to a certain class or scientific society; the text will reach at least some who can appreciate it.

In the course of time, I have made voluminous notes about the do's and don'ts of public speaking, an art which I have practiced quite a bit. Both my major subjects, stress and calciphylaxis, happen to be related one way or another to such different fields as physiology, biochemistry, morphology, and a good many specialties in clinical medicine. Since our own group could only make limited contributions to the development and practical application of our concepts in all these domains, I had to depend considerably upon the cooperation of others who have facilities and master techniques different from our own. That is why I give an extraordinarily large number of lectures (sometimes up to eighty in a single year) on organized lecture tours that take me to virtually every country where medical research is actively pursued. For reasons which I shall explain later, I never use a manuscript. Hence, in the course of my travels I have had to speak off-the-cuff in ten languages (some of which I speak very poorly), and I have also been forced to adjust my remarks to the field of interest of the most diverse audiences. I think I can say without bragging that I have committed every error that a lecturer can make; I have become an expert experienced in the craft of platform blunders. Since it is the principal purpose of these Notes to let you profit by my mistakes, let us start with what I consider to be the worst.

The Five Mortal Sins in Lecturing

1. *Unpreparedness.* When my teacher, Professor Biedl, launched me on my first public lecture, he said, "In a lecture, never use more than 3 per cent of your knowledge about the subject." This advice has stood me in good stead ever since. Beginners have an uncontrollable urge to tell all they know and, hence, inevitably confuse their listeners by mentioning things they do not know well. That last experiment with the "preliminary results" should be repeated; that last reference about adrenaline (or was it adrenalone?) should be looked up before we lecture about it. It is not necessary to mention even all fully verified facts if they do not add much to the point we want to make.

In a printed article, a statement on the effect of an insulin substitute upon the blood sugar may have to be backed up by the tabulation of many consecutive determinations, with the means, and the standard errors of the means, at each point of the curve. All this information will have to be listed separately for experiments on various species, e.g., the dog, rat, and rabbit. But, if the only point of all this work was to show that the agent does, in fact, depress the blood sugar in various species, it is quite sufficient in a lecture to say so, leaving it up to the listeners to ask questions, or to look up the published article, if they are interested in details.

Under no circumstances should an address correspond to the recitation of a printed publication. The only advantage of a lecture over the printed text is the immediate contact it offers between lecturer and audience. Unless a lecturer can learn—by reading the faces of his listeners, or by encouraging questions—how to make intimate contact with his audience, I can think of nothing that a lecture does better than a printed article. You can take a text home to read at your leisure; you can reread parts that you did not immediately understand or skip passages that bore you. The paper can be looked up again and again, so that you need not tax your memory with its details. The lecture has none of these advantages; therefore, it must be prepared with all these points in mind. Yet, there is such a thing as overpreparation. Of course, no experienced lecturer will recite a manuscript verbatim (unless it is the fact-studded curriculum of a speaker he has to introduce—or the text of a particularly important short statement he must make, say, at a press conference). But too detailed lecture notes can stifle your style and this is even more true of a manuscript which, though not read in full, is kept in sight as a guide.

Here again, generalizations are impossible because of the great individual variations in lecturing techniques, but I like to use lecture notes consisting of no more than about a dozen key words. These suffice to remind me of the points I want to make and the order in which I plan to present them. For example, if I were to lecture on the mortal sins of lecturers, I would use a small abstract card inscribed (very legibly and in large letters) with the following five words:

1. Unpreparedness
2. Verbosity
3. Inarticulateness
4. Introversion
5. Mannerisms

If there are especially meaningful or amusing points to make about any of these five subjects, I might add one or two words after some of these headings, but no more. If I wrote out entire sentences, I would undoubtedly forget to read them when carried away by my speech. Or else, I would read them and not be carried away. Of the two evils, the former is less serious.

It is quite impossible, even for the most experienced reader, to concentrate on the mechanics of reciting a text and yet retain the freshness, directness, and color of uninhibited free speech as it emerges still warm from the baking oven of your mind. The occasional slip of the tongue, jargon, or grammatical error that an educated person makes in ordinary conversation, detracts nothing from a lecture; on the contrary it adds spontaneity. It takes a great deal of time to polish a written text until it is letter perfect, and we are unaccustomed to absolutely flawless English in discussing things unreservedly without fears and inhibitions. That is one reason why the recitation of a perfect manuscript, be it even in the most natural tone, always has something artificial and stilted about it that puts us on our guard about the speaker and blocks intimate contact with him.

In summary, this is what I recommend:

Lecture only about the cream of what you know, leaving yourself a broad safety margin of reserve knowledge for use if you get carried away from the original plan, either by your own speech or by an audience reaction.

Never read from a manuscript (not even from the corner of your eye); a few easily legible key words should suffice as a guide.

Remember that it is better to prepare a lecture carefully than to have hindsight later. All of us who have given badly prepared speeches know those frustrating monologues during hours and sometimes days (or what is worse, nights) after an important lecture, when you go on repeating to yourself what you should have said on the platform.

But a lecture must be well prepared not only by the speaker but also by his host. Many a formal address given by a visiting scientist has been spoiled by program committees. They should remember that:

The lecture should be planned for a date when other events do not clash with it, and it should be properly announced to those who may wish to attend.

The lecture room should have good acoustics or at least a good loudspeaker system. Otherwise, to be heard, the speaker must use an artificially loud voice and concentrate too much on elocution. Especially in hotels and clubs, there is, in addition, the possibility of sonorific musical events in adjacent rooms to think of.

The optical qualities of the lecture facilities should be checked. Stray light, a dirty screen, and a weak projector spoil the most instructive colored slides. Blackboard, colored chalks and a pointer should be within easy reach.

The chairman should not regard his post as purely honorary. Directly, or through his delegates, he is supposed to supervise the smooth flow of the entire program. He must see to it that the speaker gets to the lecture hall in time (without any last-minute, frantic drive through evening traffic, even if there is a banquet in honor of the guest at the other end of town just before the address). The chairman may either introduce the lecturer himself or delegate this task to someone more familiar with the speaker and his subject. A good introduction should not be an empty formality, nor should it be a flowery eulogy in funeral oration style; it has a definite purpose: it is meant to assist the speaker in establishing close contact with his audience. The listeners are more likely to give their full attention to a man if they are reminded of the particular accomplishments that guarantee his competence in the field about which he will speak. Unless the audience consists only of a small group of specialists who know the lecturer personally, a brief, factual résumé of the highlights of his career (his chief scientific accomplishments, facts and perhaps even an anecdote that characterizes him as a person) always helps to bring him closer to his listeners.

On the other hand, a bad introduction can have exactly the opposite effect by starting the event on a platitudinous or ridiculous tone. No lecturer should be introduced with the well-worn phrase, "Doctor X needs no introduction," nor should he be embarrassed by being compared with Newton, Faraday, Pasteur and/or Einstein. The introduction should not be a lengthy biographic essay, studded with dates, that makes the audience impatient, nor should it be a detailed treatise on the subject which the speaker was asked to discuss.

The lecturer should be clearly told in advance how long he is expected to speak and what kind of audience he will be addressing, so that he may adjust his remarks accordingly.

The chairman should also protect the speaker against the usual barrage of questions on the way out through the crowd. Even with the best of will, after an exhausting lecture, the speaker is in no condition to prescribe for a patient, to think about complicated scientific questions, or to advise students on how to get fellowships, while he signs copies of his book on the backs of autograph collectors.

If I speak with some feeling about these points, it is because the oddest things have happened to me while lecturing in foreign countries. I remember one well-meaning chairman who wanted to flatter me in his halting English as best he could on the occasion of an address given to inaugurate a colossal new lecture hall. He started by saying: "I have had de greatest deaficulty to convince de governors to build dis enormous auditorium; dey said dat in dis city such a beek hall would never be fool, so I played trick on dem and invited Professor Selye; I knew he could fool de whole place and you see, he did."

Another very excited young colleague mentioned "Stress" and "Selye" so often in his introduction that eventually he gave me the floor with the remark: "... and now, I give you Doctor Stress." But this was not nearly as well received by the audience as the introduction of another chairman who, after expounding enthusiastically about the particular characteristics of my lecturing style, finished by saying: "... and now, you will hear a lecture in the inimitable style that has come to be identified throughout the world with the name of Doctor Silly." In this connection I also recall the Japanese chairman who kept referring to our group as "Professor Selye and his honorable accomplices."

As a lecturer, one runs into all sorts of peculiar situations, but the one that is most common and puzzling is the odd time-dependent enthusiasm that program committees have for lecturers. Because of my busy schedule, I once had to decline the same lecture invitation for four consecutive years, before finally—flattered by the persistence of the demand—I accepted.

At the airport, there was a whole delegation to welcome me; at the hotel, the alerted local press waited in eager anticipation for my message; the next two hours were bespoken for visits to the principal and the dean who wanted to thank me personally for coming. This was followed by a gigantic cocktail party, to meet local colleagues. There were so many of them, I could hardly do more than shake hands between drinks, but I did feel welcome!

Then came a banquet at which I was presented with a beautiful scroll, but I noticed that the chairman, to my left at the table, was preoccupied. "The program is a little behind schedule," he explained, "and we may expect to run into heavy traffic on the way to the auditorium which is at the other end of town. So, instead of the hour foreseen, could you cut your lecture to about forty-five minutes . . . perhaps forty . . . , or thirty-five? Of course, only if you think this could easily be done, but we should finish on time because I have invited a few friends to meet you, after the address, at my house. You will love the place—it is on a beautiful sunny hill about twenty-five miles east of the city—and it will do you good to relax with a nightcap after the stress (Ha-Ha!) of public speaking, before being driven back to town for a good night's rest." I was also tactfully told that not so much would be lost if I did not present all my material because attendance will probably be limited anyway on account of unforeseen conflicts. "There will be a major league game on television, and some of the members have to attend an emergency meeting of the County Medical Society in relation to matters of professional interest, the result of some outrageous suggestions made to Congress about the socialization of medicine."

Now, by cutting out half of my slides, I could have managed to adjust my speech to this schedule, had the introduction not taken up seven minutes of my precious time, and had it not been preceded first by the reading of the Society's minutes, the election of new members and the treasurer's very conscientious and detailed financial report. I finally took only thirty minutes but still felt very garrulous because I finished fifteen minutes late at that!

Now, you may think that this was an unusual occasion—and, fortunately, it was. But less crass examples of the same spirit are far from exceptional; they are the rule. Why is it that the larger a scientific meeting, the greater the fanfare, the more insistent the anticipatory enthusiasm to get the lecturer—and often the greater the honorarium—the more people are interested merely in meeting the speaker without having to listen to what he was invited to say?

2. *Verbosity.* Verbiage is perhaps the cardinal sin of public speakers. No matter how great your experience, there is always room for improving the proportion between words and substance in your speech.

Conciseness is a difficult art to acquire, especially if you speak without notes. The beginner considers his subject so complex that it could not possibly be described in a few words. Of course, the more time you have, the more you can say; but even the most complicated subject can be explained simply, understandably, and correctly, as far as the statement goes. A dictionary definition of cortisone cannot replace a monograph on the same subject, but it can satisfy the curiosity of those who have never heard the word before. As I have said elsewhere, no written article can be perfect. At best it can be perfect for a certain type of reader. The same is true of a lecture or an instruction given to an assistant; all communications must be adjusted to those for whom they are meant and to the time available for explanation. The story is told about Einstein that, in answer to a college girl's request for a simple definition of relativity, he said: "One hour on the lap of your boy friend seems like one minute; one minute on a hot stove seems like one hour. That is relativity."

The best safeguard against verbosity in lecturing is to think first about whom you are talking to and how much time you have; then put down a certain length of time after each key word on your lecture notes. After this, just stick to your schedule.

One of the worst pests at scientific meetings is the "runaway speaker" whose words act like an avalanche, each ephemeral snowflake of thought once set into motion, gathers more and more fuzzy fluff until it becomes a mighty monster, uncontrollably pushed on by its own mass and finally it breaks down into nothing but balls and more balls.

3. *Inarticulateness.* As one former child prodigy poignantly put it, most of our college courses are quite inadequate for the linguistic education of the average student. "They introduce him to the English language as one might be introduced to a delightful young lady at a cocktail party: the student has not quite caught her name and would not know her again" [Norbert Wiener [89]].

An occasional error in grammar or syntax, the odd colorful colloquialism, or (I hope for personal reasons) a slight regional or foreign accent, can be tolerated; indeed, these minor flaws may even add a certain personal flavor to a lecture. But a speaker who mumbles incomprehensibly should take a course in diction, and one whose voice is too weak must remember to stay close to his microphone. Inarticulate speech is usually the consequence of emotion, particularly tenseness and shyness. This defect tends to be worst during the first minutes. Here, it may help to learn the first few sentences by heart, or even to read them, because once a start is made the speaker thinks of his topic rather than of himself—and the stage fright disappears.

The excessive use of collegiate, or even ordinary jargon is another form of inarticulateness. Unconsciously, the speaker tries to ingratiate himself by showing through the use of common words that, despite his scientific eminence, he is just a simple, unaffected guy like the fellows in the audience. Yet, jargon is out of place in a scientific lecture, and it should not be used—or at least not frequently and not on purpose.

Finally, we must guard against the inarticulateness of sloppily prepared lantern slides, diagrams and photographs, as well as overcrowded, illegible tables and diagrams. Such carelessness is an offense to the audience and just as difficult to follow as mumbled speech.

4. *Introversion.* A good speaker must project himself outward, toward his audience, without indulging in histrionics. He must learn to assume an attitude of relaxed extroversion. Modesty is an endearing virtue, but if it takes the form of excessive shyness on the platform, it isolates the speaker from his listeners. He is afraid of detecting some trace of criticism in their faces and tends to look away, usually taking refuge in the familiar lines of his own manuscript. He knows from previous experience that, if he raises his eyes, out there in the audience he may detect all sorts of sights to block his thinking; the yawning face of an athletic-looking student; a lady who knits while listening with such disheartening equanimity to the findings that cost him years of arduous work; the bright-colored, funny hat with the dangling feather, whose coquettish femininity is so incongruous in this setting. He may even detect a boy who reads a newspaper behind the back of the fellow in front of him; worst of all, his eyes may meet a disapproving or sarcastic smile. All these are terrible ganglionic blocking agents. In a large audience, the occasional one is unavoidable—but the better the lecturer, the less the danger of seeing such sights. In any event, the best way to fight indifference and inattention is to look squarely at the faces of your listeners. Seek out a pair of eyes here and there, and speak first to one, then to

another of the people before you, directing your remarks strictly at
them just as you would in the leisurely and relaxed setting of your
office had they come to question you about your work.

Introversion is one of the worst faults in a lecturer; it is related
to all the other mortal sins enumerated here. It may stem from
unpreparedness, and often leads to nervous verbosity, inarticulateness and mannerisms, all barricades between speaker and listener.
Introversion destroys the main advantage a lecture has over a written
article; it abolishes the rapport between teacher and pupil, so necessary in continually adjusting the spoken word to the ever-changing
needs of the listeners as expressed by their reactions.

5. *Mannerisms*.   Nervous lecturers develop an astonishing variety
of mannerisms and tics. The twitch at the corner of the mouth, the
theatrical, exaggerated gesture, the stilted speech, the repetitious use
of the same platitudes, the compulsion to look down at the floor
or up at the ceiling with sightless, vacuous eyes, are all mannerisms
that stem from tension and fear of the public. Like some of the
previously mentioned expressions of introversion, these mannerisms
isolate the speaker from his audience: you feel so sorry for the
lecturer, so embarrassed by his compulsion to indulge in these antics,
that you cannot listen to the substance of his talk. It is a relief when
the lights go out for projections because now everybody looks at
the screen. And suddenly the speaker's mannerisms disappear because the darkness protects him from the terrifying experience of
seeing his listeners and being seen by them. The bad lecturer needs
this protection as the shy horse needs blinders and it is not a bad
idea for the beginner to use many slides both as a guiding manuscript-
substitute and as a smoke screen against his terrifying audience.

There are many stereotypes of speakers whose platform habits,
affectations and pretentions are not just mannerisms but bad manners. There is the aggressive lecturer who wastes his listeners' time
by lengthy, venomous diatribes against those who do not accept his
views. There is the defensive speaker who constantly asserts his
priority or underlines the importance of even his most trifling observations by devious but quite transparent arguments. Curiously,
unusual beauty of expression is also a drawback in scientific lectures
because it detracts attention from the hub of the matter to be explained. I have often caught myself being so fascinated by the
eloquence and flawless diction of a speaker, that I could hear only
the lovely music and not the message of his address. This danger is
greatest in the case of lectures delivered in particularly musical
languages, such as French and Italian.

Bad platform habits are worth analyzing because they can be

mastered. Personally, I have found it easiest to fight the mannerisms that would separate me from the audience with other mannerisms which have an opposite effect. Nothing is more conducive to a warm personal contact with your listeners than the assumption of attitudes that are quite foreign to formal oratory but natural in chatting informally with friends. Just leaning against the blackboard or the edge of the table helps to abolish formality, but the most important thing is to check the tone of your voice and your choice of words. Relax. Imagine that you are just trying to explain your work to a few colleagues who dropped in to see you in your lab.

There is a kind of diction that we have come to associate with the pulpit and the lectern. It creates an air of solemnity and respect for authority; it encourages unquestioning acceptance rather than critical analysis; it stimulates memorizing more than understanding. Avoid this style. It is not a bad thing for a scientist to break down, purposely, all awe-inspired confidence in his "stature" by the simplicity and lack of pretense in his bearing. Personal authority is based on past accomplishments; a speaker who wears it as an academic robe does not help his listeners to follow him in his efforts to judge each new fact independently and objectively only on its own convincing power.

Now that we have briefly gone over the general principles of communicating information by the spoken word, just a few remarks about some of the occasions when effective speaking is particularly useful to a scientist.

Technical Speech

Regular courses. Elementary teaching courses are not really for scientists, but you may not be able to avoid them, especially at the beginning of your career.

The problem of the scientist's participation in teaching has been dealt with elsewhere (p. 159), but regarding the technique of lecturing in regular university courses, not much can be added to what has already been said about effective public speaking in general.

Brief scientific communications. The staple oral offering of the modern scientist is the ten minute paper, delivered at a society meeting. The beginner may have to rely entirely on this medium for the direct presentation of his results outside his immediate surroundings, because formal addresses and participation in scientific round tables are arranged by invitation. Let us illustrate the problem of the brief oral communication by a scene I witnessed a couple of years ago at an International Congress in Europe.

A young American endocrinologist, whom we shall call Dr. Smith, performed an interesting series of experiments on the effect of hypophysectomy upon various blood constituents. He has never been at an international meeting before and his trouble started 'way back home because his chief disregarded the first rule of this game, namely, that the beginner must get the chance of a grand rehearsal before the members of his department, so that his attention may be called to the inevitable errors of the uninitiated. Now, he sits nervously on the edge of his chair in this huge lecture room, surrounded by all these foreigners who are shamelessly jabbering among themselves in unintelligible tongues and walking in and out of the room while the speaker is holding forth in French (or maybe it's Italian).

Smith has been waiting here in readiness for two hours, although he has been far too excited to listen even to the English papers and would have been much better off relaxing in the cafeteria. Sitting next to him, I suggest that he should go out for a snap of fresh air, but he is worried that he might be called early if one of the speakers doesn't turn up. The meeting being an hour behind schedule, there is no danger of this; but Smith does not listen to me. Time marches on. Paper follows paper and Smith becomes increasingly more restless.

Suddenly, it occurs to him that it might be well to reread his manuscript while waiting, but he can't find it. Feverishly, he goes through all his pockets. No manuscript! Smith becomes frantic. He says he couldn't possibly speak without a text. He searches desperately through the enormous stack of papers that was handed to all the delegates in a plastic briefcase. There is the program of the meeting, a list of all delegates, the plan of the city, with one red "X" over his hotel and another over the auditorium, a number of invitations to various parties, a beautifully illustrated pamphlet describing all the noteworthy sites in the surrounding district, all sorts of advertisements—but no manuscript. It seemed to me that I saw it in his hand a few minutes ago, but now Smith is sure he left it in the hotel, and gets up to retrieve it although it is obvious that he could not be back in time because the preceding paper is approaching its end. Suddenly I see the manuscript. He was sitting on it. He welcomes the somewhat crumpled document with a deep sigh of relief just as the chairman calls upon him.

We are sitting in the middle of a long row of crowded chairs and Smith is obviously worried about the time it takes him to get out to the aisle. Yet, to my surprise, he does not go toward the platform but in the opposite direction. He pulls a package of lantern slides out of his pocket and begins to explain something to the projectionist. This takes time because, apparently, the latter does not understand

Smith's midwestern American. All eyes are now on Smith who becomes increasingly more jittery. But eventually, there he stands at the lectern, looking terribly bewildered. As I found out later, he suddenly wondered whether he should say "Mr. Chairman," "Ladies and Gentlemen," "Members of the Society" or whatnot, and the problem assumed enormous importance at that moment. He finally doesn't say anything but just mumbles, away from the microphone, so that people won't realize his terrible ignorance.

Smith begins to read that manuscript. His voice is almost inaudible and hollow from fear, but it really doesn't matter because the majority of the audience can't understand the midwestern twang anyway. He goes on for what seems to be an eternity in the same colorless monotone until the first slide. It appears on the screen first upside-down, then right side left. Now it is the projectionist who becomes jittery, although Smith tries to put him at ease by telling him (in a very audible voice) not to worry about this slide because it isn't the first one anyway. Several voices from the audience tune in, in an effort to translate the widwestern accent into the local tongue or at least into school English for the baffled man at the lantern.

Finally, the right slide appears correctly oriented on the screen. The audience is manifestly relieved, but still there are difficulties. The slide contains ten columns from left to right, each with twelve rows of figures followed by $\pm$ the Standard Errors. Nobody can take in this crowded slide, although Smith comments separately on each of the 130 figures ($\pm$ S.E.). To make things worse he now turns toward the screen and away from the microphone so that his voice becomes inaudible even to those of us who can follow the accent.

When, after a few more such slides, the lights go on, the room is virtually empty. It is a big amphitheater—but Smith has emptied it. Still, he goes on reading from his manuscript although the red light has been flickering in front of him for quite some time, to show that his time is up. The chairman gets restless. He walks toward Smith with a compassionate but suggestive smile. Smith mumbles on. The chairman gently taps his shoulder, showing his wrist watch, to which Smith replies that he is almost through.

People begin to come in again for the next paper, but seeing Smith still on the platform, they leave. The situation is embarrassing and even I, who am really trying, cannot follow because I am so worried about Smith.

At last, there is a slight gap in the monotone because Smith has to wet his parched lips with a sip of water. The experienced chairman immediately seizes on this chance and puts his foot in the gap by loudly thanking Dr. Smith for his "most interesting communication" and calling for the next speaker with an air of finality, "because there is no time left for discussion." With a last uncertain look toward the Chair, then toward the audience, Smith hesitatingly leaves the platform; but the dignity of his departure is somewhat marred by the fact that, in his excitement, he stumbles over the steps and falls flat on his face.

I took the remains of Smith out to the bar for a drink which both of us needed badly, but I failed in my efforts to cheer him up. He just didn't think it was really worth his while to come all the way from America just for this paper, although he did manage to draw out his allotted ten minutes to seventeen.

Even age and experience offer no foolproof protection against embarrassing platform blunders. Far from it!

Two years ago, one of Europe's most eminent octogenarian pathologists was asked to add to the prestige of a great international convention by presenting a concluding summary of the highlights. Because of his advanced age, the text was prepared by others "under his supervision" and was kept as short as possible to protect him against fatigue. The voice of the venerable speaker was very weak and shaky, but in deference to his past accomplishments, the lecture room was crowded by pathologists who listened with rapt attention to this solemn final event. After a while, however, the affair began to take on an air of unreality; it seemed to go on and on, as the speaker placed each successive page underneath the others.

Sitting in the first row, I could hear what he said, but it was not easy to concentrate and follow the quavering monotone. Still it went on and eventually people began to drift quietly out. After an hour there were only nine of us left in the large hall: six dignitaries and a speaker on the platform, the projectionist near his lantern, and myself. Oblivious of all, the ancient voice droned on.

I could not imagine how the great old man could possibly ad lib so much out of the four or five pages in front of him. I took a firm grip on myself to overcome my near-hypnotic state and suddenly realized what was happening. In his absent-mindedness, he had been reading the pages over and over again. The scene was threatening to become slightly embarrassing and I wondered what would happen. Fortunately, the chairman, with great presence of mind, found a tactful solution. He went up to the rostrum, muttered something about the pages rustling too much into the oversensitive microphone, and then removed each finished page, one by one, next time around.

There is a moral to these stories for chairman, speaker and potential discussants alike. A brief communication, to be worthwhile, should be understandable, instructive, and conducive to discussion, otherwise it cannot stand the competition of the written article. In order to achieve these aims:

The *chairman* must keep the speakers strictly to their time schedule. If they are allowed ten minutes followed by five minutes for discussion, the warning red light should go on after eight minutes, and at the end of the tenth minute it is the sacred duty of the Chair to interrupt the speaker and open the discussion. The latter is the main purpose of the whole event. Were it not for the chance to discuss results with colleagues, there would be no point in all the delegates traveling long distances to a get-together. Of course, in the corridors and at social functions that accompany congresses, scientists can also discuss their findings in small groups, but certainly not so well as on the conference floor, immediately after the speaker's presentation, when all those interested in the subject are present. Besides, at large conventions, several sectional meetings proceed simultaneously, and delegates have to know precisely when they should be in one or the other room to hear papers that interest them.

The *speaker* should prepare his material carefully. His address must have some important point to contribute, since it is impertinent to waste the time of a large audience with insignificant trivia. The material must be thoughtfully adjusted to the special requirements of succinct oral presentation. The major points must be selected and so arranged that they can be told, in the allotted time, without undue hurry. Methodologic details and quantitative data (which are better looked up in printed papers) should be kept to the minimum necessary for the understanding of the main points. Tables should not be crowded with more figures than can be discussed during the time available. It is merely confusing to see a huge table which the speaker himself asks you to ignore except for a few selected figures. The paper should begin with a brief outline of its purpose and finish with a concise recapitulation of the principal results. Except for rank beginners or speakers not very conversant with the language in which the paper is to be given, it is very advisable to speak free from notes.

At the meeting, the speaker must recheck the order of his slides and give instructions about them to the projectionist well ahead of time. Then he takes his place near the front of the room, close to an aisle, so that he need not waste too much time in getting to the rostrum.

At scientific meetings, rules about how to address the audience are not taken very seriously, something like "Mr. Chairman, Ladies and Gentlemen," will do, or the speaker may just start in without any preliminaries. He should speak clearly and slowly. Few lecturers speak too slowly at meetings, and nothing is gained by racing at a pace which the audience cannot follow.

Especially at international congresses a speaker should watch his elocution and diction, in deference to those who do not speak his language fluently. At meetings with simultaneous translation into various languages, a slow, clear diction will also help the translators. A speaker who has to use some uncommon technical expressions should give a small glossary of them to the translators before he begins, so that they may have time to think about them. The speaker must remember to stay close to the microphone, especially when he turns toward the screen or blackboard.

The *discussant* who wants to comment on a paper should first formulate his remarks in his mind; if he has several points to make, it is well to put down key words on a piece of paper as a guide. On being recognized by the Chair, he should go to the closest microphone if there are such on the floor; if not he should stand up and speak clearly enough to be understood throughout the room.

He should begin by identifying himself, stating his name and the institution he represents. His remarks are to be limited to the paper under discussion. A discussant may mention personal observations only if they are really pertinent. The discussant who "happens to have a few slides in his pocket" and uses the discussion period for the presentation of a paper of his own, is highly objectionable.

Questions about details, which would interest only very few people in the audience, are likewise out of order on the floor; they can be discussed with the speaker later, in private.

The Formal Address

The formal address is a special lecture delivered by invitation. Normally, one hour or even more is allotted for it and it represents the only, or at least the principal, event at a special meeting of a scientific society. Since this type of address served as our example for the discussion of the general characteristics of public speaking (p. 366), we need not say much more about it here.

The formal address is probably the most difficult medium for the verbal communication of scientific thought. Its usual purpose is the presentation of a major field of study by a recognized authority to a large and often somewhat heterogeneous audience of scientists. This type of lecture should not be a poor substitute for a review article. Here, as in all other media for the verbal communication of scientific information, the spoken word has only one advantage over the written text: it brings the speaker into direct contact with his listeners. This should be remembered in planning a formal address. Many of the listeners will already be familiar with at least some of the speaker's writings. Often the main reason for their coming is to see what kind of a person he is and to learn things that they could not get equally well from his writings. These expectations can be fulfilled only by a personal presentation well adjusted to the level of the audience in the room. The speaker may even mention trivial, yet interesting, incidental facts that played an important part in directing his work, but which are unsuitable for publication or at least have not been published.

Formal addresses are always given to large audiences; hence, they do not lend themselves well to general discussion, because only a very small proportion of the listeners can have a chance to speak. However, often one or two invited discussants are asked to make comments and raise questions that are representative of the interests of the particular audience which the speaker addresses.

If the lecture is, nevertheless, open to general discussion, the chairman has a difficult time. In a very large auditorium there is always an odd crackpot who makes embarrassingly silly remarks, a narcissist who uses the opportunity to show off his own wisdom, or a runaway speaker who monopolizes badly needed time, merely because he cannot think of a suitable closing sentence. Against these menaces the chairman is the only protector of speaker and audience alike; it is clearly up to him to find tactful ways of disarming the saboteurs.

It may be difficult for the speaker to adjust his talk to audience requirements when he has had little or no previous contact with his listeners. As I think back on formal addresses which I gave to the most diverse scientific societies—in such places as New York, Leningrad, Berlin, Paris, London or Buenos Aires, and occasionally even in Montreal—I can remember many highly stimulating and many shatteringly embarrassing moments. There would be material here for a special chapter, but the essential lesson from it all can be summarized in a single word: Adaptability.

I tried to get close to all these people, to learn something about them first during personal discussions and visits to their labs, and then to lecture about what might interest them in our own work. In all these respects it was of the greatest value to me that in most of the places I could speak the language of my hosts. My grammar wasn't always very good and I tended to mix related languages (e.g., Russian and Czech, or Portuguese and Spanish), but I am sure, had I always had to force English upon my foreign colleagues, I could not have got nearly so close to them, made so many real friends among them nor profited so much from their experience. Of course, nowadays all educated medical research men speak English to some extent—but the extent varies. I still remember how isolated I felt on my lecture tour through Japan. Although my immediate entourage spoke English quite well, my lectures had to be translated, and I do not think they accomplished nearly as much as the Japanese translations of my books. The auditoriums were crowded, but I suspect that people came mainly to see what I looked like—and, I am afraid, they were disappointed.

Round-table discussions.   Just as the formal address offers the greatest possibility for teaching a well established subject to a large number of people, so the round table is the best setting for very advanced discussions of unfinished work with a small group of specialists.

The ideal round table consists of no more than a dozen people. In larger groups free discussion is handicapped by the fact that each participant must wait too long for his turn to speak. When a question is raised, the discussion may have drifted to an entirely different subject before the one member who knew the answer could speak up. Conversely, someone may wish to ask a question but, not wanting to interrupt the speaker, misses his chance before the topic changes.

The main advantage of the round table as a forum for discussion is its informality, and everything should be done to avoid conventionality. To my mind, the best round tables are those not meant for subsequent publication and not even registered on tape. Here, speakers can concentrate on what they really want to say or ask, without having to worry about what they want to be quoted on. For the same reasons it is best not to have a gallery of silent observers. It is true that beginners can learn a great deal from listening to a discussion among experts. But, once there is a larger audience, the speakers invariably tend to speak to the gallery, and face-saving begins to displace simple thirst for knowledge.

Except in very small gatherings of three or four people, I believe it is always useful to have a chairman, responsible for keeping the discussion on the subject at hand. This can be done quite unobtrusively and without stilted formalities. I have seen it accomplished admirably and still quite rigidly at gatherings where we were all on first name terms with each other and sat around the table in shirt sleeves, surrounded by ash trays and beer mugs. Parenthetically, these meetings, in which the most complex and important scientific subjects are discussed with great informality, always impressed me as the epitome of intellectual elegance; conversely, at formal academic gatherings, surrounded by dignitaries in medieval robes, I can never help feeling ridiculous while listening to the recitation of the customary stilted and vacuous phrases.

Scientific conversation. In a section on "How to Speak" we certainly must not forget ordinary everyday conversation about our work. After all, this is the medium of communication that we use most frequently. It can be very stimulating but if abused, it can waste a lot of time and energy.

In our lab, we have become very conscious of style in ordinary conversation. Here, as in all types of scientific communication, the motto must be clarity and conciseness; curiously, the greatest danger is an exaggerated preoccupation with courtesy. Courtesy should be the keynote of intercourse among cultured people, but like its sisters, modesty and dignity, it has produced the most monstrous caricatures ever since the earliest recorded periods of man's history. The potentate who must be addressed by an enumeration of all his exalted titles, the ruler who insists upon being greeted by his kneeling subjects through the kissing of his feet, still have too many counterparts in university life, especially in Europe and the East, even if the expressions of respect are somewhat modified.

A simple conversational tone implies no disrespect, and I would much sooner have an assistant, technician, or even animal caretaker come right to the point instead of starting off by the "If I may interrupt you, sir, I would like to ask you a question" gambit. In the course of a day an enormous amount of time can be wasted by this kind of chatter and I think mutual respect is expressed much better by the studied avoidance of such formalities, which shows that we do not consider each other so vain as to insist on homage.

For example, the daily rounds through our laboratories are meant to give us a quick, up-to-date view of where we stand with our work. Usually, the assistant in charge of a lab reports about anything of importance that happened since yesterday in each experiment. We have a great deal of ground to cover, and courtesy here consists not in elaborate speechifying but in taking the trouble to look over each experiment carefully before the rounds and to prepare the report so that it will be as short and as clear as possible. If the first few remarks and a glance at the protocol are sufficient, I would like to go on to the next experiment which may require a more lengthy discussion. Formerly, I could not think of a better way of doing this than by saying something like: "That's fine, thank you very much. But I think this much information brings us quite up-to-date here, so perhaps we might go on to the next experiment." Of course, it is ridiculous to repeat this same sentence thirty times in a row if you have thirty experiments to survey, so you must think of variations. If this situation repeats itself day in, day out, it can become not only time consuming but grotesque. Now all I say, when I want to go on, is "Next." We just agreed among ourselves that this "Next" will be a symbol, invested with all the courtesies of the more complicated, lengthy, formal phrases of transition.

During his first days in the lab, a new man may be shocked by the abruptness of this "Next," but after a week or two, he begins to use it himself whenever he wants to go on to the next item. This "Next" has become quite symbolic of our style, not only at lab rounds, but also in discussions among ourselves or at staff meetings. It always means, "Thank you very much for the courtesy of explaining this to me, I have understood you perfectly and now you really need not bother to go on with additional explanations."

There is no need to give any further examples, but the constant effort to improve our way of saying things as simply and clearly as possible is not only a time-saver but also an excellent exercise in the clear formulation of thought. Right now, for example, I feel that some transitional sentence would be in order to go on to the next section, but all I really need say is "Next."

Nontechnical and Semitechnical Speech

In the course of his career, every modern scientist will be called upon from time to time to speak on some nontechnical or semitechnical subject. He may have to explain his work or his philosophy at the luncheon meeting of a club, at board meetings of his sponsors or of the university governors; he may have to address the public at large on radio or television; he may be asked to make an after-dinner speech or just to "say a few words" quite unexpectedly to a class of students when he visits a colleague's laboratory. Last, but not least, sooner or later he will be interviewed by reporters. It may be appropriate therefore, to touch briefly on the problems presented by such occasions.

Club meetings. With the increasing interest of the public in basic research, various business, political, and social clubs invite scientists to speak. These addresses usually take the form of after-luncheon or after-dinner speeches of twenty to thirty minutes before an audience whose interests are totally different from the scientist's—and I must say I have never been able to establish a satisfactory rapport with a club audience. This failure may be due to lack of experience, because I can rarely accept such invitations. Then again, it may be that I don't like to accept them because I am very bad at this game. In any event, I am not the man to give advice on this form of public speaking; all I can do is to describe the situation as I see it.

I agree that those who have a decisive influence upon the economy of the country, the representatives of its commerce, industry, and finance, should want to know what is going on in basic research. I also agree that even if these men are not trained in research a scientist should be able to prepare a brief and yet understandable résumé of his work for them, an outline which is instructive and correct, at least as far as it goes. My difficulty lies not in preparing the summary, but despite all my lecturing experience, in being unable to deliver it properly. I usually manage to make what I think is an adequate plan, but at the last minute, something invariably puts me off. Some scientists do not want to, or do not even feel they should, speak to laymen about their work, but this is not so in my case; in principle, I think that I should. But when I meet "worldly men" I find that I simply cannot face them.

Only last week I was called upon to speak on stress before a very large and influential group of businessmen here in Montreal, and I prepared my lecture notes carefully with a real desire to succeed. When I arrived at the hotel, I was first ushered into a room to meet the distinguished group of people who were to sit at the speaker's table. Immediately, I was introduced to the very cream of Canada's *Who's Who* in commerce, finance and industry. I was impressed by the well-known names, but we had time only for a brief handshake —because the television people were waiting with their equipment set up in a corner of the room. I had to step up quickly in front of the strong lights and answer a few questions before the cameras: "What is stress?," "In what way will your work on calciphylaxis be applicable to clinical medicine?," "What do you think should be done to promote basic research in Canada?" I had five minutes to answer all three questions!

Then I was handed a cocktail, introduced to a few latecomers of the head-table party, and asked to meet the reporters in another corner of the room. These were visibly disappointed that I did not

384 *From Dream to Discovery*

have a manuscript and asked me to give a brief résumé of what I was going to say after lunch. This I did as best I could to the accompaniment of clicking cameras and flashing light bulbs. By then I felt somewhat dizzy and quite incompetent because I knew, of course, that during the time available and under the circumstances, I had not succeeded in properly answering any of the broad questions put to me. Yet, the program had to go on.

Two or three more photographs in a rapidly staged "natural attitude of easy conversation" with the officials of the Club, and the procession was formed to begin its solemn march to the head table. Once there I began to chat with my neighbors, trying to find out a little more about the interests of my prospective listeners. I learned that the previous speakers had almost all been businessmen, financiers and politicians, but that the members were very interested in research, or they would not have invited me. In fact, many of them had sizeable research units within their companies; they were doing research on ways of improving the manufacture of their products, on the psychology of labor relations and, of course, market research which is concerned with the objective assessment of the demands for their products and ways to increase these demands. But when my ignorance in all these fields became apparent, the conversation drifted on to golf, hunting, fishing and ice hockey, all activities of which I thoroughly approve but, unfortunately, without being able to discuss them interestingly from personal experience.

By the time we reached the dessert, I was left out of the conversation as a hopeless dud with whom one cannot speak about anything. By now I was thoroughly intimidated; I could not imagine how any of the remarks I had proposed to make could possibly interest anyone here. This feeling of inadequacy was but temporarily assuaged by the compassionate remark of one of my neighbors who, seeing me so dejected, said that he had very much enjoyed *The Stress of Life*. Unfortunately, his honesty compelled him to add that he could not understand it—and that is why he was looking forward so much to this occasion when I would undoubtedly explain all about stress in understandable terms. My feelings about being able to do this in my present condition within twenty minutes—having evidently failed to accomplish it in the 324 pages of my carefully prepared book—were far from reassuring.

I looked around the room; it was crowded. The chairman told me that there was an overflow audience, and apart from the people at the tables, I saw many standing along the walls and even out on the corridor. On all other occasions I am encouraged by heavy attendance at my lectures, but this time the sight of the crowd just made me feel like a cheat. All these people came because they had heard from others that what I had done was important. And these others had heard it from yet others or had read it in the semifictional accounts published in magazines. Now they came to learn the facts firsthand; but I knew I couldn't deliver the goods as advertised. Under the circumstances, I could not speak about stress even as well as the science writers, for while I was closer to stress, they were closer to the public. They could tell a story which, though not the true story of stress, would, for these people, symbolize it better than my own account. Here, my detailed technical knowledge gave me no advantage over the science writer; neither of us could use more than the most primitive facts known to both of us. Of course, the same is true when we compare the discoverer of a fact with the college teacher who learned it from books; at an elementary level of teaching, neither of them is hampered by lack of factual knowledge. The discoverer has only the intangible asset of having been an eyewitness at the discovery. This advantage is of immense value in teaching other discoverers how to find a fact, but it does not help those who just want to learn the already discovered fact.

I realized that my only usable asset here was the public's confidence in my authority; we had no way of communicating with each other on the basis of common, firsthand experience. I was terrified of abusing this confidence by dishing out oversimplified platitudes which my listeners would invest with profound meaning; I have no taste for success based on Delphic pronouncements.

At this point in my meditations, I vaguely heard the well-meaning chairman as he introduced me in the customary way by comparing me with all the giants in the history of science. He wanted to raise even further the public's acceptance of me on authority, not knowing that thereby he was only adding to my paralyzingly embarrassing scruples.

Finally, I find myself at the lectern, with all eyes attentively directed toward the oracle. Nowhere is there any sign of levity or inattention. The faces are those of intelligent, well-balanced men, willing to listen to reason—but to reason only. They look satiated after a good luncheon and they look prosperous. They seem highly competent to earn money, status, and all the other rewards that are recognized by society. But they do not seem prepared to question their value. My whole life was spent in questioning the generally accepted. How could I establish rapport with this audience!

Throughout my lecture, there was no sagging of attention, but neither was there any sign of sympathy that would have revealed understanding beyond the mere comprehension of the facts related. At the end the applause was hearty, but it belonged to my image in their minds, not to me. Perhaps they did not know it, but I knew the lecture had failed to fulfill its purpose.

There is a moral to this story too: don't give any luncheon-club lectures—or learn the art from a better teacher.

Board and committee meetings. No scientist can forever succeed in avoiding participation, at least to some extent, in administrative meetings. He may be called upon to explain his research before the board of a scientific foundation, to represent his department on committees or before the governors of his university, and if he belongs to a large department, he will find it difficult to avoid participation in the internal committees which administer it.

For reasons which I have explained elsewhere, I have very little experience with, or talent for, committee work. On the few occasions when I cannot avoid it, I prepare a few notes on the points I wish to make, and, if they concern the department, I usually discuss them first with those of my assistants who have personal experience with the topics to be presented.

If I am in the Chair, I try to keep things rolling as rapidly as possible, mercilessly silencing all runaway speakers and those who deviate into irrelevancies; if I am not in charge, my major task is to fight boredom. I can remember no committee meeting of any length that did not bore me for at least part of the time, and most of them caused me excruciating boredom all of the time. This response is almost unavoidable, except for people who enjoy small talk and use committee meetings as a form of social intercourse to while away the time. It cannot be helped, because it is inconceivable that each participant of a large group should be equally interested in all subjects to be discussed. However, fortunately, not everybody is equally sensitive to boredom. I suffer from it acutely and, since doodling (the traditional remedy for committee-room boredom) gives me no relief, I usually take along some reading matter, experimental protocols, or a manuscript that can be tactfully camouflaged by the documents needed for the meeting. With such assistance, I have actually found some committee meetings to be quite profitable; but I prefer to do this kind of work alone in my office.

Of course, the best treatment is prevention. If at all possible, *just don't go.* Be particularly on guard against invitations to participate in "only one or two sessions at which your advice would be especially valuable." This never works. Eventually you get sufficiently involved to become a permanent member, and then you are lost. Committees, like living organisms, breed their own kind. The main committee creates little subcommittees which grow into full-fledged committees that make their own subcommittees. Before you know it, you have ceased to be a scientist and become an administrator.

Radio, television, and teaching films. Whenever I had to speak on radio or television, my troubles always stemmed from two reasons: 1. I did not have the "feel" of the audience; 2. there was not enough time to put meaning into what I was asked to explain.

Radio separates you almost completely from your audience: you don't see them and they don't see you. Besides, in conveying factual information, a printed text—which can be read slowly and, if need be, repeatedly—is difficult to surpass by any form of oral communication. Hence, the scientific radio talk must lean on its one special asset: the personality of the speaker as reflected by his voice and diction. My only reason for listening to a discoverer's account over the radio, rather than reading about it at leisure, would be a desire to hear him talk, to try to get something of the man behind the discovery.

I remember having heard Einstein explain relativity over the Viennese radio many years ago when I was still a schoolboy. I did not understand much of what he said, but it impressed me deeply that here I was listening to Einstein. To me this was a solemn, memorable, and elevating experience which was only enhanced by the poor diction which made the Olympian figure almost human. Whatever I am capable of understanding about relativity, I learned later by reading. But that is not the point. The dramatic value of such a situation depends upon the importance of the speaker; and, if I am sufficiently interested in any subject to learn something about it, there is an added pleasure in hearing it summarized by the discoverer.

Scientific radio talks on basic research are constantly in demand, and the same investigator may be asked to speak several times in one month—but always only for five or ten minutes. Not many scientific subjects worthy of the public's attention can be made clear to laymen in such a short time. But on the few occasions when I had half an hour or more and could extend the scope of my talk, I am sure the listeners understood me less well. No one can listen attentively that long to a disembodied voice explaining a complex subject.

None of this is too important, however, if we try not to be overly pedantic and ambitious about a scientific radio talk, but if we merely exploit its one great strength: the personal warmth of the human voice. The ideal solution is to limit technical information to the minimum that makes the gist of the matter understandable to most educated people (the uneducated may be discounted since they don't listen to such talks anyway). If possible, we should say something about probable future developments or practical applications. Even the history of the discovery or an amusing incident may be worth mentioning if they will help the listener to know you better.

On *television*, the speaker still misses the stimulating effect of a visible audience (although this is now provided in the studio by some networks), but here he can be heard and seen. Visual contact gives the audience more opportunity to discover what kind of person he is.

For the scientific talk, television's greatest advantage is that it permits visual teaching by the demonstration of objects in motion. This possibility should be exploited to the limit by developing a concept before the audience through schematic blackboard sketches, animated cartoons and even actual experiments. The more you do along these lines and the less you speak formally into the camera, the better.

Television is admirably suited even to strictly academic lectures for students and scientific societies, especially when experiments have to be shown which cannot be directly inspected by more than a few people (e.g., microsurgery). Ever since I first saw a television screen, I have wondered about the possibility of creating a "super university of the air," in which each lecture would be given (with demonstrations wherever possible) by our greatest specialist in the matter at hand. All the drudgery of teaching the same course over and over again, year after year, mostly out of textbooks and from second-hand knowledge, would be eliminated. Every professor would be asked to teach only his pet subject (about which he loves to speak), and the students of every university would get a chance to see the nation's most eminent scholars in action.

Just imagine what a course this would make! The professor could prepare his single lecture at leisure throughout the year and perform even the most laborious and expensive experiments for this one occasion. Here, also, would be the ideal solution to the old problem of giving students a chance to learn from career research men without blocking the scientific productivity of the latter by heavy teaching duties. The idea has been widely discussed, but, apart from a few abortive attempts, very little has yet been done about it.

Essentially the same can be accomplished with even greater technical perfection by colored *teaching films* with sound tracks. Films have the additional advantage of always being ready for immediate showing to classes or scientific societies.

A few years ago, we made such a film on stress and the diseases of adaptation (Pfizer Medical Film Library, New York, N.Y.) which, having been provided with sound tracks in different languages, was shown throughout the world and spared me many speeches and trips. The film demonstrates numerous experiments and illustrations of complex interrelations by animated cartoons which could not have been presented in lectures. For regular courses the only disadvantage of the film compared with annually repeated television shows is that it tends to become obsolete after a while. But the task of bringing it up-to-date is usually not too difficult.

The press. In 1945, our government sent me to Moscow to represent the Royal Society of Canada at a jubilee meeting of the Soviet Academy of Sciences. It was quite a trip. Crossing the Atlantic would have been too dangerous during the war, so they dispatched me in a small Canadian fighter plane from Montreal to Fairbanks, Alaska, whence a large Soviet bomber took me across Siberia to Moscow.

It was a very exciting and stimulating six weeks, visiting Soviet research institutions in the company of some of the most eminent scientists of our time (among others: Harlow Shapley, Irving Langmuir, D. W. Bronk of the United States; Lord Radnor, Sir Robert Robinson, Sir Julian Huxley and Lord Adrian of Britain; the Joliot-Curies of France; Albert Szent-Györgyi of Hungary). We were on the go all the time, either inspecting labs or being feted at banquets (including one given by Stalin, in the Kremlin). As I was the only foreign delegate who spoke some Russian, they constantly kept me busy making "thank you speeches" and acting as translator for the group.

After this strenuous experience, I returned on the plane of the U.S. delegation, and, since we crossed the international dateline on the fourth of July, we lived through this day twice in succession, with my American colleagues vigorously celebrating their national holiday during forty-eight uninterrupted hours. Finally, we arrived on North American soil, semicomatose from fatigue, at four o'clock in the morning. We were immediately assaulted by a mob of eager reporters who asked hundreds of questions about this, the first large international scientific convention to be held in Russia since the beginning of the war. Realizing that in my enfeebled state I might easily say something silly that could be misunderstood, I restricted myself to the most innocuous banalities. However, I vaguely heard one of my colleagues comment about the excellent treatment accorded to members of the U.S.S.R. Academy by their government. He off-handedly added that, by comparison, the Fellows of the Canadian Royal Society were treated "like garbage-can collectors."

Next morning at breakfast, on opening the paper, we were confronted with the following headline: "Fellows of Royal Society treated like garbage-can collectors, delegate says."

The delegate in question was none too pleased although he philosophically assured me that nothing could be done about these things. Only a few months before, he pointed out, our Governor General made a speech about public health in Western Canada, expressing concern about the overcrowding of mental hospitals. Thereupon, one paper captioned his address: "Insanity rampant in our West, Governor General says." Allegedly, this was also resented in certain high quarters.

Still, I felt very smug about my own ability to deal with the press until a few days later, when I arrived home in an even more exhausted condition after another transcontinental flight in a small fighter plane. Again, I had to meet the reporters immediately (they were waiting in our living room), and again I thought I was doing very well, saying not a word that could have been embarrassing even if quoted out of context. By 2 A.M. the reporters had withdrawn, except for one lady who stayed for a cup of coffee with the family while I was unpacking. She expressed interest in some rather nice pieces of antique church embroidery that I retrieved from my suitcase. I modestly explained that they were far beyond my means, but the dealer had offered them in exchange for a pair of striped pants for which I had little use on this trip after the official receptions were over. (Apparently, striped pants were much in demand then to caricature capitalists on the stage.)

The arrival of the paper next morning rudely shattered any illusions I might have kept about having a knack for public relations. My interview was captioned: "McGill Professor Loses Pants to Reds." The text reported almost none of my enthusiastic comments on the activities of the Soviet Academy and dealt mainly with my one barter transaction. No wonder this document gave a somewhat one-sided picture of how I spent my time in Moscow. To make things worse, several other dailies reproduced this version of my interview, with which my Russian hosts were understandably disgusted. Soon, both *Izvestia* and *Pravda* registered great disappointment about the Canadian delegate who, instead of attending scientific meetings, spent his time buying and selling old junk. Conversely, several

American papers gallantly sprang to my defense. *Time Magazine* remarked in its column on "International Affairs" that *"Pravda screaming like a fishwife soundly lambasted Selye"* whose "homecoming interview contained nothing about the outstanding scientific event" and dealt exclusively with the "pants-tapestry deal" (*Time* July 30, 1945). I certainly did not foresee that such a storm would be raised by one playful remark made over a cup of coffee, long after the reporters' ominous notebooks had been sheathed.

Actually, in all these reports the most embarrassing parts were the *headlines*. But after the incident my lady reporter phoned me especially to say that she had had nothing to do with the title of her story; captions are added by anonymous specialists against whose wording the reporter has no recourse.

There is little to be learned from these sad experiences. No matter what you say at an interview, its meaning can still be ridiculously distorted by the addition of a sensational last-minute headline. The best you can do is to check the accuracy of the text by requesting a copy before publication; most serious science writers welcome this assistance, and some journals may even change a title you really object to. Of course, this verification is rarely possible when dealing with reporters whose stories are required for immediate publication; but, here, a carefully worded press release can do much to avoid ambiguity.

Nowadays, when public understanding of research plays such an important role in our social structure, it is fortunate that the popularization of science has become a journalistic speciality. As a rule, professional *science writers* are genuinely interested in research and well versed, at least in the general aspects of certain fields; some of them even hold an academic degree. But newsworthy discoveries tend to be rather sophisticated, avant-garde stuff, and no one can be expected to be fully informed on all subjects. Scientific interviews are often further complicated by the fact that they take place at a time when the scientist is greatly excited and very busy as a consequence of some recent discovery; hence, he is inclined to be impatient in explaining what seem to him self-evident, primitive preliminaries. I do not know why so few science writers use shorthand or portable tape recorders, but I have difficulty in concentrating on my verbal report if I have to wait while my interviewer slowly writes out each sentence in longhand. My associates and I try to remedy this situation by sharing the task of conveying the necessary information. First, they show the science writer through our labs and explain the broad outlines of our work on the basis of technical papers and manuscripts. After this preparation, it is easier for me to give meaningful answers on any special points.

Except on the occasion of very important discoveries, jubilees, the inauguration of new laboratories or other particularly noteworthy events, scientists rarely need to hold actual *press conferences.* Here, the preliminary preparation is best accomplished by distribution of a detailed press release, formulated in generally understandable terms.

"Say a few words." Sooner or later every scientist is faced with the request: "Won't you say a few words to them? They would be thrilled." Now, "they" may be a classroom of students, the staff of a hospital or research lab, your companions around a dinner table, or the guests at the wedding of a colleague. "They" may be young or old, ignorant or highly sophisticated, and usually you know very little about them or their interests. Indeed, if "they" are foreigners, you may not even be very familiar with their language.

Yet, there you are, stuck with the problem of addressing them impromptu because you have been publicly and most charmingly invited to do so and it would not be very gracious to refuse. All eyes are directed imploringly at you but they also unmistakably reflect your own embarrassment as you weakly ask, "Well, what do you want me to say?" The reply is, of course, "Oh, anything. Anything at all, they would be delighted to hear you. They have been looking forward to your visit for so long. Just say a few words. It will be a thrill and an inspiration they will long remember."

On the surface, it doesn't look like a tall order; it ought to be easy to say a few words of encouragement. But even the most shameless, conceited, cocksure egomaniac shakes in his boots when first faced with this task. He may be quite immodest and self-confident in the lab and he may habitually exceed his allotted time on the lecture platforms of the most sophisticated scientific societies, but when it comes to "say a few words about anything at all," he suddenly becomes sheepishly shy and behaves like a six-year-old when asked to recite for the guests.

Eventually, he accepts—what else can he do? But while his host gratefully introduces him, he still hasn't the slightest idea of what he is going to say. The problem of giving birth to an "inspiration they will long remember" begins to assume gigantic proportions. Calmly straightening his tie and buttoning his coat, he can add only one short, brain-racked moment in his frantic search for a topic— and if he is inexperienced, the result is rarely inspiring although it may be long remembered.

Even the forewarning, say at the beginning of a dinner, that you should say something afterward, rarely accomplishes more than to spoil your appetite. You are reminded only of the ancient Christian who saved his life in the Roman arena by whispering into the lion's ear that he would be expected to say a few words after the meal.

My earliest recollection of this problem takes me back to a banquet kindly arranged in my honor by the professors of the Collège de France in Paris, at the termination of my first formal lecture series on stress. Several of my distinguished hosts made beautiful speeches, while I, shivering in terror, awaited my turn. In desperation, I turned to my neighbor, Professor Courrier. I told him that my simple French would sound ridiculous after all this polished oratory, and yet, I did so much want to express my heartfelt thanks for all the trouble these men had taken to give me such a warm reception. He looked at me with a cordially reassuring smile and simply said, "Well, say just that. Lack of polish can be even more effective by contrast; it reflects unretouched sincerity."

The more usual technique is to have a few general topics ready for such occasions but I prefer to follow Courrier's advice. It has helped me many times since that memorable banquet. Whenever I am asked to "just say a few words," I quickly appraise the situation, asking myself: Just who are these people? Why did they ask me to come? What would interest them? Then I make a few unpretentious remarks in unpolished conversational language, about whatever seems most appropriate. I doubt that much more can be accomplished by "just a few impromptu words."

Afterthoughts

Well, John, this ends my report. There were so many loose notes on so many things that struck me as significant during a lifetime, it took me longer than I thought to edit them for you. But here they are, legibly typed and neatly arranged, freed of the superfluous as far as my loquaciousness permits. These are the reflections and events that most decisively influenced my life. Whatever may be the worth of such a record, I, myself, have profited immensely from this systematized confession. It has helped me to put order into my thoughts; order—and peace, too. For we are less worried by our conscience once we know why we do things the way we do, once we have established to our satisfaction that, being what we are, this is the way we have to act.

As I look back on what I have written, I am mainly surprised—as probably you will be—by its one-sidedness: directly or indirectly it is virtually all about science; it says almost nothing about other values. I seem to have been uncommonly blunt to most things that give pleasure to other people, but actually, I think I found them all in science. The elevating experience of beauty, the majesty of greatness, the wonder of mystery—and even the relaxation that comes from merely playing and puttering about—are all around me here in the lab. Whenever I looked for any of these satisfactions elsewhere I was disappointed; what I gained always seemed trivial by comparison. Before the judgment of my one-sided sensitivity, no manmade beauty or tour de force of power could possibly compete with the creations of Nature.

And now that I have put all this down on paper, what is the essence of it all? How can you profit from my account? I would like these Notes to plead for three things in science: simplicity, honesty and charity.

First, they should serve as a plea for simplicity in thought and action. This is a crucial time in the history of science, especially in biology and medicine. A preoccupation with detail and the complex machinery necessary to appraise detail threatens to kill the art of observation by our natural senses and the gift for the broad-scale coordination of highlights. Some people say that my old-fashioned way of doing research has been made obsolete by modern technology. It has been claimed that all those aspects of life that can be seen with the eyes and elucidated by simple experiments have already been described. In these Notes I have tried to show by many examples that this is not so. Some of the most fundamental discoveries in medicine have been and still are being made by people who use no complex machinery but only their intuitive feeling for the way Nature works and a keen eye for what she camouflages. Of course, the application of chemistry and physics, the mathematical analysis of biologic phenomena, and the construction of complex instruments has much to offer—no one doubts this. It is the leading principle taught at our universities; it needs no protagonist. Let me then be the advocate of the naturalist, of the simple observer and coordinator, of the old school in biology that is threatened with extinction. To my mind, the correlator, who skims the surface and is no specialist in any field—in our case the general practitioner of medical research —still has a great deal to offer and will never become dispensable.

Secondly, I want these Notes to act as an exercise in honesty, a frank uncensored case report of a man who has lived almost exclusively in, on, and for science. He is an extreme case, I admit, an oddity not necessarily to be emulated but one which, like so many curiosities of Nature, may have a lesson to teach. In any case, like all living beings, he desperately wants to perpetuate his kind before it is too late, and he feels that he can do so only by finding you, John. If you are the man I want you to be, you would not have listened trustfully had I embellished my account by smoothing over the rough spots. And I wanted you to see that on the road before you, another man, subject to weaknesses like anybody else, found happiness and fulfillment, not in spite of being human but because of it.

Last but not least, I wanted to make a plea for charity. Nowadays, most of the really gifted young men and women—the ones I would like to reach—are more likely to be attracted to physics, chemistry, space research, and other fields whose breathtaking current progress offers a seductive challenge to the intellectually minded. Yet, in the final analysis what could be more noble and important than to fight disease, aging and death?

The United States government intends to spend some twenty to forty billion dollars in order to reach the moon. There may be something worth having on the moon. Undoubtedly, the first nation to reach another planet will earn much admiration and prestige. And yet—as I have said ever since operation Sputnik proved to be a success—there is no reason to doubt that, with an equal investment of money and (more important) talent, a systematic attack on cancer, heart disease, and premature aging, would be less likely to succeed than our dreams of interplanetary travel. I find it very difficult to imagine that any treasure found on another planet could be more important to mankind and more conducive to gratitude and prestige than the cure, say of cancer or insanity.

You give little thought to disease and death while you are young and strong, but your outlook changes after you have spent a great deal of time in hospitals. Everything else seems so terribly unimportant by comparison when you see those patients with the signature of death on their washed-out, hazy eyes. Try to remember them when you are in the lab. Try to remember their expressionless faces which reflect only total indifference. They do not even bother to answer a friendly smile—it isn't worth the effort. Try to imagine that worst thing in the realization of impending death: the humiliation of it. It is so terribly degrading for them to learn that they are suddenly excluded from all the strivings, the competitive games of life, from all the preparations for the future which normally guide our every action. Their progress along the road was so exciting. It was such fun always to anticipate the pleasures of the next step— and now there is no next step, just a precipice. They were so used to fighting for knowledge, money, fame, power, things that can be stacked away for the future. And now suddenly there is no future.

Our colleagues in the exact sciences, in physics, chemistry or mathematics, share with us and, in many respects, surpass us in everything I have said about the beauty of science for its own sake. But nothing can be of greater concern to man than the agony of excruciating pain and the humiliation of certain death which wipes out all our motives. No matter how hard I try to remain objective and to appreciate the importance of other professions, I cannot see what else you could do with your life, John, that would be more meaningful and satisfactory than medical research. Even the grandeur of conquering the universe, or the fear that war may break out, or that our world may become overpopulated, seems to pale at the bedside of a patient who will die because we were remiss in our efforts to learn more about disease.

Glossary and Brief Definitions

The following brief explanations deal with technical terms only as far as required for the understanding of the text. They are not intended as complete scientific definitions.

ACTH. Abbreviation for the adrenocorticotrophic hormone.

adaptive hormones. Hormones produced for adaptation to stress.

adrenalectomy. Removal of the adrenal gland.

adrenaline. One of the hormones of the adrenal medulla.

adrenals. Endocrine glands which lie (one on each side) just above the kidneys. They consist of a whitish outer cortex, or bark, and a dark-brown medulla, or core.

adrenocorticotrophic hormone (ACTH). A pituitary hormone which stimulates the growth and function of the adrenal cortex.

alarm reaction. The first stage of the general adaptation syndrome.

aldosterone. One of the mineralocorticoids.

anacalciphylaxis. An inverse form of calciphylaxis through which the organism can protect certain organs from calcification.

anaphylactic shock. A state of general shock that accompanies severe anaphylaxis.

anaphylactoid reaction. A response which resembles anaphylaxis but develops without any previous sensitization by an antigen.

anaphylaxis. A hypersensitivity reaction which develops following the injection to an antigen into a sensitized organism.

androgen. A virilizing or male hormone.

antagonist. An agent which acts against another agent.

antibiotics. Antibacterial substances, most of which are prepared from molds or fungi (e.g., penicillin, streptomycin).

antibodies. Substances produced in response to infection or to inoculation with antigens. They play an important part in immunity and hypersensitivity.

antigen. Any substance which stimulates the production of antibodies.

anti-inflammatory corticoids. Adrenocortical hormones which inhibit in-

397

flammation, for example, cortisone or cortisol. They have a marked effect upon glucose metabolism and are therefore also known as glucocorticoids.

arteriosclerosis. Hardening of the arteries.

atrophy. Shrinkage of an organ.

basal metabolism (BMR). The rate of metabolism under basal resting conditions.

bioassay. Determination of the potency of a substance by comparing its effect on a living organism with that of a standardized preparation.

calcergy. Direct calcification. It is induced by an agent upon contact with tissue and requires no special sensitization.

calcinosis. Abnormal calcification, particularly the incrustation of soft tissues with calcium salts.

calciphylaxis. A biologic mechanism through which the organism can send large amounts of calcium and phosphate selectively to certain regions (see also *anacalciphylaxis*).

chromafin cells. Endocrine cells (particularly numerous in the adrenal medulla) which stain with chromium salts.

collagen. An insoluble fibrous protein which is the chief constituent of connective-tissue fibrils.

conditioning factors. Substances or circumstances which influence the response to an agent, for instance, to a hormone.

connective tissue. A tissue consisting of cells and fibers; it is a kind of living cement which connects and reinforces all other tissues. Inflammation develops mainly in connective tissue.

cornification. Horny transformation (e.g., of the vaginal surface epithelium during the estrous phase of the sexual cycle).

corticoids. Hormones of the adrenal cortex. It is customary to subdivide them into the anti-inflammatory glucocorticoids and the proinflammatory mineralocorticoids.

cortisol. One of the anti-inflammatory corticoids.

cortisone. One of the anti-inflammatory corticoids.

desoxycorticosterone (DCA). One of the proinflammatory corticoids.

DHT. An abbreviation for dihydrotachysterol.

Dihydrotachysterol. A compound closely related to vitamin D.

diseases of adaptation. Maladies which are principally due to imperfections of the general adaptation syndrome (G.A.S.), as for instance, to the production of an excessive or insufficient amount, or an improper mixture, of adaptive hormones.

duodenum. The first part of the small intestine, which comes immediately after the stomach.

ecology. The totality of the relationships between organisms and their environment.

-ectomy. A suffix indicating extirpation, or surgical removal, of an organ (e.g., adrenalectomy = adrenal removal).

edema. A swelling of tissues owing to imbibition with water.

electrolyte. A substance which in solution is capable of conducting the electric current. Water-soluble salts belong to this group.

endocrine kidney. A kidney that has been so modified by surgical operation that it ceases to produce urine but continues to elaborate hormonally active substances.

endocrines. Ductless glands which secrete their products, the hormones, directly into the blood.

endogenous. Arising within the organism.

eosinophil leukocytes. White blood cells which stain with the dye eosin.

erythrocytes. Red blood corpuscles.

estradiol. An estrogenic ovarian hormone.

estrogen. An ovarian hormone inducing the estrous, or heat, phase of the sexual cycle.

extract. A preparation containing the essence of the substance from which it is derived.

folliculoid. Synonym of estrogen.

formalin. An irritating aqueous solution of formaldehyde.

G.A.S. Abbreviation for general adaptation syndrome.

general adaptation syndrome. The totality of the manifestations of stress in the body; these develop in three distinct stages: alarm reaction, stage of resistance, stage of exhaustion.

gonadotrophic hormones. Hormones which stimulate the growth and function of the gonads (ovary, testis).

glandulotrophic hormones. Hormones which stimulate the growth and function of certain glands.

glucagon. An insulin-antagonizing hormone.

glucocorticoids. See *anti-inflammatory corticoids*.

granuloma. Inflamed connective tissue.

granuloma pouch. A pouch formed by inflamed connective tissue. It is used as an experimental model of inflammation and is produced in animals by the subcutaneous injection of air and an inflammatory irritant.

gymnasium. In Austria, Hungary and several other European countries, a secondary school whose curriculum stresses the classics, history, mathematics, and modern languages; it prepares students for the university.

histochemistry. A science concerned with the chemical constitution of tissues, combining histologic and chemical methods.

histology. The study of the minute microscopic structure of tissues.

homeostasis. The body's tendency to maintain a steady state despite external changes; physiologic stability.

hormones. Chemical substances released into the blood by the endocrine glands to stimulate and coordinate distant organs. Bodily growth, metabolism, resistance to stress, and sexual functions are largely regulated by hormones.

hunch. A strong intuitive impression that something will happen. A sudden flash of intuition.

hypercalcemia. An increase of the blood calcium level above normal.

400 *From Dream to Discovery*

hypocalcemia. A drop of the blood calcium level below normal.

hypophysectomy. Removal of the hypophysis, or pituitary.

hypophysis. Synonym for the pituitary.

infarct. An area of necrosis, or tissue death [e.g., in the heart after obstruction (thrombosis) of an artery].

inflammation. The typical reaction of tissue (particularly of connective tissue) to injury. Its main purpose is to barricade off and to destroy the injurious agent by which it was elicited.

insulin. The antidiabetic hormone produced by the pancreas.

intuition. Knowledge obtained without recourse to reasoning. Immediate apprehension or cognition, as contrasted with speculative or mediate knowing. A hunch.

in vitro. Literally "in glass." In the test tube outside the living body.

in vivo. In the living body.

involution. Shrinkage or decline of an organ.

-itis. A suffix indicating inflammation (e.g., appendicitis = inflammation of the appendix).

lipids. Fatty substances.

luteotrophic hormone. One of the gonadotrophic hormones.

lymphatic tissues. Tissues containing mainly lymph cells, for example, the thymus, the lymph nodes.

lymph nodes. Nodular organs, consisting of lymphatic tissue, in the groin, under the armpits, along the neck, and in various other parts of the body.

MAD. Abbreviation for methylandrostenediol, an androgenic substance.

mast cell. A hormone-producing cell irregularly distributed throughout the connective tissue. It contains granules which apparently can bind certain substances such as calcium.

metabolism. The transformation of foodstuff into tissue and energy, a process which occurs in the body.

Methylandrostenediol. See MAD.

mineralocorticoids. See *proinflammatory corticoids.*

morphology. The branch of biology that deals with the form and structure of tissues, comprising anatomy and histology.

necrosis. Localized tissue death within a surviving organism.

neoplasm. An abnormal tissue growth (e.g., a cancer).

nephritis. Inflammation of the kidney.

nephrosclerosis. A kidney disease often causing hypertension.

nephrosis. A kidney disease which leads to dropsy and loss of protein through the urine.

neurotropic. Anything having a specific affinity for nerves.

ovaries. The female sex glands.

pancreas. An endocrine gland which produces insulin.

parathyroids. Very small endocrine glands, closely attached to the thyroid. Their main function is to regulate calcium and phosphate metabolism, mainly through their action upon the renal elimination of these elements and upon the bones.

pathogen. A disease-producing agent.

pathology. The study of disease.

periarteritis nodosa. A form of arterial inflammation.

pineal gland. A small, presumably endocrine organ attached to the brain.

pituitary. A little endocrine gland embedded in the bones of the skull just below the brain; also known as *hypophysis.*

polymyxin. An antibiotic which discharges the granules contained in mast cells.

polypeptide. A constituent part of the protein molecule.

preputial glands. Small accessory sex glands.

progeria. Premature aging.

progesterone. An ovarian hormone.

proinflammatory corticoids. Adrenocortical hormones which stimulate inflammation, as for example, aldosterone, desoxycorticosterone. They have marked effects upon mineral metabolism, and are therefore also known as *mineralocorticoids.*

psychoanalysis. The method of analyzing an abnormal mental state by having the patient review his past emotional experiences and relating them to his present mental life. The technique furnishes hints for psychotherapeutic procedures.

puerperal fever. Childbed fever.

reaction. In biology, the response of the body, or of one of its parts, to stimulation.

renal. Pertaining to the kidney.

rheumatic fever. An acute and often recurring disease, most common in children and young adults. It is characterized by fever with inflammation of the joints and the heart valves. It often follows upon infection in the tonsils.

rheumatism. A vague term which includes rheumatic fever, rheumatoid arthritis, and several allied conditions.

rheumatoid arthritis. A more or less chronic disease, characterized by an inflammation of the joints, with swelling, pain, stiffness, and deformity. There are several variants in which one or the other among these manifestations predominates.

salt. A substance that results from the reaction between acids and bases (e.g., sodium-chloride or kitchen salt).

scleroderma. A skin disease characterized by connective-tissue proliferation and often accompanied by calcium deposition.

sclerosis. A pathological hardening of tissues, usually produced by overgrowth of fibrous tissue sometimes with calcification (as in arteriosclerosis).

serology. A branch of science which deals with serums and their ingredients such as antigens and antibodies.

somatotrophic hormone. A pituitary hormone which stimulates the growth of the body in general.

stage of exhaustion. The final stage of the adaptation syndrome.

stage of resistance. The second stage of the adaptation syndrome.

steroids. Compounds having a polycyclic structure like that of the sterols, vitamin-D derivatives and certain hormones (e.g., cortisone).

steroid anesthesia. The induction of sleep by steroid hormones or their derivatives.

steroid hormones. Hormones chemically related to cholesterol. To this group belong the male and female hormones, as well as the corticoids.

STH. The somatotrophic, or growth hormone.

stimulus. In biology, anything that elicits a reaction in the body or in one of its parts.

stress. The sum of all nonspecific changes caused by function or damage; also defined as the rate of wear and tear in the body.

stressor. That which produces stress.

syndrome. A group of symptoms and signs which appear together.

synergist. An agent which facilitates the action of another agent.

target area. The region upon which a biologic agent acts.

testoid. Synonym of androgen.

thymicolymphatic. A generic designation for the thymus, the lymph nodes and related structures.

thymus. A large lymphatic organ in the chest, probably concerned with immunity and resistance in general.

thyroid. An endocrine gland in the neck, which regulates metabolism in general.

thyrotrophic hormone. A pituitary hormone which stimulates the growth and function of the thyroid.

thyroxin. A thyroid hormone.

tissue. An aggregate of cells and intercellular substances forming one of the structural materials of the body. Each type of tissue (nervous, muscular, connective) has a different specific structure.

ulcer. Inflammation and erosion on a surface.

uremia. Poisoning caused by insufficient urinary excretion of toxic products.

viruses. Living agents, even smaller than bacteria, which can cause infectious diseases. For instance, measles, mumps, poliomyelitis, and the common cold, are produced by viruses.

Bibliography

1. ALLBUTT, T. C.: *Notes on the Composition of Scientific Papers*. London: Macmillan, 1923.
2. ALMACK, J. C.: *Research and Thesis Writing*. Boston: Houghton Mifflin, 1930.
3. ALVAREZ, W. C.; CLEGG, H.; MARTI-IBAÑEZ, F.; SELYE, H.; and SIGERIST, H. E.: *Medical Writings*. New York: MD Publications, 1956.
4. ANDERSON, J. A.: "The preparation of illustrations and tables." Am. Assn. Cereal Chemists, Transact., *3*, 74 (1945).
5. BAKER, J. R.: *The Scientific Life*. London: George Allen & Unwin, 1942.
6. BANCROFT, W. D.: "The methods of research." In: The Rice Institute Pamphlet, *15*, 167. Houston: The Rice Institute, 1928. By permission of The Rice Institute.
7. BARTLETT, J.: *The Shorter Bartlett's Familiar Quotations*. New York: Doubleday (Permabooks), 1953.
8. BARZUN, J.: *Teacher in America*. New York: Doubleday, 1955.
9. BERNARD, C.: *Introduction à l'étude de la médecine expérimentale*. Paris: Flammarion, 1865. *An Introduction to the Study of Experimental Medicine*, Copyright 1949. All rights reserved. Reprinted by permission of Abelard-Schuman Ltd. and of Flammarion.
10. BETT, W. R.: *The Preparation and Writing of Medical Papers for Publication*. London: Menley & James, 1953.
11. BEVERIDGE, W. I. B.: *The Art of Scientific Investigation*. Melbourne, London, Toronto: William Heinemann Ltd., 1951. First published in the United States of America, 1950. Revised edition, 1957. W. W. Norton & Company, Inc., New York, N.Y. All rights reserved. Reprinted by permission of the publishers.
12. BOOLE, G.: *An Investigation of the Laws of Thought on Which Are Founded Mathematical Theories of Logic and Probabilities*. New York: Dover Publ. First ed. 1854.
13. BRIDGMAN, P. Q.: *Reflections of a Physicist*. New York: Philosophical Library, 1955.
14. BULLOCH, W.: *History of Bacteriology*. London: Oxford University Press, 1938.
15. BURTON, A. C.: "The human side of the physiologist, prejudice and poetry." Proc. Am. Physiol. Soc., *1*, 1 (1957).
16. CANNON, W. B.: *The Way of an Investigator*. A Scientist's Experience

in Medical Research. New York: W. W. Norton, 1945. By permission of the publisher.

17. CARNAP, R.: *Logical foundations of probability.* Chicago: University of Chicago Press, 1950.
18. CARREL, A.: *L'homme cet inconnu.* Paris: Librairie Plon, 1935.
19. COCHRAN, W. G., and COX, G. M.: *Experimental Designs.* New York: John Wiley, 1950.
20. COHEN, M. R., and NAGEL, E.: *An Introduction to Logic and Scientific Method.* New York: Harcourt, Brace, 1943.
21. COLLIP, J. B.; SELYE, H.; and THOMSON, D. L.: *Beiträge zur Kenntnis der Physiologie des Gehirnanhanges.* Virchows Archiv, *290,* 23 (1933).
22. CONANT, J. B.: *Modern Science and Modern Man.* New York: Double-day, 1952. By permission of Columbia University Press.
23. CONANT, J. B.: *On Understanding Science.* New York: Mentor, 1953. By permission of Yale University Press.
24. CURIE, E.: *Madame Curie.* New York: Copyright 1937 by Doubleday and Company, Inc. Reprinted by permission of the publisher.
25. DALE, H. H.: "Accident and opportunism in medical research." Brit. med. J., Sept. 4th, p. 451 (1948).
26. DARWIN, F.: *Autobiography of Charles Darwin.* London: The Thinker's Library, No. 7, Watts, 1950. By permission of the publisher.
27. DE KRUIF, P.: *The Microbe Hunters.* New York: Pocket Books, 1926.
28. DER GROSSE BROCKHAUS. Leipzig: F. A. Brockhaus, 1930.
29. DEWEY, M.: *Decimal Classification.* New York: Forest Press, 1951.
30. DEWEY, M.: quoting Rider. In: *Decimal Classification.* New York: Forest Press, 1951.
31. DUCLAUX, E.: *Pasteur: Histoire d'un Esprit.* Paris: Sceaux, 1896.
32. EINSTEIN, A.: *Mein Weltbild.* Amsterdam: 1934; Zürich: Europa Verlag, 1953. (Engl. Translation: *Ideas and Opinions,* by S. Bargmann. New York: Crown Publishers, 1953). By permission of the publishers.
33. EINSTEIN, A.: Preface in: *Where Is Science Going?* by Max Planck. (Translation by James Murphy). London: George Allen & Unwin Ltd., 1933.
34. *Encyclopaedia Britannica:* Chicago: William Benton, Publisher, 1962.
35. FISHBEIN, M.: *Medical Writing.* New York: McGraw-Hill, 1957.
36. FISHER, R. A.: "Has Mendel's work been rediscovered?" Ann. Sci., *1,* 115 (1936).
37. FLOREY, H.: "Steps leading to the therapeutic application of microbial antagonisms." Brit. Med. Bull., *4,* 248 (1946).
37A. GEORGE, W. H.: *The Scientist in Action.* London: Williams & Norgate, 1936.
38. GOETHE, J. W.: *Faust.* (Translation by J. Anster.) London: The Oxford University Press, 1949.
39. GOODMAN, N.: *Fact, Fiction and Forecast.* London: The Athlone Press, 1954.

40. HELMHOLTZ, H. von: *Vorträge und Reden*. Braunschweig: F. Vieweg, 1903.
41. HERTER, C. A.: Chapter entitled "Imagination and Idealism" in *Medical Research and Education*. New York: Science Press.
42. HILL, A. B.: *The Principles of Medical Statistics*. London: The Lancet Ltd., 1948.
43. HUET, E.: *Manuel pour la classification décimale des écrits et documents relatifs à la stomatologie et à l'odontologie*. Bruxelles: Fédération Dentaire Internationale, 1920.
44. JONES, E.: *The Life and Work of Sigmund Freud. Years of Maturity, 1901–1909*. New York: Basic Books, 2, 1955.
45. KEKULE, F. A.: Quoted by Schutz, G.: Ber. deut. chem. Ges., 23, 1265 (1890).
46. KOCH, R.: *Investigations into the Aetiology of Traumatic Infective Diseases*. Translation by W. W. Cheyne. London: The New Sydenham Society, 1880.
47. KOENIGSBERGER, L.: *Hermann von Helmholtz*. Translation by F. A. Welby. Oxford: Clarendon Press, 1906.
48. METCHNIKOFF, E.: Quoted by Fried, B. M.: Arch. Path., 26, 700 (1938).
49. MOE, H. A.: *Report of the Secretary*, John Simon Guggenheim Memorial Foundation, 1957–1958.
50. NICOLLE, C.: *Biologie de l'Invention*. Paris: Alcan, 1932.
51. NELSON, J. R.: *Writing the Technical Report*. New York: McGraw-Hill, 1947.
52. NERVO, A.: *Obras Completas*, Vol. 2. Madrid: Aguilar, 1956.
53. *Nouveau Petit Larousse*. Paris: Librairie Larousse, 1954.
54. *Oxford Dictionary of Quotations*, Second Edition. London: The Oxford University Press, 1953.
55. PLANCK, M.: "Sinn und Grenzen der exakten Wissenschaft." (Vortrag, gehalten in November 1941), 6. Auflage 1958, Johann Ambrosius Barth Verlag, Leipzig. Reprinted by permission.
56. PLATT, W., and BAKER, R. A.: "The relation of the scientific 'hunch' to research." J. Chem. Educ., 8, 1969 (1931).
57. POINCARE, H.: *Science et méthode*. Paris: Flammarion, 1924.
58. RAPOPORT, A.: *Operational Philosophy: Interesting Knowledge and Action*. New York: Harper, 1953.
59. RICHET, C.: *Le Savant*. Paris: Librairie Hachette, 1923.
60. RUSSELL, B.: *Human Knowledge. Its Scope and Limits*. London: George Allen & Unwin Ltd., 1948.
61. SCHILD, A.: "On the matter of freedom: the university and the physical sciences." Canad. As. Univ. Teachers (C.A.U.T.). Bulletin, 11, 4 (1963).
62. SCHILLER, F.C.S.: "Scientific discovery and logical proof." In: *Studies in the History and Method of Science*. Oxford: Clarendon Press, 1917.

63. SCHLESINGER, A. M., JR.: "The decline of heroes." In: *Adventures of the Mind*. New York: Vintage Books, 1960. By permission of the author.

64. 1958 PARLIAMENT OF SCIENCE conducted in Washington, D.C., March 15–17, by the AAAS, SCIENCE, *127*, 856 (1958).

65. SELYE, H.: "The nomenclature of steroid hormones." Pharm. J., *149*, 98 (1942).

66. SELYE, H.: *Textbook of Endocrinology*. Montreal: Acta Inc., Med. Publ., First ed. 1947; Second ed. 1949.

67. SELYE, H.: *Encyclopedia of Endocrinology*. Section I: Classified Index of the Steroid Hormones and Related Compounds (4 vols.). Montreal: A. W. T. Franks Publ. Co., 1943.

68. SELYE, H.: *Stress*. Montreal: Acta Inc., Med. Publ., 1950.

69. SELYE, H.: *Annual Reports on Stress*. (In collaboration with G. Heuser and A. Horava.) Volumes I–V. Montreal: Acta Inc., Med. Publ., 1951–55/56.

70. SELYE, H.: *The Stress of Life*. New York: McGraw-Hill, 1956.

71. SELYE, H.: *The Chemical Prevention of Cardiac Necroses*. New York: The Ronald Press Co., 1958.

72. SELYE, H.: "What makes basic research basic?" In: *Adventures of the Mind*. New York: Vintage Books, 1960.

73. SELYE, H.: *The Pluricausal Cardiopathies*. Springfield: Charles C Thomas Publ., 1961.

74. SELYE, H.: *Calciphylaxis*. Chicago: The University of Chicago Press, 1962.

75. SELYE, H., and STONE, H.: *On the Experimental Morphology of the Adrenals*. Springfield: Charles C Thomas Publ., 1950.

76. SELYE, H., and EMBER, G.: *Symbolic Shorthand Systems for Physiology and Medicine*. Montreal: Acta, Med. Publ., 1964.

77. SHAW, G. B.: *Man and Superman*. New York: Brentano's, 1903.

78. SINCLAIR, W. J.: *Semmelweis, His Life and Doctrine*. Manchester University Press, 1909.

79. SMITH, T.: "The influence of research in bringing into closer relationship the practice of medicine and public health activities." Am. J. Med. Sci., *178*, 740 (1929).

80. SMITH, T.: "Letter to Dr. Krumbhaar." J. Bact., *27*, 19 (1934).

81. SNEDECOR, G. W.: *Statistical Methods*. Applied to experiments in agriculture and biology. Iowa State College Press, Ames, 1956.

82. STEPHENSON, M.: "F. Gowland Hopkins." Biochem. J., *42*, 161 (1948).

83. TRELEASE, S. F.: *The Scientific Paper, How to Prepare It, How to Write it*. Baltimore: Williams and Wilkins, 1951.

84. TROTTER, W.: *Collected Papers of Wilfred Trotter*. London: Oxford University Press, 1941.

85. UNIVERSITY OF CHICAGO PRESS: *A Manual of Style*. Chicago: The University of Chicago Press, 1950.

86. WALLACE, A. R.: *My Life*. London: Chapman & Hall Ltd., 1908.

87. WALLAS, G.: *The Art of Thought.* New York: Harcourt, Brace, 1926. By permission of the publisher.
88. WEBSTER: *New International Dictionary.* Springfield: G. G. Merriam, Second ed., 1953.
89. WIENER, N.: *Ex-Prodigy: My Childhood and Youth.* New York: Simon & Schuster, Copyright © 1953. By permission of the publisher.
90. WOODGER, J. H.: "The technique of theory construction." In: *International Encyclopedia of Unified Science, 2* No.5. Chicago: The University of Chicago Press, 1939.
91. WOLF, A.: "Scientific method." In: *Encyclopaedia Britannica.* Chicago: William Benton, Publisher, *20,* 127, 1943.
92. ZINSSER, H.: *As I Remember Him.* (The Biography of R. S.) Boston: Little, Brown & Co., 1940.

Index

Boldface numerals (e.g., **17**) refer to principal discussions of a subject. There are many *quotations* in this book; some appear as introductory aphorisms following captions, others as supporting statements incorporated in the text itself. With few exceptions these are indexed only under the author's name. Human interest stories are conjointly indexed under *"Anecdote,"* brief reference being made to their content.

Methodology, 202
Methods; cf. Techniques
Meticulousness, 81
"Mimosa," 26
Minkowsky, Oskar, 45, 90
"Misunderstood geniuses," 93
Mnemonic symbols of the SSS, 233
Models of disease, 222
Modesty, 142
"Monkey trials," 125
Monographs, 349
Montaigne, Michel de, 39
Motivation of the researcher, 5
Morbus pilaris mirabilis, 104
Morley, Viscount John, 363
Morphology, as an experimental approach, 83
Moscow trip (1945), 389
Multiple causes, 318

Nagel, E., 258, 264
"Narcissist," 26
National and international scientific cooperation, 177
Nature, contact with, 9, 77
  harmony of, 6
  how to question, 284
  love of, 7
Natural phenomena, 222
"Navel-cord-cutting time" of young scientist, 115
Nelson, J. R., 334
Neologisms, 339
Neurotics, 187
Newton, Sir Isaac, 8, 278, 281
Nicolle, Charles J. H., 47, 131
Nietzsche, Friedrich Wilhelm, 38
Noguchi, Hideyo, 319
Nonspecific features of disease, 51
Nontechnical and semitechnical speech, 382
Norsemen discover America, 88

Observation, 77
  accidental, 93
  by the naked eye, 83
  "corruptive optimism" in, 85
  evaluation of, 83
  techniques of, 215
"Operation Nightingale," 145
Optimism, 157

Order of precedence in experimentation, 116
  of the SSS, 233
Organization, 183
  of research teams, 161
Originality, 42
Overspecialization, 203
  avoidance of, 95
"Ox-faced children," 154

Pagination, 352
Parascientific interests, 145
Parathyroid extract, method of injection, 221
Parliament of Science, 121
Pasteur, Louis, 78, 79, 84, 92, 107, 149, 152, 155, 333
Pavlov, Ivan Petrovich, 74
Period of severance, 114
"Period of the scapeogats," 115
Peripheral vision, 44, 78, 81
Perseverance, 31
Personal conduct, 135
Personality-centeredness, 162
  types, 21
Personnel, management and supervision of, 179
  selection of, 162
Perspective, balance of, 94
Phagocytosis, 49
Pharmacologic techniques, 218
"Pharmacology of dirt," 35
  of steroid hormones, 240
Photographs, 343
Physical examination of animals, 217
Physical facilities, 132
Pirquet, Clemens Peter, 152, 155
Planck, Max, 11, 14, 266, 280
Plato, 158
Platt, W., 47, 56, 62, 65
Plutarch, 13, 127, 149
Poincaré, Henri, 50, 62, 266, 354
Political attitudes of scientists, 193
Polymyxin, mast-cell discharger, 100
Pomposity, 338
Pónos, 341
Pound, Ezra, 153
Prayer, 41
Prejudice, control of, 43
  in scientific research, 85
Preliminary experiments, 116

ABOUT THE AUTHOR

Dr. Hans Selye is without question one of the great pioneers of medicine. In 1936 his famous and revolutionary concept of stress opened up countless new avenues of treatment through the discovery that hormones participate in the development of many nonendocrine degenerative diseases, including coronary thrombosis, brain hemorrhage, hardening of the arteries, certain types of high blood pressure and kidney failures, arthritis, peptic ulcers, and even cancer.

More recently, he has been working on a dramatic new concept relating the process of aging to the body's disposition of products of its own metabolism, and especially calcium. Promising new approaches to the prevention of the aging process have been shown to be feasible in animal experiments, and further work may reveal medical applications of the idea.

Dr. Selye was born in Vienna in 1907 and studied in Prague, Paris, and Rome. He received his medical degree from the German University of Prague in 1929 and two years later took his Ph.D. at the same university. He was then awarded a Rockefeller research fellowship which brought him to Johns Hopkins University and later to McGill University, where he became Associate Professor of Histology. Subsequently he received honorary degrees from eight other universities. Since 1945 he has served as director of the Institute of Experimental Medicine and Surgery. Dr. Selye makes his home in Montreal with his wife and four children.

Dr. Selye is the author of a large number of books and articles addressed to students and specialists in medicine, as well as *The Stress of Life*, an exposition of his stress theory for the layman, published in 1956.